COLLINS

Advanced Modular Sciences

Physics

AS

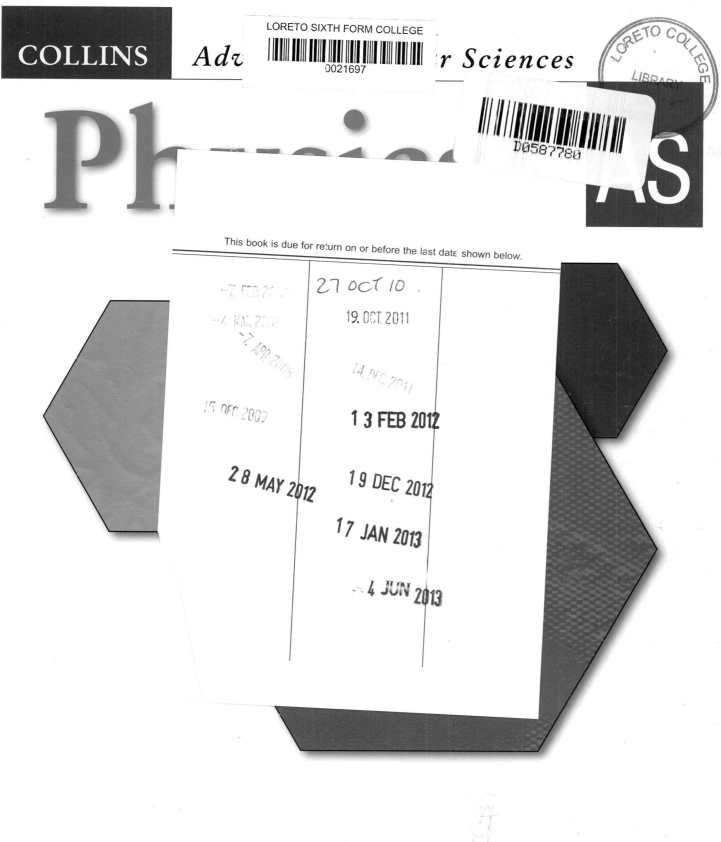

Series Editor: John Avison

Frank Ciccotti

Dave Kelly

This book has been designed to support AQA Physics specification A.
It contains some material which has been added in order to clarify the
specification. The examination will be limited to material set out in the
specification document.

Published by HarperCollins*Publishers* Limited
77–85 Fulham Palace Road
Hammersmith
London
W6 8JB

Browse the complete Collins catalogue at
www.collinseducation.com

20 19 18 17 16 15 14 13 12 11

ISBN-13 978 0 00 327755 5
ISBN-10 0 00 327755 0

David Kelly and Frank Ciccotti assert the moral right to be identified as
the authors of this work.

All new material in this book has been written by Dave Kelly.
This book draws on some sections from *Physics Core* by Dave Kelly and
Frank Ciccotti, and *Particles, Principles and Possibilities* by David Brodie.
Key Skill Assignments by Alan Yate.

British Library Cataloguing in Publication Data
A catalogue record for this publication is available from the British Library

Cover design by Chi Leung
Design by Derek Lee
Edited by Mike Nugent
Illustrations by Barking Dog Art, Tom Cross, Jerry Fowler, Hardlines,
Illustrated Arts, Mark Jordan and Alan Trewartha
Picture research by Caroline Thompson
Production by Kathryn Botterill

Printed and bound by Printing Express, Hong Kong

The publisher wishes to thank AQA for permission to reproduce
examination questions.

You might also like to visit:
www.harpercollins.co.uk
The book lover's website

Particles, Radiation and Quantum Phenomena

Chapter 1	**Atomic physics**	6
Chapter 2	**Antimatter, neutrinos and leptons**	23
Chapter 3	**The fundamental particles**	36
Chapter 4	**Waves, refraction and optical fibres**	54
Chapter 5	**Atomic spectra and photons**	72

Mechanics and Molecular Kinetic Theory

Chapter 6	**Dynamics**	86
Chapter 7	**Forces in equilibrium**	98
Chapter 8	**Work, energy and Newton's laws of motion**	113
Chapter 9	**Energy transfer**	126
Chapter 10	**Molecular kinetic theory**	138

Current Electricity and Elastic Properties of Solids

Chapter 11	**Electricity**	150
Chapter 12	**The cathode-ray tube**	171
Chapter 13	**Strength of materials**	182

Glossary	196
Answers to questions	202
Data section	213

Acknowledgements

Every effort has been made to contact the holders of copyright material, but if any have been inadvertently overlooked the publishers will be pleased to make the necessary arrangements at the first opportunity.

The publishers would like to thank the following for permission to reproduce photographs
(T = Top, B = Bottom, C = Centre, L = Left, R = Right):

Advertising Archives, 133;
Professor J F Allen, Department of Physics, St Andrews University, 138CR;
Allsport/D Cannon, 86, T Duffy, 88, 94TL, B Martin, 90CL, Vandystadt, 90TR&BL, 101L, 182TR, M Powell, 95TL, J Nicholson, 106L, S Cazenave/Vandystadt, 106C, P Roundeau, 118; S Bruty, 129;
BBC Photograph Library, (Harry Enfield and Chums), 56TL;
Barnaby's Picture Library, 101T;
Photos from www.John Birdsall.co.uk, 62TL, 139, 175;
Chris Bonington Photo Library, 182BR;
Neill Bruce, 115T, 165;
Peter Roberts Collection/Neill Bruce, 151;
BT Corporate Picture Library: a BT photograph, 54T;
University of Cambridge, Cavendish Laboratory, Madingley Road, Cambridge, England, 10L;
Michael Cole Camerawork, 92;
Bruce Coleman Ltd/A J Purcell, 182L;
A Cooley, 187T;
Fiat (UK) Ltd, 156;
Ford Motor Company, 113T;
Vivien Fifield, 7L&CR, 10B, 21, 140BL;
© 1998 - GM Corp. Used with Permission of GM Media Archives. All rights reserved, 150BR, 152, 153;
Peter Gould, 62TR;
Ronald Grant Archive, 126T;
ICCR (Institute for Cosmic Ray Research), the University of Tokyo, 32TL, 41;
Mark Jordan, 36CL, 158, 178C;

Kos Picture Source, 105TL;
Andrew Lambert, 55L, 56CR, 59B&TR, 72BL, 144, 155, 190L;
Dr M R Lindsay, Physical Education, University of Leeds, 95BL;
The Military Picture Library/Robin Adshead, 55R;
Mirror Syndication International, 117;
NASA, 20TR, 114BL;
NHPA/S Dalton, 193;
Panos/Betty Press, 184;
Pictures Colour Library, 98;
Rapra Technology Ltd, 185;
Redferns/Mick Hutson, 57T;
Rex Features Ltd, 138TL,
School of Materials, University of Leeds, 190C, 191CL;
Science Photo Library, 6, 7CL&R, 9, 19, 20B, 23, 24, 25, 27, 28, 29, 32R&BL, 36TL, 37, 39, 42, 43, 46, 48, 51, 54B, 57B, 59TL, 60BR, 62B, 64, 65, 69, 72T, 73, 74, 77, 78, 81, 83, 100, 123, 126B, 127TR, 128, 130, 131, 132, 138TR, 150, 161, 171C, 172, 173, 191T;
SHOUT, 140CR;
Skishoot/Offshoot/J Parkington, 105TR;
Sony UK, 171TL, 178T;
Giboux/Liaison/FSP, 150TL,
Starland Picture Library, 36TR;
The Stock Market, 101BR, 107;
Tony Stone Images, 10T, 20TL, 103, 108, 110, 121, 127, 140TL, 167B, 171CR, 192;
Telegraph Colour Library, 101TR;
C & S Thompson, 60TL;
Volvo Car UK Ltd. 113CR, 114BR, 116;

Front cover:
Science Photo Library (top left, top right)
Tony Stone Images (centre)

To the student

This book aims to make your study of advanced science successful and interesting. Science is constantly evolving and, wherever possible, modern issues and problems have been used to make your study stimulating and to encourage you to continue studying science after you complete your current course.

Using the book

Don't try to achieve too much in one reading session. Science is complex and some demanding ideas need to be supported with a lot of facts. Trying to take in too much at one time can make you lose sight of the most important ideas – all you see is a mass of information.

Each chapter starts by showing how the science you will learn is applied somewhere in the world. At other points in the chapter you may find more examples of the way the science you are covering is used. These detailed contexts are not needed for your examination but should help to strengthen your understanding of the subject.

The numbered questions in the main text allow you to check that you have understood what is being explained. These are all short and straightforward in style – there are no trick questions. Don't be tempted to pass over these questions; they will give you new insights into the work. Answers are given in the back of the book.

This book covers the content needed for the AQA Specification A in Physics at AS-level. The Key Facts for each section summarise the information you will need in your examination. However, the examination will test your ability to apply these facts rather than simply to remember them. The main text in the book explains these facts. The application boxes encourage you to apply them in new situations. Extension boxes provide extra detail not required for your examination. These are interesting to read and will support your studies beyond AS-level.

Words written in bold type appear in the glossary at the end of the book. If you don't know the meaning of one of these words check it out immediately – don't persevere, hoping all will become clear.

Past paper questions are included at the end of each chapter. These will help you to test yourself against the sorts of questions that will come up in your examination.

The Key Skill Assignments allow you to practise for any Key Skill assessments you may have. The assignments are often starting points for work and you will need to access other books and sources of information to complete the activity.

1 Atomic physics

What is matter made of? This critical question has perplexed scientists for centuries. It has led to a search on a smaller and smaller scale for the fundamental building blocks of our Universe. Now, at the start of the 21st century, physicists are hot on the trail of what might be the final missing piece in this particle physics jigsaw. There is a strong feeling that a mysterious particle known as the Higgs boson will be observed within the next few years. The Higgs boson is thought to be responsible for giving mass to all the other particles. Its existence is predicted by the current theory of particle physics known as the standard model. So far the predictions of the standard model have proved remarkably successful.

The tracks left by sub-atomic particles. These are the clues that may lead us to answers about the nature of matter.

Some scientists have suggested that the discovery of the Higgs boson will signal the end for particle physics. They argue that, whilst there may be some details to sort out, most of the basic questions have been answered. Others disagree. There are some nagging anomalies which may mean that the discovery of a deeper, underlying structure still awaits us.

Strangely enough the situation is very similar to that in physics 100 years ago. By the end of the 19th century Faraday had successfully linked electricity and magnetism together, Maxwell had developed equations describing electromagnetic waves and Newton's laws seemed sufficient to describe forces and motion. The main work of physics appeared to be complete. But only a few years later physics had been turned upside down. One cause for this was the accidental discovery of radioactivity. Radioactive decay proved hard to explain for 19th century scientists who were still arguing about whether atoms really existed or not.

The large electron–positron (LEP) accelerator at CERN, the European Organisation for Nuclear Research, in Geneva, accelerates electrons and positrons (positively charged electrons) in opposite directions around adjacent pipes. According to some estimates the LEP accelerator may be capable of reaching the energies necessary to reveal the Higgs boson.

1.1 The evidence for atoms

Early ideas

The first atomic theory originated 2500 years ago. The Greek philosopher Democritus suggested that matter is not continuous but is made of discrete building blocks called atoms. These atoms were the smallest components of all matter. Democritus believed that there was an infinite number of different atoms, but none of them could be divided or changed into anything else.

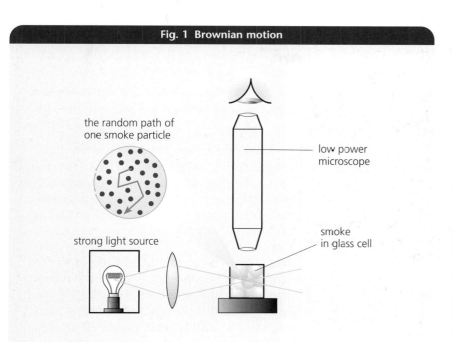

Fig. 1 Brownian motion

the random path of one smoke particle

low power microscope

strong light source

smoke in glass cell

There were no significant developments in atomic theory until the start of the 19th century. John Dalton realised that there was only a limited number of different atoms. Each type corresponded to one of the chemical elements, 18 of which were known at the time. Dalton's ideas were used to help construct the periodic table. Despite this, many chemists were not convinced that atoms actually existed. Physicists felt otherwise. They needed real atoms to understand such things as the behaviour of gases. Gas pressure, for example, can be explained by assuming that a gas is composed of small particles, molecules or atoms, which are always moving, constantly colliding with the walls of a container.

Brownian motion

In 1827 the botanist Robert Brown used his microscope to look at fine particles, like pollen or soot, suspended in water. He noticed that the particles moved with a random, jerky motion. The smaller the particles of soot, the more vigorously they moved. If the particles were any bigger than about 1/1000th of a millimetre (1×10^{-6} m) then the 'Brownian motion' became imperceptible. At first Brown thought the motions were due to microscopic living organisms, but it was soon realised that the soot particles were being battered about by impacts from the water **molecules**. The water molecules, too small to be seen themselves, move with random velocities and are constantly colliding with the soot particles. At any instant an imbalance in the number of molecules hitting a soot particle on one side would give it a push in a particular direction (Fig. 1).

Up to the end of the 19th century the existence of atoms was still a hotly debated topic.

'The atomic doctrine is at best an assumption.'

Faraday 1844

'The atom must remain a tool ... like the functions of mathematics.'

Ernst Mach 1910

'The atoms out of which the Earth is built remain unbroken and unworn. They continue this day as they were created, perfect in number, measure and weight.'

Maxwell 1873

Boltzmann developed atomic theory to explain the nature of heat. He became depressed when the scientific community did not accept the reality of the atom and he committed suicide in 1906.

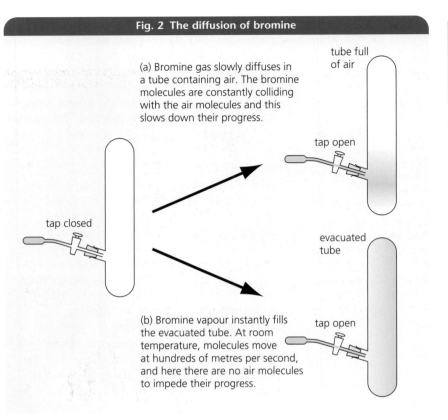

Fig. 2 The diffusion of bromine

(a) Bromine gas slowly diffuses in a tube containing air. The bromine molecules are constantly colliding with the air molecules and this slows down their progress.

tube full of air

tap open

tap closed

evacuated tube

(b) Bromine vapour instantly fills the evacuated tube. At room temperature, molecules move at hundreds of metres per second, and here there are no air molecules to impede their progress.

tap open

1 Brownian motion tends to increase if the soot particles are smaller or if the liquid is heated. Explain why these observations support the idea that it is collisions with molecules of water that moves the soot particles around.

The **diffusion** of one gas into another is another important piece of evidence that suggests that gases are composed of very small particles. Diffusion experiments suggest that molecules in a gas are moving very quickly, and are making about 1000 million (10^9) collisions every second. On average a gas molecule in the bromine experiment (see Fig. 2) moves about 10^{-7} m between every collision. This distance is called the **mean free path**. Molecules could be closer to each other than this, since a gas molecule is unlikely to collide with its nearest neighbour. This suggests that gas molecules may be 10^{-8}–10^{-9} m apart. This gives an upper limit for the size of a gas molecule.

2 How would you expect the rate of diffusion to vary with either the mass of the molecules or the temperature?

APPLICATION

The scale of things

Physics often deals with the inordinately large, like the diameter of the Universe, and the infinitesimally small, such as the distance across an atomic nucleus. We use scientific notation to write down numbers that would otherwise be strings of zeros across the page. It is usual to use powers of 10 that go up in steps of 1000, or 10^3. In the SI system of units these are given standard prefixes.

3a The power output of a particular nuclear power station is 1 450 000 000 W. Express this using an appropriate standard prefix.

b The radius of an aluminium atom is 142 pm. Express this in metres.

Multiplication factor		Prefix	Symbol	Scale (order of magnitude)
1 000 000 000 000	10^{12}	tera	T	5.9 Tm = Radius of Pluto's orbit
1 000 000 000	10^9	giga	G	0.4 Gm = Mean Earth–Moon distance
1 000 000	10^6	mega	M	6.37 Mm = Mean radius of Earth
1 000	10^3	kilo	k	320 km from Manchester to London
0.001	10^{-3}	milli	m	Microwave wavelength
0.000 001	10^{-6}	micro	μ	Wavelength of visible light: 0.4 to 0.7 μm
0.000 000 001	10^{-9}	nano	n	Approximate atomic diameter
0.000 000 000 001	10^{-12}	pico	p	Wavelength of a gamma ray
0.000 000 000 000 001	10^{-15}	femto	f	Approximate diameter of an atomic nucleus
0.000 000 000 000 000 001	10^{-18}	atto	a	Range of weak nuclear force

Note: it is important to use *capital* letters only for the first three prefix symbols: T, G and M.

EXTENSION

How big is an atom?

One way to find a rough value for an upper limit to the size of an atom is to let a small drop of oil fall on to the surface of some water (Fig. 3). The drop will spread out into a very thin film. If we know the volume of the oil drop and the area of the film, we can calculate the thickness of the oil film. The oil molecules cannot be bigger than this, and an atom must be smaller still, so we can arrive at the maximum size for *one* atom.

Oleic acid is often used, dissolved in alcohol. When the drop hits the water, the alcohol dissolves, leaving the oleic acid behind. A fine powder is sprinkled on to the surface of the water to make it easier to see the extent of the oil film.

Suppose that we use a solution of 1 part oleic acid to 499 parts alcohol. If 100 drops of the solution has a volume of 502 mm^3, then the volume of oleic acid is:

$$\frac{1}{100} \times \frac{1}{500} \times 5.02 \times 10^{-6} \text{ m}^3$$

$$= 1.004 \times 10^{-10} \text{ m}^3$$

If the oil film spreads to a diameter of 245 mm then its area is:

Area of oil film $= \pi r^2$
$= \pi \times (12.25 \times 10^{-2} \text{ m})^2$
$= 0.047 \text{ m}^2$

Since

$$\text{thickness of the film} = \frac{\text{volume of drop}}{\text{area of film}}$$

the thickness is

$$\frac{1.004 \times 10^{-10}}{0.047} = 2.14 \times 10^{-9} \text{ m}$$

This sets the upper limit for the size of an oleic acid molecule. These molecules are actually long chains about 20 atoms long which orientate

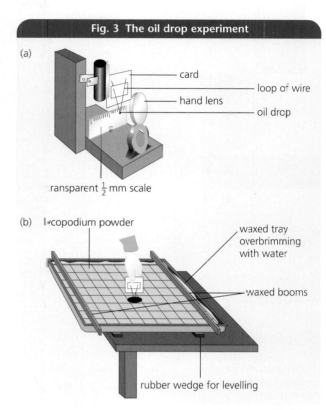

Fig. 3 The oil drop experiment

(a) card — loop of wire — hand lens — oil drop — transparent $\frac{1}{2}$ mm scale

(b) lycopodium powder — waxed tray overbrimming with water — waxed booms — rubber wedge for levelling

themselves at right angles to the water surface. This gives an approximate size of an atom as 1×10^{-10} m. Modern measurements give the atomic radius of a hydrogen atom as 46 pm (1 pm = 1 picometre = 1×10^{-12} m).

4 Explain why this experiment gives an upper limit for the size of an atom.

5 Why are 100 drops of solution used to measure the volume?

6 Estimate how many atoms thick this sheet of paper is.

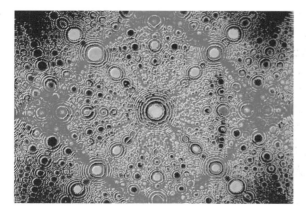

It wasn't until the 1950s that we could actually see images of atoms. This field-ion micrograph shows a plane of platinum atoms.

In the first few years of the 20th century the arguments over whether atoms really exist were forgotten as scientists came to accept the theory.

Two discoveries moved the scientific debate forward rapidly. In 1897, J. J. Thomson discovered the electron. The discovery of radioactivity at about the same time soon led people to believe that not only was the atom real, but that it had a structure and could be taken apart. The search to understand the composition of the atom had begun.

1.2 Atomic structure

Before 1900 the atom was considered to be a **fundamental particle**: it had no structure and no constituents. One or two scientists suspected that there could be something rattling around inside the atom. This could help to explain the existence of atomic spectra (see Chapter 5), but no-one suspected that the atom itself could be taken apart. Thomson's discovery of the electron changed that: he suggested that the electron was part of the atom that had been torn away.

The electron

Physicists in the 19th century had two wonderful new pieces of technology: the vacuum pump and the induction coil. The vacuum pump could be used to create a very low pressure in a glass tube. The induction coil was used to generate a large potential difference across electrodes placed in the tube. The vacuum tubes produced in this way were the first particle accelerators.

In Thomson's discharge tube (Fig. 4) a large potential difference was applied across two metal plates inside an evacuated glass tube. This caused the fluorescent coating at the end of the tube to glow. Thomson was working on the hypothesis that the glow was caused by a

The Cavendish Laboratory in Cambridge where the electron was discovered at the turn of the last century. In the years after the discovery there was a toast at the annual dinner, 'The electron: may it never be of use to anybody'.

Together, the vacuum pump and the induction coil led to the demonstration of radio waves by Hertz, the transmission of telegraph signals without wires by Marconi, the discovery of X-rays by Röntgen and the discovery of the first sub-atomic particle, the electron, by J. J. Thomson.

The passage of electrons through low pressure gases is a familiar sight today.

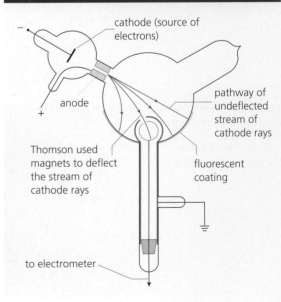

Fig. 4 Thomson's experimental set-up

cathode (source of electrons)

anode

pathway of undeflected stream of cathode rays

Thomson used magnets to deflect the stream of cathode rays

fluorescent coating

to electrometer

CATHODE RAYS.

By J.J.THOMSON, M.A., F.R.S.,
Cavendish Professor of Experimental Physics, Cambridge.

THE EXPERIMENTS discussed in this paper were undertaken in the hope of gaining some information as to the nature of cathode rays ... According to the almost unanimous opinion of German physicists they are due to some process in the aether ... another view of these rays is that ... they are in fact wholly material, and that they mark the paths of particles of matter charged with negative electricity ... The following experiments were carried out to test some of the consequences of the electrified-particle theory.

Two coaxial cylinders with slits in

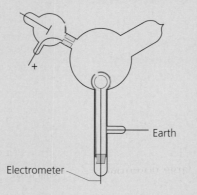

Earth

Electrometer

them are placed in a bulb connected with a discharge tube; the cathode rays... do not fall upon the cylinders unless they are deflected by a magnet. The outer cylinder is connected with the Earth, the inner with the electrometer. When the cathode rays (whose path was traced by the phosphorescence on the glass) did not fall on the slit, the electrical charge sent to the electrometer ... was small and irregular; when, however, the rays were bent by a magnet so as to fall on the slit there was a large charge of negative electricity sent to the electrometer. I was surprised at the magnitude of the charge ... Thus this

experiment shows that however we twist and deflect the cathode rays by magnetic forces, the negative electrification follows the same path as the rays, and that this negative electrification is indissolubly connected with the cathode rays.

[Thomson goes on to discuss the effect of an electric field on cathode rays ...]

Deflexion of the Cathode Rays by an Electrostatic Field

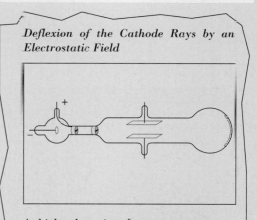

At high exhaustions [a strong vacuum, or low pressure] the rays were deflected when the two aluminium plates were connected with the terminals of a battery of small storage-cells; the rays were depressed when the upper plate was connected with the negative pole of the battery, the lower with the positive, and raised when the upper plate was connected with the positive, the lower with the negative pole. The deflexion was proportional to the difference of potential between the plates, and I could detect the deflexion when the potential difference was as small as two volts. It was only when the vacuum was a good one that the deflexion took place.

stream of charged particles. The particles, which were called **cathode rays**, seemed to be emitted from the negatively charged plate (the cathode). The rays then travelled at high speed across the tube, finally striking the fluorescent coating. Thomson showed that he could deflect the beam with a magnet. The beam could also be deflected by using electrically charged plates. This proved that the cathode rays carried a negative charge.

The plum pudding atom

Physics is often concerned with constructing models that describe some aspect of the real world, such as the kinetic theory of gases, or the big-bang model for the Universe. If electrons could be pulled out of atoms, physicists wanted to know how the atom was constructed. A first thought was that atoms were made entirely of electrons. A hydrogen atom might consist of around 1 000 electrons.

EXTENSION   Thomson's balancing act

Fig. 5 Electrostatic and magnetic deflection

(a) Electrons are attracted to the upper plate. They follow a parabolic path whilst they are in the electric field.

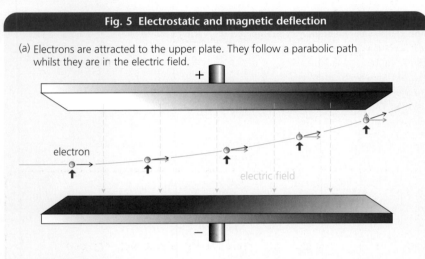

(b) In a magnetic field electrons are made to travel in a circular path. The direction of the force at any instant can be predicted using Fleming's left-hand rule:

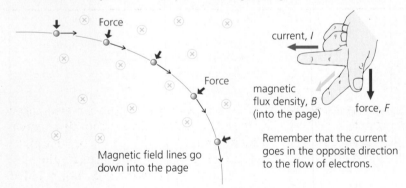

Magnetic field lines go down into the page

current, *I*

magnetic flux density, *B* (into the page)

force, *F*

Remember that the current goes in the opposite direction to the flow of electrons.

(c) Thomson balanced the effects of the magnetic and electric fields so that the electron travelled in a straight line.

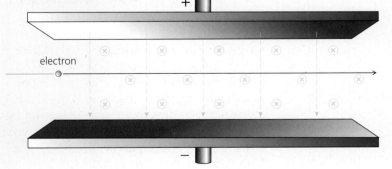

Thomson was able to measure the charge-to-mass ratio for the cathode rays. This ratio is referred to as e/m where e is the charge carried by the electron and m is its mass. He found a value that was 770 times bigger than that of hydrogen. Either the cathode rays carried a very large charge or they had a much smaller mass than an atom. Thomson opted for the latter: 'On this view we have in the cathode rays matter in a new state, a state in which the subdivision of matter is carried very much further'.

Thomson was able to reach this conclusion by using his new method of crossed electric and magnetic fields. This apparatus had electric and magnetic fields arranged so that the deflections exactly cancelled out and the cathode rays carried on in a straight line (Fig. 5). Thomson then applied his method to the particles emitted by the photoelectric effect (see Section 5.3) and found that they had the same value for e/m as cathode rays. In 1899 Thomson concluded that cathode rays were 'a splitting up of the atom, a part of the mass of the atom getting free and becoming detached from the original atom'. Thomson had discovered the electron. He measured its charge and so arrived at a value for the mass of the electron of 3×10^{-29} kg. This is respectably close to the modern measurement of 9.109×10^{-31} kg.

There is no evidence yet to suggest that the electron has any structure of its own, or has any other constituents. It is still considered to be a fundamental particle.

7   Why did the experiments on cathode rays depend on getting a good vacuum, i.e. a very low pressure, in the tube?

But there had to be some positive charge to cancel out the negative charge carried by all those electrons. This was necessary or the whole atom would be pushed apart by electrostatic repulsion. How much mass did this positive charge have and where was it? Thomson's **plum pudding** model (Fig. 6) pictured the atom as a uniform, positively charged cloud with tiny electrons embedded in it like plums in a pudding.

The plum pudding atom had problems though. An atom with stationary electrons cannot be stable, so the electrons had to move around. The problem is that whenever a charged particle changes direction it emits electromagnetic radiation. Electrons moving around in the atom would radiate energy and slow down. Sooner or later all atoms would become unstable. The end of the plum pudding model was finally decided by experiments carried out at Manchester University in 1909.

Fig. 6 The plum pudding model

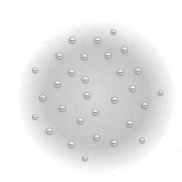

The term 'pudding' is rather misleading; the low density of the positive part of the atom makes it more like a cloud than a pudding.

KEY FACTS

- The electron is a fundamental particle.

- The electron has a mass of 9.1×10^{-31} kg and carries a negative charge of 1.6×10^{-19} C.

- The plum pudding model pictured atoms as having tiny electrons embedded in a positively charged background.

1.3 The discovery of the nucleus

Fig. 7 Geiger and Marsden's experimental set-up

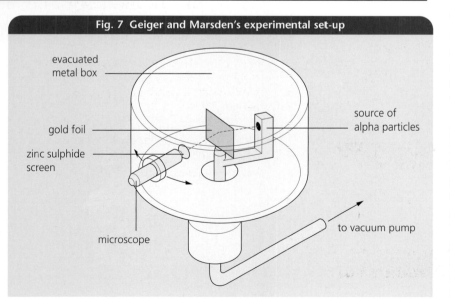

evacuated metal box

gold foil

zinc sulphide screen

microscope

source of alpha particles

to vacuum pump

The first steps in nuclear physics were taken early in 1909. Hans Geiger and his research student Ernest Marsden were conducting an experiment designed to investigate the scattering of alpha particles as they collided with gold atoms (Fig. 7).

A radioactive sample of radium was used to beam alpha particles towards a thin gold foil. Each alpha particle was detected by a flash of light emitted when it hit a zinc sulphide screen. In hours of painstaking observations, Geiger and Marsden counted how many scintillations there were at different angles. Rutherford suggested that they should look for alpha particles directly reflected from the metal surface. To their great surprise a small fraction of the alpha particles, about 1 in 8000, was bounced back from the metal foil.

Alpha particles have a positive charge, known to be twice the charge on the electron. They are also relatively heavy, about 8 000 times as massive as an electron. An alpha particle travelling at $10\,000\,\text{km s}^{-1}$ shouldn't have been bounced back by a gold atom that consisted of a few tiny electrons stuck into a positive atom. Rutherford was amazed. He said later, 'It was quite the most incredible event that has ever happened to me. It was almost as incredible as if you fired a 15 inch shell at a piece of tissue paper and it came back and hit you'.

The plum pudding model of the atom had to go. Rutherford deduced that all the positive charge, and almost all the mass, of an atom must be concentrated in the centre of the atom. He called this the nucleus.

Rutherford suggested that the electrons carried all the negative charge and that they orbited the nucleus through empty space, a relatively long way from the nucleus. Most of the alpha particles passed through the gold foil with small or zero deflections simply because they were too far away from the nucleus of the gold atoms to be affected by it. Very occasionally an alpha particle passed so close to the nucleus that it would be repelled by its positive charge and suffer a large deflection (Fig. 8).

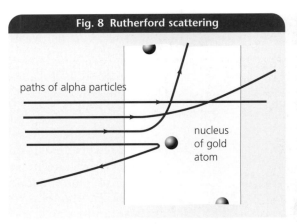

Fig. 8 Rutherford scattering

paths of alpha particles

nucleus of gold atom

Rutherford used the results of this scattering experiment to calculate the size of the nuclear atom. The nucleus has a radius of approximately 10^{-15} m, compared to the radius of the atom which is about 10^{-10} m. Rutherford's model of the atom is often pictured as a miniature solar system: the electrons orbit the nucleus rather like planets orbiting the Sun. This image does not really reflect the true scale of the atom. If we picture the atom scaled up so that the nucleus was the size of the Sun, the electrons would orbit ten times further from the nucleus than Pluto is from the Sun. The atom is almost all empty space with an extremely small, dense nucleus.

Table 1 Nuclear data					
Nuclide	Nucleon number, A	Atomic number	Radius, R/fm	Atomic mass, u	Atomic mass, 10^{-27} kg
$^{12}_{6}\text{C}$	12	6	3.04	12.000	19.932
$^{16}_{8}\text{O}$	16	8	3.41	15.945	26.485
$^{28}_{14}\text{Si}$	28	14	3.92	27.977	46.470
$^{40}_{20}\text{Ca}$	40	20	4.54	39.963	66.378
$^{51}_{23}\text{V}$	51	23	4.63	50.944	84.618
$^{88}_{38}\text{Sr}$	88	38	5.34	87.905	146.010
$^{115}_{49}\text{In}$	115	49	5.80	114.904	190.856
$^{197}_{79}\text{Au}$	197	79	6.50	196.966	327.161

Nuclear density

Electron diffraction patterns give the radius of an oxygen nucleus as 3.4×10^{-15} m.

Modern measurements of nuclear radii are carried out using **electron diffraction** (Fig. 9). Just as radio waves diffract around a hill, a beam of high energy electrons can be made to diffract around a nucleus. This may sound odd; after all we usually imagine electrons to be tiny particles rather than waves. However, in some circumstances electrons can behave like waves. This double nature is referred to as **wave–particle duality** (see Chapter 5).

Electron diffraction measurements show that nuclei with more **nucleons,** neutrons and protons, are larger (Table 1). This seems logical, though the pattern is not a simple one. The relationship between nuclear radius and nucleon number is shown in Fig. 10.

We can use these measurements to calculate the density of an atomic nucleus, like gold for example.

An atom of gold has 79 electrons orbiting its nucleus. The mass of a gold atom is 3.27×10^{-25} kg. The radius of a gold nucleus is 6.5×10^{-15} m. To find the density of its nucleus we first assume that the nucleus is spherical.

Nuclear volume = $\frac{4}{3}\pi r^3$, where r is the radius of the nucleus

$$= \frac{4}{3}\pi (6.5 \times 10^{-15})^3 \text{ m}^3$$

To find the mass of the nucleus we must subtract the mass of 79 electrons;

electron mass = 9.81×10^{-31} kg.

Mass of nucleus
= $(3.27 \times 10^{-25} \text{ kg}) - (79 \times 9.31 \times 10^{-31} \text{ kg})$
= 3.21×10^{-25} kg

$$\text{Density} = \frac{\text{mass}}{\text{volume}},$$

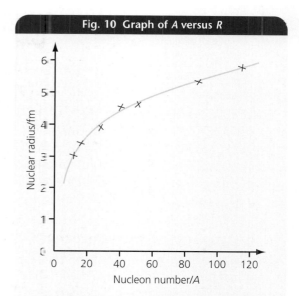

Fig. 10 Graph of A versus R

The radius, R, of a nucleus depends on the nucleon number, A. In fact, $R = r_0 A^{1/3}$, where r_0 is a constant which represents the radius of a single nucleon.

so the density of the nucleus is

$$\frac{3.21 \times 10^{-25}}{\frac{4}{3}\pi (6.5 \times 10^{-15})^3} = 2.79 \times 10^{17} \text{ kg m}^{-3}$$

Notice that subtracting the mass of the electrons makes very little difference because the mass of the electrons is only about 0.02% of the total mass of the atom.

It turns out that all nuclei have approximately the same density, around 2×10^{17} kg m^{-3}. A matchbox full of nuclear matter would have a mass of around 8 thousand billion tonnes, that is 8×10^{12} kg.

8 Use the data in Table 1 to calculate the density of the nucleus of a carbon atom.

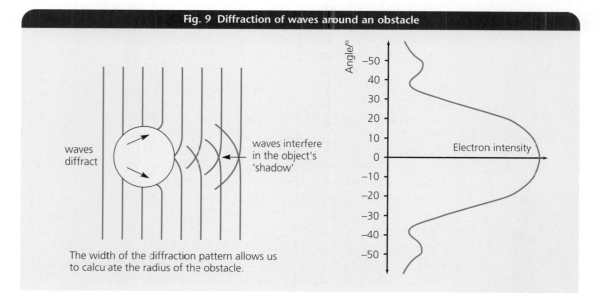

Fig. 9 Diffraction of waves around an obstacle

waves diffract

waves interfere in the object's 'shadow'

The width of the diffraction pattern allows us to calculate the radius of the obstacle.

Angle/°

Electron intensity

Inside the nucleus

Rutherford's model of the nuclear atom has a positively charged nucleus orbited by negatively charged electrons. The particles that carry the positive charge in the nucleus are known as **protons**. The number of protons in the nucleus is known as the **proton number**, or the **atomic number**, and is given the symbol Z. In a neutral atom, that is an atom that carries no overall charge, the number of protons in the nucleus is balanced by the number of electrons orbiting the nucleus. The atomic number of an atom is also the number of electrons in the neutral atom. The atomic number is used to place elements in the periodic table. Hydrogen, with $Z = 1$, has one proton in its nucleus and one electron in orbit. Helium, with $Z = 2$, has two protons and two electrons, and so on through the periodic table, until the heaviest naturally occurring element, uranium, which has 92 protons and 92 electrons.

The strong nuclear force

However, a nucleus composed entirely of positive charges would not hold together. Positive charges repel each other. At the short distances inside the nucleus, the electrostatic forces pushing the protons apart are very large. There is another force acting inside the nucleus, known as the **strong nuclear force** or **strong interaction**, which pulls the nucleus together.

The strong nuclear force has a very short range; it has no effect at separations greater than about 5 fm (5×10^{-15} m). When two protons are 5 fm apart, or closer, the strong interaction acts as an attractive force, pulling the protons closer together. This happens until the separation is less than 1 fm. The strong interaction is then strongly repulsive (Fig. 11). The overall effect of the force is to pull the nucleus together, but the repulsive action prevents it from collapsing to a point.

At distances of less than about 2 fm, the strong nuclear attraction between two protons is larger than the electrostatic repulsion so the nucleus is held together (Figs. 12 and 13).

The neutron

For larger nuclei there is still a problem. The strong nuclear force acts over a much shorter range than electrostatic repulsion. It just isn't

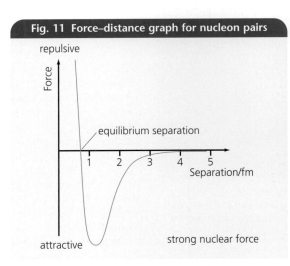

Fig. 11 Force–distance graph for nucleon pairs

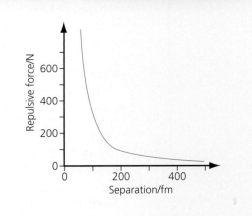

Fig. 12 The electrostatic force between protons

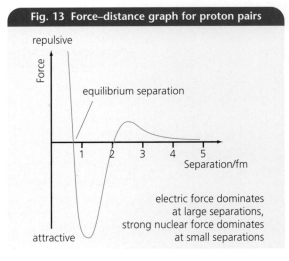

Fig. 13 Force–distance graph for proton pairs

possible to get all the protons close enough together for the strong nuclear force to overcome the electrostatic repulsion. There must be some other particle or particles in the

Table 2 Proton, neutron and electron data			
	Proton	**Neutron**	**Electron**
Symbol	$_1^1p$	$_0^1n$	$_{-1}^0e$
Charge (C)	$+1.602 \times 10^{-19}$	0	-1.602×10^{-19}
Mass (kg)	1.6726×10^{-27}	1.6749×10^{-27}	9.1096×10^{-31}

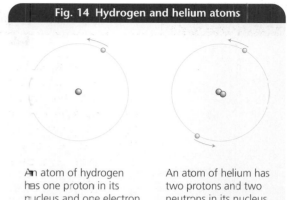

Fig. 14 Hydrogen and helium atoms

An atom of hydrogen has one proton in its nucleus and one electron in orbit around it.

An atom of helium has two protons and two neutrons in its nucleus, and two electrons in orbit around it.

nucleus that helps to glue it together. Chadwick discovered the **neutron** in 1932.

The neutron is a particle with a mass almost identical to that of the proton, but the neutron carries no electric charge (Table 2). It does exert a strong nuclear attraction on protons and on other neutrons. The number of neutrons in a nucleus is known as the neutron number, N.

Protons and neutrons are the only particles in the nucleus. They are referred to as **nucleons**. The strong nuclear force acts between *any* pair of nucleons, whether that is two protons, two neutrons or a proton and a neutron. Electrostatic repulsion acts only between two protons.

Building nuclei

The simplest atom of all is hydrogen. It has one proton in its nucleus and no neutrons. It has only one electron orbiting the nucleus. Helium has two protons and two neutrons in its nucleus, and therefore there are two electrons in orbit around it (Fig. 14).

The total number of nucleons in the nucleus of an atom is referred to as its nucleon number, A. This is the number of protons plus the number of neutrons, so $A = Z + N$.

The nuclear composition of an atom can be described using symbols. The most common form of carbon has six protons and six neutrons in its nucleus. It can be written as $_6^{12}C$. The upper figure is the nucleon number, A, and the lower figure is the atomic number, Z.

In general an element X with an atomic number Z and nucleon number A is written as $_Z^A X$. Using this system, hydrogen is represented as $_1^1H$, and helium is represented as $_2^4He$. The nucleon number is also known as the **atomic mass number**.

The atomic mass number is always an exact integer, since it counts the number of nucleons in the nucleus. The **relative atomic mass** of an element is slightly different. It is found by comparing the mass of the atom to that of the most common form of carbon atom, $_6^{12}C$, whose mass is 19.92×10^{-27} kg. This atom is defined as having a mass of exactly 12 'units'. This 'unit' is known as the unified atomic mass constant, u, and has the value 1.66×10^{-27} kg.

The relative atomic mass of hydrogen is 1.0078 u, which is almost the same as its atomic mass number. Similarly helium, with atomic number 4, has a relative atomic mass of 4.0026 u. Indeed *all* nuclei have relative atomic masses which are very close to their atomic mass numbers. To an accuracy of three significant figures the mass of a proton, the mass of a hydrogen atom and the mass of a neutron are all equivalent to 1 atomic mass unit = 1 u = 1.66×10^{-27} kg (see Table 3).

Table 3 The first five elements in the periodic table					
Element	**Symbol**	**Atomic number, Z**	**Neutron number, N**	**Atomic mass number, A**	**Relative atomic mass, u**
Hydrogen	H	1	0	1	1.0078
Helium	He	2	2	4	4.0026
Lithium	Li	3	4	7	7.016
Beryllium	Be	4	5	9	9.012
Boron	B	5	6	11	11.009

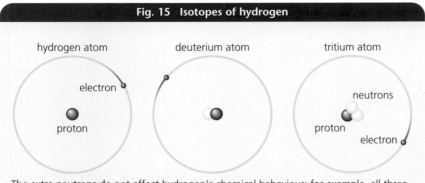

Fig. 15 Isotopes of hydrogen

hydrogen atom   deuterium atom   tritium atom

electron   neutrons

proton   proton   electron

The extra neutrons do not affect hydrogen's chemical behaviour; for example, all three isotopes combine with oxygen to make water.

Isotopes

Elements can exist in more than one atomic form. Though the simplest atom, hydrogen, usually has only one proton in its nucleus some hydrogen atoms have one or two neutrons as well. These different forms of hydrogen are called isotopes (Fig. 15).

The different isotopes of an element have identical chemical behaviour. This is because their atoms have the same number of electrons. Isotopes also have the same number of protons in their nucleus. The difference between isotopes of the same element is simply the number of neutrons

that they have. This makes some isotopes heavier than others. The most common form of carbon has six protons and six neutrons in its nucleus; this isotope is referred to as carbon-12. Carbon-13 has six protons and seven neutrons; carbon-14 has six protons and eight neutrons (see Table 4).

9 An isotope of uranium, atomic number 92, has 235 nucleons in its nucleus. How many protons, neutrons and electrons are there in a neutral atom of uranium-235?

10 Uranium-238, $^{238}_{92}U$, is another isotope of uranium. How does it differ from uranium-235?

11 The lighter elements, like carbon and oxygen, tend to have equal numbers of protons and neutrons in their nuclei. In heavier elements there are always more neutrons. Explain why this is so.

12 List the properties of the strong nuclear force.

Table 4 Isotopes of carbon					
Isotope	Atomic number, Z	Number of electrons	Neutron number, N	Mass number, A	% abundance
Carbon-12	6	6	6	12	98.89
Carbon-13	6	6	7	13	1.11
Carbon-14	6	6	8	14	< 0.001%

KEY FACTS

■ The diameter of a nucleus is about 10^{-15} m. The diameter of an atom is 100 000 times larger.

■ The nucleus contains two different particles of roughly equal mass, the neutron and the proton.

■ Protons are positively charged. Neutrons are uncharged. Both particles are affected by the strong nuclear force which holds the nucleus together.

■ The proton or atomic number, Z, counts the number of protons in a nucleus. The mass or nucleon number, A, gives the total number of nucleons in a nucleus. The nucleus of an element X can be represented by $^A_Z X$.

■ Isotopes of an element have the same number of protons and electrons. They are chemically identical. Different isotopes have different numbers of neutrons in their nuclei.

1.5 Fundamental forces

Although gravity is the dominant force on the scale of planets and stars, it is the weakest of the four fundamental forces.

The search inside the atom revealed a new force, the strong interaction, which acts alongside gravity and electromagnetism to control the motion of particles in the Universe. How many other 'new' forces might there be? Scientists now believe that there are only four different types of forces which act between objects. Some consider that these are all different aspects of the same truly fundamental force (Fig. 16 and Table 5).

The electromagnetic force holds atoms together. It ties electrons into orbits and binds atoms into molecules. This force acts between all charged particles. Electromagnetic forces have an infinite range, though the strength of the interaction decreases with distance. Because there are two charges, positive and negative, the electromagnetic force can either be attractive or repulsive. Two similar charges repel each other, two particles carrying opposite charges will attract each other.

Electromagnetism is responsible for most of the everyday forces between objects. Contact forces, friction, air resistance and tension are all electromagnetic in origin.

Gravity is the other force that has a noticeable impact on our lives. All particles feel the force of gravity. Every mass in the Universe attracts every other mass because gravity is always an attractive force and it has infinite range. The strength of the attraction between two objects depends on their masses and on the distance between them. On the atomic and nuclear scale the effect of gravity is totally negligible.

The strong nuclear force acts inside protons and neutrons and holds them together. The attraction is strong enough to act between nucleons and it is this force which holds the nucleus together. Although it is the strongest of the four forces, it has no effect outside the nucleus. This is because its range is so short, $\approx 10^{-15}$ fm.

The weak interaction is the fourth of the fundamental forces. It exerts its influence on all particles. Despite its name the weak interaction is significantly stronger than

Table 5 The four fundamental forces		
Force / N	Relative strength (within the nucleus)	Range
Strong nuclear	1	10^{-15} m
Weak interaction	10^{-5}	10^{-18} m
Electromagnetic	10^{-2}	Infinite
Gravity	10^{-39}	Infinite

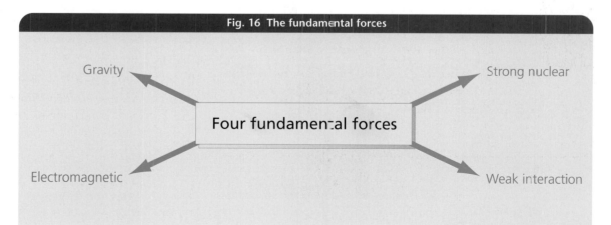

Fig. 16 The fundamental forces

Gravity

Strong nuclear

Four fundamental forces

Electromagnetic

Weak interaction

Most of the forces acting on the skier are electromagnetic. The tension in the tow rope, the drag from the air and water and the buoyancy from the water are all due to the interaction between charged particles.

gravity; however it acts only over an extremely short range, $\approx 10^{-18}$ m. The weak interaction is responsible for beta radiation and has an important role to play in nuclear reactions.

Because there is no negative mass, nothing can be shielded from the effects of gravity. The only way to leave the Earth is by expending a lot of energy.

APPLICATION

In the heart of the Sun

Deep inside the Sun nuclear fusion is gradually converting hydrogen to helium. The reaction

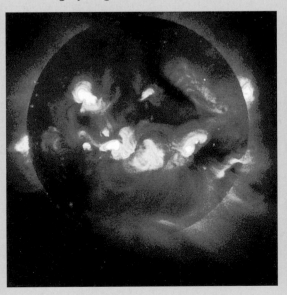

which starts this process involves the fusion of two protons. Two protons have to react to form a deuterium nucleus, a positron (a positive electron), e^+, and an electron-neutrino, ν_e (see next chapter).

$$p^+ + p^+ \rightarrow {}_1^2H + e^+ + \nu_e$$

The probability of this reaction occurring is incredibly small, only 1 in every 10^{31} collisions between protons will result in fusion. This makes winning the National Lottery, with odds of around 1 in 10^7, look like a racing certainty! Even though a typical proton in the Sun undergoes 10^{14} collisions every second, it will take an average of 10 billion years before it eventually reacts in this way with another proton. Without this highly improbable reaction there would be no sunshine, and no life on Earth. The force that is responsible for this reaction is the **weak interaction**.

- There are four fundamental interactions between particles.

- The strong interaction is short range and acts inside the nucleus, holding nucleons together.

- The weak interaction is even shorter range and is responsible for some forms of radioactivity.

- The electromagnetic force acts on charged particles and is responsible for holding atoms and molecules together.

- Gravity is also a fundamental force, but it is insignificant within the atom.

1.6 Grand unified theories

Figure 18.5. Cartoon depicting Michael Faraday at the Royal Institution. Due to A. de Rujula.

Michael Faraday felt that the different forces could be unified. After linking electricity and magnetism Faraday tried to link gravity into the scheme but was unsuccessful No-one has succeeded in this since.

In 1850 Michael Faraday carried out experiments to prove that the forces of magnetism and electricity were different aspects of the same force. Over a hundred years later in 1967 the Pakistani physicist Abdus Salaam and the Americans Steven Weinberg and Sheldon Glashow put forward a theory that linked the weak interaction with the electromagnetic force. The theory predicted the existence of three new particles, the W^+, W^- and Z^0 particles. In 1983 these particles were discovered by Carlo Rubbia's team at CERN in Geneva. The results were in such good agreement with the theory that the electroweak theory is now widely accepted. The search is on for the other particle predicted by the theory, the Higgs boson.

New theories known as grand unification theories (GUTs) are trying to link the electroweak and strong interactions together. Most of these predict that the proton is not stable at all, but will decay with a mean lifetime of 10^{30} years. These decays are difficult to detect, since the lifetime of the Universe so far is only 10^{10} years. Physicists are looking in huge tanks containing about 8000 tonnes of water, trying to catch the one proton per day which should decay. The results so far are inconclusive.

Radiocarbon dating and archaeology

BC, AD or BP?

Most people know what BC and AD mean, but what about BP? It means 'before present', which is taken as 1950. In this year, a baseline measurement was calibrated for radioactive carbon (carbon-14) in living material. All radiocarbon dating depends on this baseline. Before the technique was developed, archaeologists had to rely on evidence such as written accounts and illustrations to date an object. Much of this evidence was unreliable. Scientists needed a way to count time that did not depend on flimsy, circumstantial evidence. This was provided by measuring the rate of decay of radioactive isotopes.

The isotope carbon-14 ($^{14}_{6}C$) is produced naturally when high-energy neutrons in cosmic rays react with nitrogen in the atmosphere: $^{14}_{7}N + ^{1}_{0}n \rightarrow ^{14}_{6}C + ^{1}_{1}H$.

Carbon-14 then reacts with oxygen and is taken in by plants as carbon dioxide.

Carbon-14 decays at a slow, constant rate. After 5730 years, half the carbon-14 atoms in a sample will have decayed to give nitrogen and a high-energy electron – a beta particle: $^{14}_{6}C \rightarrow ^{14}_{7}N + ^{0}_{-1}e$

The time it takes for half of the carbon-14 atoms in any sample to decay is called the **half-life**. The half-life of a particular isotope is constant and provides exactly the type of clock archaeologists need to measure the age of objects.

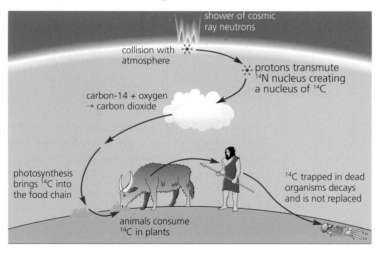

shower of cosmic ray neutrons

collision with atmosphere

protons transmute ^{14}N nucleus creating a nucleus of ^{14}C

carbon-14 + oxygen → carbon dioxide

photosynthesis brings ^{14}C into the food chain

^{14}C trapped in dead organisms decays and is not replaced

animals consume ^{14}C in plants

The US researcher Willard Libby showed that the ratio of ^{14}C to ^{12}C is roughly constant in all organisms while they are alive – about 1 carbon atom in 12×10^{12}. As this carbon-14 breaks down, it is replenished by the natural exchange of carbon that takes place in all living things.

After death, however, active exchange with the world stops. Any carbon-14 that decays now is not

replaced. After about 6000 years, the proportion of carbon-14 in an object has dropped to half of its original value. After another 6000 years, the value is down to a quarter of the original. In this way, it is possible to use the carbon-14 proportion to calculate the time since the death of the object.

1 We often don't use the more accurate figure of 5730 years in dating samples. Why do you think it doesn't matter?

2 Suggest a way that Libby could have checked his new dating technique for reasonable accuracy.

3 Carbon dating becomes unreliable when the level of carbon-14 in the sample reaches 1% of its original value. Calculate the oldest object that could be reliably dated using radiocarbon.

4 The proportion of carbon-14 to carbon-12 in a living being is 1 part in 12×10^{12}, which has a value of 8.33×10^{-14}. Assuming the half-life of carbon-14 is 6000 years, draw a graph to show the way that the proportion of carbon-14 in a sample changes over 20 000 years.

5 Use your graph (or calculator) to find the approximate ages of the following artefacts:

Object	Proportion of carbon-14/ carbon-12
A fragment of cloth	8.33×10^{-14}
Wood from a Viking longship	7.42×10^{-14}
Corn from an Egyptian pyramid	5.56×10^{-14}
Bones from a Stone Age camp	4.68×10^{-14}

A modern technique of radiocarbon dating

A new technique called accelerator mass spectrometry is used to date most radiocarbon samples by distinguishing heavier carbon-14 from lighter carbon-12 and comparing quantities. This allows us to use much smaller samples of the valuable artefact in dating procedures.

A complication for dating is that samples can be contaminated with other materials of different age. For example, ancient fabric can be impregnated with materials of much earlier or later date in the place they are found.

6 Suggest a way to overcome the problem of contamination of samples.

2 Antimatter, neutrinos and leptons

In the early Universe, radiation dominated, but now there is very little radiation left, and matter dominates the Universe.

Fig. 1 Chronology of the Universe

	life	Now
	galaxy discs	5 billion years
	quasars galaxy spheroids	3 billion years
	protogalaxies; first stars	1 billion years
	decoupling	3 000 000 yr
	matter domination	10 000 yr
hydrogen plasma		
	nucleosynthesis	3 min
	electron–positron pairs annihilate	1 s
q q	protons and neutrons created	10^{-5} s
electron–quark soup	weak and electromagnetic	10^{-11} s
Z W	forces separate	
q	baryon genesis	10^{-33} s
	inflation	10^{-35} s
+–	grand unification	10^{-43} s
Planck epoch (quantum gravity)		
Radius of Universe ⟶		The big bang

The material world around us is almost entirely made from just three particles: protons, neutrons and electrons. These are particles of ordinary matter. We know now that for each of these particles there exists an antiparticle. The antiparticles are identical to their ordinary matter twins in mass, but they carry the opposite charge. There is an antielectron, known as a positron, an antiproton and an antineutron. Occasionally one of these antiparticles puts in an appearance, perhaps as a result of a radioactive decay or as part of a shower of cosmic rays. These antiparticles don't exist for very long. When they meet their ordinary matter equivalents they annihilate each other, sending out a burst of radiation. The puzzle is, why is our Universe made from matter and not antimatter?

The very early Universe, only 10^{-35} s after the big bang, contained almost equal quantities of matter and antimatter. By 10^{-5} s almost all the particles had decayed, but there was a small excess of protons left. Originally there must have been an imbalance in the matter–antimatter divide; for some reason the early Universe had more protons than antiprotons. The initial asymmetry was only one part in a billion, but without it the Universe would have been a very different place (Fig. 1).

2.1 Particles and antiparticles

The creation of particles and antiparticles was first observed in 1932. Scientists now believe that matter–antimatter pairs are constantly being created from radiation. Even out in the vacuum of space it seems that particles and antiparticles are popping into existence, and subsequently annihilating each other. This conversion of energy into mass and back again was predicted by Einstein and turns out to be an important idea in nuclear physics.

This event shows the creation of matter and antimatter; a particle and its antiparticle are created and then spiral away from each other in a magnetic field.

Mass and energy

A helium nucleus consists of two protons and two neutrons. Strangely, the mass of the helium nucleus is less than the total mass of its nucleons.

Mass of two protons	$= 2 \times 1.0073\,u$	$= 2.0146\,u$
Mass of two neutrons	$= 2 \times 1.0087\,u$	$= 2.0174\,u$
Total mass of the nucleons		$= 4.032\,u$
Measured mass of helium nucleus		$= 4.0026\,u$

This 'missing mass', the difference between the mass of the nucleus and the total mass of the nucleons, is called the **mass defect** of the nucleus. For helium the mass defect is:

$$4.032 - 4.0026 = 0.0294\,u = 4.88 \times 10^{-29}\,kg$$

The explanation for this missing mass was provided by Einstein. One of the consequences of his special theory of relativity is that mass is just one form of energy. Einstein's theory predicts that under the right circumstances mass can be transferred into energy, and vice versa. The missing mass has been radiated away in the form of energy. This energy, known as the **binding energy**, would have to be returned to the nucleus in order to separate it back into two neutrons and two protons. The binding energy can be calculated using the Einstein relation:

Energy = mass defect × (speed of light)^2

$$E = mc^2$$

Note: the mass is in kg, the speed of light is in m s^{-1} and the energy is in J.

So the binding energy of the helium nucleus is:

$$E = 4.88 \times 10^{-29} \times (3 \times 10^8)^2$$
$$= 4.39 \times 10^{-12}\,J$$

The idea that mass is not created or destroyed now has to be broadened so that it is part of the principle of conservation of energy. The total mass–energy in any system is conserved, but energy and mass may be converted from one to the other. Indeed it is the conversion of mass to energy which powers radioactivity and nuclear fission.

The electronvolt

The joule is rather a large unit of energy to use in atomic and nuclear physics. In practice physicists use the **electronvolt** as a convenient unit of energy. An electronvolt (eV) is the amount of energy gained by an electron as it accelerates through a potential difference (voltage) of 1 volt (Fig. 2).

$1\,eV = 1.6 \times 10^{-19}\,J$.

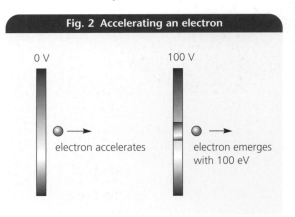

Fig. 2 Accelerating an electron

0 V   100 V

electron accelerates   electron emerges with 100 eV

The energy acquired by particles as they pass through accelerators is usually given in electronvolts. The cathode ray tubes used by Thomson achieved electron energies of around 1 keV (one kilo-electronvolt or 1×10^3 eV). Modern particle accelerators are pushing towards energies of 1 TeV (tera-electronvolt, or 1×10^{12} eV). Even though this is a very large energy for one particle, it is still only a small fraction of a joule:

$$1\,TeV = 1 \times 10^{12}\,eV$$
$$= 1 \times 10^{12} \times 1.6 \times 10^{-19}\,J$$
$$= 1.6 \times 10^{-7}\,J.$$

Fig. 3 A simple cloud chamber

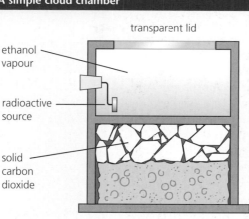

A cloud chamber contains a gas, often air, and a supersaturated vapour. Ionising particles such as beta particles ionise the air as they pass through the chamber. The ions produced act as sites for the vapour to condense around. The liquid droplets that form along the trails of ionised air are just big enough to see and photograph.

transparent lid

ethanol vapour

radioactive source

solid carbon dioxide

The first evidence of a 'positively charged electron' (the track moves down the picture and curves to the left).

Measuring mass in electronvolts

Because mass can be transferred into other forms of energy, we can use units of energy to measure mass. Since

$$E = mc^2$$

then

$$\text{mass} = \frac{E}{c^2}$$

We can use units of GeV/c^2 to measure the mass of small particles. On this scale the mass of an electron is

5.11×10^{-4} GeV/c^2.

The atomic mass unit, u (see Chapter 1) is equivalent to 1.66×10^{-27} kg.

Using $E = mc^2$ this is equivalent to an energy of

$1.66 \times 10^{-27} \times (3 \times 10^8)^2 = 1.5 \times 10^{-10}$ J

or

9.34×10^8 eV.

Therefore 1 atomic mass unit could be expressed as 0.934 GeV/c^2.

1. An electron that is accelerated by a particular X-ray tube gains an energy of 100 keV. Convert this energy to joules.

2. Some of the most energetic cosmic rays have energies of 100 GeV. How many joules is this?

3. A muon is an elementary particle similar to the electron. Its mass is 0.106 GeV/c^2. Convert this to kg.

Antimatter

It was the British physicist, Paul Dirac, who first predicted the existence of a particle with exactly the same mass as the electron, but with a positive charge. Indeed he suggested that all charged particles must have a 'mirror image', a particle of identical mass but opposite charge. Dirac called these particles **antiparticles**.

It wasn't long before the first antiparticle was discovered. In 1932 Anderson was observing tracks made by cosmic rays, high energy particles coming from outer space. He was able to see the tracks left by high energy electrons using a cloud chamber (Fig. 3). Anderson used a strong magnetic field to curve the path of these electrons. He detected tracks that seemed identical to his electron tracks, except they curved in the opposite direction. These were either electrons moving upwards through the apparatus or antielectrons, carrying a positive charge, moving downwards through the apparatus. Anderson put a piece of lead across the middle of his apparatus. This would show which way these particles were moving, since they would slow down after passing through the lead and the curvature of the track would be greater. Anderson found that the particles were indeed moving down through the chamber. He had discovered the electron's antiparticle which he christened the **positron**. Since then other examples of antimatter have been observed.

When a particle meets its antimatter twin the particles are drawn ever closer together by electrostatic attraction, until they **annihilate** each other. The mass of the two particles is converted to energy and appears as a pair of photons of electromagnetic radiation. This is a very clear example of mass–energy equivalence, as predicted by Einstein's special theory of relativity.

4. Explain why a curved track in the photograph top left could be an electron moving upwards, or a positron moving downwards. How would Anderson have known that the curved track was a positron, rather than an electron?

Pair production

Annihilation is the conversion of matter to energy. The opposite process, where matter is 'created' from energy, is referred to as **pair production** (Fig. 4). In this process a **photon** of electromagnetic energy, a gamma ray for example, is converted into a pair of particles. There are always two particles created; one is conventional matter and the other is its antimatter twin. This satisfies the conservation of charge, since before the event there is only a photon, which carries no charge. After the pair production there are always two particles of opposite charge, making the total charge zero.

A gamma ray would have to have a minimum energy of 1.02 MeV before it could create an electron–positron pair. This is because the mass of the pair has an energy equivalence of 1.02 MeV. If the photon had more energy than this, the surplus energy would appear as kinetic energy carried by the positron and the electron.

In 1955 the first antinucleon was discovered. The Berkeley accelerator could accelerate protons up to energies of 6 GeV and collide them into protons in a fixed target. The collision produced antiprotons by the reaction

$$p + p \rightarrow p + p + p + \bar{p}$$

This really is a remarkable reaction. By colliding two protons together we have produced an extra proton and an antiproton. If this happened when two snooker balls

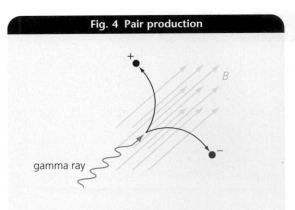

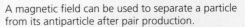

Fig. 4 Pair production

A magnetic field can be used to separate a particle from its antiparticle after pair production.

collided, the table would fill up with extra balls! The extra mass needed to create the proton–antiproton pair has come from the energy of the initial protons. The minimum energy required to do this is

$2 \times$ mass of the proton $\times$ (speed of light)^2

Minimum
energy $\quad = 2m_{\mathrm{p}}c^2$

$\qquad = 3.0096 \times 10^{-10}$ J or 1.8 GeV

A year later the antineutron was produced by using antiprotons to collide into protons:

$$\bar{p} + p \rightarrow n + \bar{n}$$

The mass of a particle is always identical to its antiparticle, but other properties, such as charge, are opposite.

KEY FACTS

■ Every particle has an antimatter equivalent. The antiparticles have equal mass and equal, but opposite, charge.

■ Mass and energy can be converted to each other. The formula linking the conversion is $E = mc^2$.

■ Particle–antiparticle pairs can form from radiation if the energy is high enough. The process is called pair production.

■ When a particle meets its antiparticle, they annihilate each other, releasing energy as radiation.

■ Atomic energy is often measured in electronvolts, eV. 1 eV = 1.6×10^{-19} J

APPLICATION **PET scanning**

Matter–antimatter annihilation (Fig. 5) is used in the medical technique of PET (positron emission tomography) scanning. A radioactive isotope, such as carbon-11, which emits positrons, is injected into the body. When a positron is emitted it only travels about 1 mm in the body before it meets an electron and is annihilated. Because two gamma rays are emitted in opposite directions it is relatively easy to locate the exact position of the radioactive isotope.

This technique, using carbon-11 as a positron emitter, is used in brain imaging (Fig. 6). The patient inhales a small dose of carbon monoxide 'labelled' with carbon-11. Carbon monoxide molecules attach themselves to the

haemoglobin in red blood cells and are transported around the body. When the carbon-11 decays it reveals areas of high blood flow which correspond to active regions in the brain. PET scans can show which areas are busy when the patient is reading, listening or just sitting with their eyes closed.

We can calculate the energy of the two gamma rays emitted when an electron and a positron annihilate each other. The mass of an electron is 9.1×10^{-31} kg.

The mass of the positron is exactly the same as the electron, so

total mass = 1.82×10^{-30} kg

Using $E = mc^2$,

energy released $= 1.82 \times 10^{-30} \times 9 \times 10^{16}$
$= 1.638 \times 10^{-13}$ J

In electronvolts this is

$$\frac{1.63 \times 10^{-13}}{1.6 \times 10^{-19}} = 1.06 \times 10^6 \text{ eV}$$

$$= 1.06 \text{ MeV}$$

This energy is shared between the two gamma rays, so each one has an energy of 511 keV.

5 How much energy is released when a proton meets an antiproton?
Mass of a proton = 1.672×10^{-27} kg.

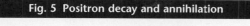

Fig. 5 Positron decay and annihilation

Positron decay

Carbon-11 is an artificially produced positron emitter. When it decays, a proton is transformed into a neutron and a positron:

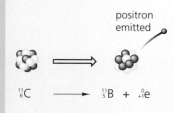

positron emitted

$$^{11}_{6}\text{C} \longrightarrow ^{11}_{5}\text{B} + ^{0}_{+1}\text{e}$$

Positron annihilation

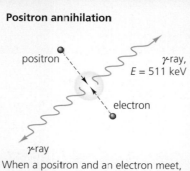

positron

γ-ray, $E = 511$ keV

electron

γ-ray

When a positron and an electron meet, they annihilate each other. Two identical gamma rays of energy 511 keV are emitted in opposite directions.

Fig. 6 Positron emission tomography

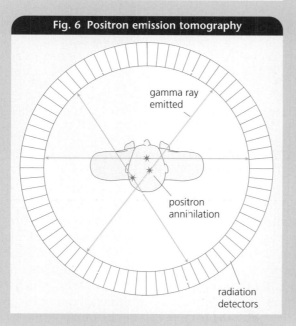

gamma ray emitted

positron annihilation

radiation detectors

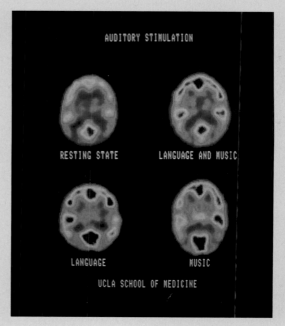

Heisenberg's uncertainty principle

Producing pairs of particles from the energy of photons may seem odd, but it gets odder: pairs of particles can be created from no energy at all! According to a law of physics called Heisenberg's uncertainty principle, an amount of energy ΔE can be borrowed for up to a time Δt as long as the product of ΔE and Δt is not bigger than a certain value, h. This value is 6.626×10^{-34} J s, and is called Planck's constant:

$$\Delta E \times \Delta t < h$$

This process of 'borrowing' allows short-lived events to occur that would otherwise need extra energy. At the very small scale, energy is creating and destroying 'virtual particles' all the time, even in a 'vacuum'. What was once imagined as literally *nothing* is now imagined as a bubbling soup of virtual particle–antiparticle pairs.

These are **virtual particles**, rather than real ones. They are not directly observable. Energy is 'borrowed' from the vacuum to create the particle pairs, and then paid back when the particles annihilate again. The more massive the particle, the more energy has to be borrowed and the shorter the lifetime of the particle.

Although these particles are virtual they should leave behind their signature. The theory says that they should have an effect on the energy levels in atoms, which in turn affects the light given out by the atom. The effect, known as the Lamb shift, is only about one part in a billion. This strange prediction has been verified by laboratory experiments.

The spectrum from the vapour of an element. The light that is emitted has wavelengths that are known precisely. The creation of virtual particles shifts these lines by one part in 10^9.

2.2 Dark matter

Detailed astronomical observations of hundreds of galaxies have revealed a puzzle. There is simply not enough visible mass in each galaxy to cause the gravity needed to hold them together. A similar problem exists on the huge scale of galactic clusters; there isn't enough detectable matter to give rise to the huge gravitational forces needed to pull the galaxies together. Astronomers have come to believe that much of the matter in the Universe is invisible. Perhaps as much as 90% of the mass in the Universe is in the form of what is called 'dark matter'.

It may be that some of this dark matter is in the form of ordinary particles, like protons and neutrons, with which we are already familiar. However, current theories suggest that most of the dark matter in the Universe must be of a different kind. Some of the candidates are exotic particles, such as magnetic monopoles or WIMPs (weakly interacting massive particles). One theory, known as supersymmetry (affectionately abbreviated to SUSY), suggests that every known particle has a supersymmetric partner. For example, the photon is supposed to have a supersymmetric partner known as the photino, which has mass. This theory would double the number of known particles. Though there is some supporting evidence for this theory, no SUSY particles have yet been detected.

Another possibility is that the neutrino, a particle that we can detect here on Earth, has mass. For some time it was assumed that the neutrino was massless, but new experiments have suggested that it has a small, non-zero, mass. This would be very significant because neutrinos are so numerous. The extra gravitational attraction could be enough to reverse the expansion of the Universe and pull the Universe back together into a final 'big crunch'.

Physicist Sheldon Glashow was sceptical when a new massive particle, the magnetic monopole, was discovered on St Valentine's Day, 1982. One year later no-one had managed to replicate the discovery. Glashow sent the 'discoverer' a special Valentine's message

Roses are red:
Violets are blue.
The time is now right
For monopole two.
It still hasn't turned up!

2.3 Neutrinos

Cosmic Gall

Neutrinos, they are very small.
They have no charge and have no mass
And do not interact at all,
The Earth is just a silly ball
To them through which they simply pass,
Like dustmaids down a drafty hall
Or photons through a sheet of glass.
They snub the most exquisite gas,
Ignore the most substantial wall,
Cold-shoulder steel and sounding brass,
Insult the stallion in his stall,
And, scorning barriers of class,
Infiltrate you and me! Like tall
and painless guillotines, they fall
Down through our heads into the grass,
At night, they enter at Nepal
And pierce the lover and his lass
From underneath the bed – you call
It wonderful; I call it crass.

John Updike

Neutrinos are probably the most numerous particles in the Universe. They outnumber the protons and neutrons of ordinary matter by a factor of 1 000 000 000. Neutrinos created at the time of the big bang still permeate the Universe. There are about 100 or so of them in each cubic centimetre of space.

Neutrinos are also emitted by radioactive nuclei and from nuclear reactions. The Earth is bathed in neutrinos from the Sun. Every second about 60 thousand million solar neutrinos pass through every square centimetre of the Earth's surface.

Despite this, neutrinos are extremely difficult to detect. They are not charged and so they do not feel electrostatic attraction or repulsion. In fact, neutrinos only interact with other matter very weakly indeed; the vast majority of neutrinos that strike the Earth pass straight through with no deviation at all. Experiments that are looking for neutrinos often use large tanks of water, usually placed well underground, surrounded by sensitive light detectors. They are looking for the very occasional flash of light that signifies that a neutrino has interacted with a neutron, or that an antineutrino has interacted with a proton.

The existence of the neutrino was first predicted by Wolfgang Pauli in 1930. At the time, physicists were struggling with a problem caused by beta radiation. Beta particles are fast moving electrons emitted by the nuclei of some radioactive atoms. Unlike alpha particles, which are emitted with a well defined energy, beta particles are emitted with a range of energies (Fig. 7).

Beta particle emission seemed to contravene the principle of the conservation of energy. If a certain amount of energy is

Fig. 7 Energies of alpha and beta particles

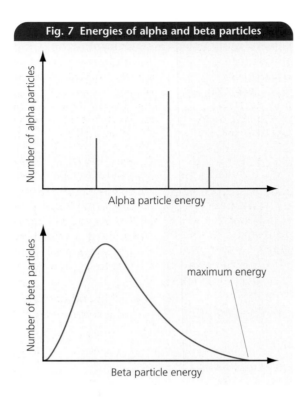

Number of alpha particles

Alpha particle energy

Number of beta particles

maximum energy

Beta particle energy

Fig. 8 Neutrino and antineutrino

10^{12} neutrinos pass through your body every second. Don't worry, it is extremely unlikely that even one of them will ever interact with any of the particles of your body. Even if it did, you wouldn't notice it. Neutrinos are unaffected by the electromagnetic or strong nuclear forces. They interact with other particles through the weak interaction, which is very short range, 10^{-18} m. Their mass, if they have any at all, is extremely small. Neutrinos have no charge but they do carry energy. They also have a property known as 'spin'.
In fact, since neutrinos are not charged, the main difference between a neutrino and an antineutrino is the direction of its spin.

transferred by each radioactive decay, why did the emitted beta particle have a range of possible energies? Pauli suggested that another particle, the neutrino, is also emitted in beta decay. The neutrino carries away the balance of the energy, so that the total energy of the decay is always constant.

The neutrino is represented by the symbol v_e. The subscript, e, stands for 'electron' and these neutrinos are more properly referred to as electron-neutrinos. The neutrino also has its antiparticle, the antineutrino, which is written as $\bar{v}_e$ (Fig. 8). This antineutrino is emitted during beta decay.

6 Read Pauli's letter below. Which of Pauli's predictions about the neutrino proved to be correct? Where do we now believe he was mistaken?

Pauli was unable to attend a nuclear physics conference, as he had to go to a ball, so he sent a letter proposing the existence of a new particle. At the time only three particles were known to exist, the electron, the proton and the photon, so predicting a new particle was quite courageous.

Zurich
December 4, 1930

Dear radioactive ladies and gentlemen,

I beg you to listen most favourably to the carrier of this letter. He will tell you that, in view of the … continuous beta spectrum, I have hit upon a desperate remedy to save the law of conservation of energy. This is the possibility that electrically neutral particles exist which I will call neutrinos,[1] which exist in nuclei … and which differ from the photons also in that they do not move with the speed of light. The mass of the neutrinos should be of the same order as that of the electrons and should in no case exceed 0.01 proton masses. The continuous beta spectrum would then be understandable if one assumes that during beta decay a neutrino is emitted with each electron in such a way that the sum of the energies of the neutrino and electron is constant …

I admit that my remedy may look very unlikely, because one would have seen these neutrinos long ago if they really were to exist. But only he who dares wins … Hence one should seriously discuss every possible path to rescue …

Your most obedient servant,

W. Pauli

---

[1] *Pauli actually called his new particle the neutron, but the particle we now call the neutron was discovered two years later. Pauli's predicted particle was re-christened by the Italian Enrico Fermi, it became known as the neutrino … the little neutral one!*

First catch your neutrino

It was 26 years before Pauli's courageous proposition could be confirmed. The problem is that neutrinos are so difficult to detect. On average a neutrino emitted from a beta decay would pass through a light-year's thickness of lead and only interact once. The only way of finding a few of these elusive particles is to look in a place where there should be a huge number of them. In 1956 Cowan and Reines set up their apparatus next to the Savannah River nuclear reactor. The neutrino flux was expected to be 10^{13} neutrinos per second through each cm^2.

Cowan and Reines were actually looking for the antineutrinos, $\bar{v}_e$, that are emitted from beta decay. In beta-minus decay, a neutron, n, decays into a proton, p, and an electron, e⁻. An antineutrino is also emitted. The decay can be written

$$n \rightarrow p + e^- + \bar{v}_e$$

The experiment was designed to look for the reaction of the antineutrino with a proton:

$$p + \bar{v}_e \rightarrow n + e^+$$

Cowan and Reines used large tanks of liquid scintillator with a high hydrogen content. The liquid also contained a cadmium compound. The idea was that the positron would annihilate almost immediately and release two gamma rays, which would cause a prompt flash of light in the scintillator. A short, but predictable, time later the neutron would be absorbed by the cadmium and would emit a gamma ray, which would lead to another flash of light. The neutrino would reveal itself by the right coincidences between the flashes of light. After three years of experiments Cowan and Reines were able to telegraph Pauli to say that they had found the neutrino.

7a Why did the liquid scintillators need a high hydrogen content?

b Why do you think the experiment was installed next to a nuclear reactor?

2.4 Leptons

The electron and the neutrino are fundamental particles of the **lepton** family. The term 'lepton' comes from the Greek word *leptos*, meaning small. Leptons are not affected by the strong nuclear interaction. Because the neutrino carries no charge, it is not affected by the electromagnetic force either. The neutrino only interacts with other particles through the weak interaction. This explains why 1000 billion of them can pass through your body each second without you noticing.

A fierce debate still rages about the mass of the neutrino. For some years it was believed to have zero mass, but recent experiments (1998) suggest that neutrinos do indeed have a small mass, much less than that of an electron. If this is true, it will be a significant result since mass will be a property of all matter. A non-zero mass for the neutrino would also affect our calculations of the mass and the gravitational force in the Universe, simply because the number of neutrinos in the Universe is so huge.

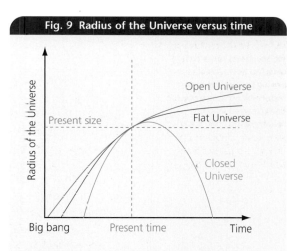

Fig. 9 Radius of the Universe versus time

The future of the Universe depends on the density of matter. If there is not enough mass in the Universe, it will keep expanding forever (an 'open Universe'). If there is enough mass in the Universe, it is said to be 'closed': gravity will eventually stop the expansion and pull the Universe back towards a 'big crunch'.

The solar neutrino problem

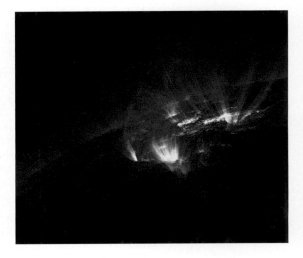

Deep inside an old Japanese mine, one kilometre underground, is the world's largest neutrino telescope. The Super Kamiokande detector consists of 50 000 tonnes of ultra-pure water, surrounded by 11 000 highly sensitive light detectors. The detectors are looking for the flash of light that comes when an electron hurtles away at high speed after being hit by a neutrino. Even in such a large tank of water this is a rare event.

One of the experiments at the Super Kamiokande is designed to detect neutrinos from the Sun. We know that the neutrino flux from the Sun is caused by nuclear reactions deep within the solar core. These reactions are well understood and the theory is in excellent agreement with measurements, except for one thing. Over half of the solar neutrinos seem to disappear on their way to Earth.

How is it that these neutrinos go missing? One theory is that the neutrinos oscillate: they change from one type of neutrino to another *en route* to Earth. If this really does happen, it implies that neutrinos do have mass. The latest results from Kamiokande confirm this idea.

The muon was discovered by detectors flown high in the air, looking for particles in cosmic rays. It still isn't clear why the Universe needs another, heavier, version of the electron.

The muon

From 1930, until the building of high energy particle accelerators in the 1950s, most of the new discoveries in particle physics came from studies of cosmic rays. Cosmic rays are high energy particles that emanate from space, from exploding stars for example. Fortunately the Earth's atmosphere protects us from most of this radiation. However, some of the rays penetrate to the surface of the Earth, and many interact with atoms in the atmosphere, showering the Earth's surface with the products of nuclear reactions. Cosmic ray detectors are often flown high in the atmosphere using high-altitude balloons in order to detect more particles.

It was cosmic ray experiments that first revealed the existence of the **muon**, μ^-, in 1937. The muon turned out to be a close relative of the electron. The muon carries the same charge as the electron but its mass is about 207 times greater.

In 1962 it was shown that the neutrinos that accompany muons are not the same as electron-neutrinos. The muon-neutrino, v_μ, and its antiparticle, $\bar{v}_\mu$, are also fundamental particles which carry no charge.

The tau particle

In 1978 yet another member of the lepton family was discovered. The tau-minus, τ^-, particle was observed by a team working on electron–positron collision at Stanford in the USA. The tau particle has the same charge as the electron and the muon but is much more massive, around 3 500 times the mass of the electron.

The Stanford team collided electrons and positrons together to produce a tau-minus and its antiparticle, the tau-plus:

$$e^+ + e^- \rightarrow \tau^+ + \tau^-.$$

For several months these results were not generally accepted, until a team working in Germany managed to replicate the results.

It seems logical to suppose that this new, heavier version of the electron has its own type of neutrino and antineutrino, the v_τ and the $\bar{v}_\tau$. These have not been observed (summer 1999) but this is not really worrying, since the particles will be very difficult to detect. Recent work has suggested that there may not be any other members of the lepton family, though no-one has yet been able to explain why there are three types of electron and why they should have the masses that they have.

	Symbol	Charge (in terms of proton charge)	Mass (in terms of electron mass)
Table 1 A summary of leptons and antileptons			
Leptons			
electron	e^-	−1	1
electron-neutrino	v_e	0	≈0
muon	μ^-	−1	207
muon-neutrino	v_μ	0	≈0
tau	τ^-	−1	3 500
tau-neutrino	v_τ	0	≈0
Antileptons			
positron	e^+	+1	1
antineutrino	$\bar{v}_e$	0	≈0
antimuon	μ^+	+1	207
muon-antineutrino	$\bar{v}_\mu$	0	≈0
antitau	τ^+	+1	3 500
tau-antineutrino	$\bar{v}_\tau$	0	≈0

KEY FACTS

■ The leptons, and their antiparticles, antileptons, are believed to be fundamental particles.

■ There are three charged leptons, the electron, the muon and the tau particle.

■ Each of these charged leptons has an associated neutrino.

■ Each of the charged leptons has an antiparticle which has an identical mass but whose other properties, charge for example, are opposite.

Money to burn?

When physicists started research into the basic building blocks of matter, they had no idea that useful applications would spring from their work. This was called 'blue sky' research because it was research for the sake of knowledge rather than applied research, which aims to improve a particular technology. CERN in Switzerland is the home of much blue sky research and is supported by funds from American and European governments. This kind of research is amongst the most expensive in the World. But do we need this kind of research? Should the funds be used for things that are more immediately useful?

1 Prepare for a discussion about what sort of research governments should support. Do you want to fund CERN's hyper-expensive machines?

Preparing for your discussion

When you prepare for a discussion you need to think about:

- What are your starting points? Note down the attitudes and ideas you already have on a scrap of paper.
- Now take a long look at your assumptions. Try to sort then into statements of fact and statements of opinion.
- Now look at the statements of fact. Do any need to be checked? Can you find the evidence to back up your facts? If you can't – are you sure your 'fact' is correct?
- Then look at your opinions. Can you unpick the reasons behind them? Since they are opinions not facts you will not be able to find something that will prove them to be correct – but you should be able to find some evidence to suggest that they are reasonable.
- Finally decide which of your opinions you feel strongest about. What are the things you are extremely unlikely to change? This is not always a bad thing – to believe in something very strongly is not wrong – but do recognise that a strongly held belief is not as strong in an argument as a simple fact.
- As well as deciding on your strongest opinions, look for areas where you are uncertain or willing to be convinced. Where do you feel able to compromise?

Making a successful discussion

After you have assembled your thoughts and some evidence you should be able to join the discussion. Again a few simple rules:

- Make sure you listen – and check that you understand what people are saying. Ask questions like 'So are you saying…?' and try to paraphrase what someone has said. They can correct you if you have misunderstood them.
- Hear what people are saying – people who *listen carefully* learn much more from discussions than the people who *talk continually*.
- Remember that some opinions will annoy and irritate you. Don't let your feelings interfere with your thinking!
- Be prepared to learn and change your position on some issues. And when you agree with people – tell them.
- Try not to tell people they are stupid – even if they are! Insults rarely work as a way of convincing someone.

Remember that discussions should be win–win situations. Even if you end up disagreeing with someone you can learn something by understanding their point of view. Not every discussion is an attempt to convince someone that you are completely right in every detail and that they need to change their ideas to match yours.

Rounding off your discussion

At the end of your discussion try to agree a statement that summarises the opinions of the whole group. This might contain two lists of statements:

- Statements everyone can support
- Statements most of the group can support

Question for Chapter 1

1 a Describe the principal features of the *nuclear model of the atom* suggested by Rutherford. (4)

b When gold foil is bombarded by alpha particles it is found that most of the particles pass through the foil without significant change of direction or loss of energy.

A few particles are deviated from their original direction by more than 90°.

Explain, in terms of the nuclear model of the atom and by considering the nature of the forces acting,

(i) why some alpha particles are deflected through large angles,

(ii) why most of the alpha particles pass though the foil without any significant change in direction or significant loss of energy. (5)

(AQA PH01 Sample 2000 Q1)

Question for Chapter 2

2 A particle accelerator is designed to accelerate antiprotons through a potential difference of 2.0 GV and make them collide with protons of equal energy moving in the opposite direction. In such a collision, a proton–antiproton pair is created as represented by the equation:

$$p + \bar{p} \rightarrow p + \bar{p} + p + \bar{p}$$

You may assume that the rest energy of the proton is 940 MeV.

a State how an antiproton differs from a proton.

b Give the total kinetic energy of the particles, in GeV, before collision.

c State the rest energy of the antiproton.

d Calculate the total kinetic energy of the particles, in GeV after the collision.

3 The fundamental particles

Hubble telescope.

The Hubble telescope allows us to look deeper into space than ever before. This photograph taken by Hubble's Deep Field Camera shows the most distant objects that have ever been seen. The photograph shows us the Universe when it was only one third of its current age.

'The Universe began 15 thousand million years ago in a violent explosion. After 10^{-35} seconds the Universe was 3 mm across and had a temperature of 10^{28} degrees Kelvin. From this hot 'big bang' the Universe expanded rapidly, cooling as it grew, until today the visible Universe has a radius of 3×10^{24} m and its temperature has dropped to 3 degrees Kelvin (–270 °C)'

This is the current view of the creation of the Universe. The 'big bang' theory is almost universally accepted amongst physicists, though many questions remain to be answered. How did matter form? Why do particles have particular masses? How are the different forces between particles connected?

To answer these questions we need to look back in time, to see what conditions were like in the early Universe. This is not as difficult as it sounds: every time we look at the night sky we are also looking back in time. The light from the nearest star takes four years to reach us; the light from the our neighbouring galaxy, Andromeda, is

1.5 million years old when we see it. Hubble's Deep Field Camera can detect light that left its source over 10 thousand million years ago. Perhaps a larger, more powerful telescope would let us look further away, and so further back in time until we could see light from the very beginning of the Universe? Unfortunately this approach does not work.

In the early Universe conditions were too hot for neutral atoms to exist. Until the Universe was about 300 000 years old it was composed of charged particles which were constantly emitting and absorbing radiation. Light could not travel freely and so the early Universe was opaque. Even with an infinitely powerful telescope we could not see the Universe before it was about 300 000 years old. However, high energy particle physics is now giving us a way of recreating the conditions in the early Universe.

The particle accelerators at CERN, in Geneva, are designed to collide matter together at very high energies. These collisions create new particles that would have been common in the early Universe. The highest energies created so far can simulate the conditions that would have existed only 10^{-10} s after the big bang. Physicists who are probing the nature of matter are also hoping to answer questions about how the Universe began.

3.1 The particle explosion

The muon turned up most unexpectedly. The particle physicist Isadore Rabi was eating in a Chinese restaurant when he heard of it, 'Who ordered that?' he demanded.

Until 1937 it seemed that the particle physics world was a fairly simple one. Its only massive inhabitants were the neutron, the proton and the electron. There was also the massless photon which transferred electromagnetic energy. The first antiparticle, the positron, had been discovered in 1931, after the existence of antimatter was predicted by Paul Dirac, and scientists expected to find antiparticle equivalents for the proton and neutron. Other than that, the picture seemed complete.

The first indication that life might not be so straightforward came in 1937 when the muon was discovered in cosmic rays. The muon turned out to be a big brother for the electron. Before long other new particles were discovered. By the 1960s there were hundreds of known particles. The situation was similar to that in chemistry a hundred years before: many elements had been discovered but scientists felt that there couldn't be so many different fundamental particles. Indeed it turned out that all the atoms and isotopes were made from different combinations of just three particles: the neutron, the proton and the electron. Perhaps the bewildering array of different sub-atomic particles was also indicative of a simpler, underlying structure.

Table 1 The particle explosion: the discovery of elementary particles				
Year	Particle	Discoverer	Source of particles	Approximate energy
1897	Electron	J. J. Thomson	Cathode ray tube	keV
1911	Nucleus	Rutherford	Alpha particles	MeV
1931	Positron	Anderson	Cosmic rays	MeV–GeV
1932	Neutron	Chadwick	Alpha-particle source	MeV
1937	Muon	Neddermeyer/Anderson	Cosmic rays	GeV
1947	Pions	Powell (Bristol University)	Cosmic rays	GeV
1948–	K-mesons			
	τ, Ξ, Λ, θ, Σ and other particles		Cosmic rays	GeV
1955	Antiproton/antineutron	Berkeley	Synchrotron	GeV
1957	Neutrino		Nuclear reactor	
1961	Muon-neutrino			
1964	Ω⁻ particle	Brookhaven		
1969	Up and down quarks	Stanford (SLAC)	Linear accelerator	10 GeV
1974	J/ψ (charmed quark)	SLAC/Brookhaven		
1976	Tau-lepton	SLAC		
1977	Y hadron (bottom quark)	Fermilab		
1983	W, Z bosons	CERN, Geneva	Proton synchrotron	500 GeV
1995	Top quark	Fermilab		
???	Higgs boson	?		
???	Supersymmetry particles?	?		
???	Exotic dark matter	?		

Classifying particles

Current theories now suggest that there are only three families of particles, the **leptons**, the **hadrons** and the **gauge bosons** (Fig. 1). We will learn about these families in the course of this chapter.

Leptons

There are twelve different members of the lepton family: three types of electrons and the three types of neutrinos and all their antiparticles (Fig. 2). All the leptons are fundamental particles and cannot be broken down into other particles. (The leptons were discussed in Chapter 2.)

Hadrons

By the 1960s cosmic ray and accelerator experiments had revealed a large number of different particles in addition to all the leptons described above. Particles now known as pi-mesons, kaons and delta mesons were discovered, all of which had masses much larger than the leptons (Table 2). This group of particles is referred to as hadrons (hadron is from the Greek word, *hadros*, meaning bulky).

Some hadrons were found to carry charge, some did not. All the hadrons, except the proton, were found to be unstable. Like radioactive atoms, after a certain time they decay into something else. Even the neutron is unstable when it is free of the nucleus. The neutron decays with a half-life of around 11 minutes via the reaction:

$$n \rightarrow p + e^- + \bar{v}_e$$

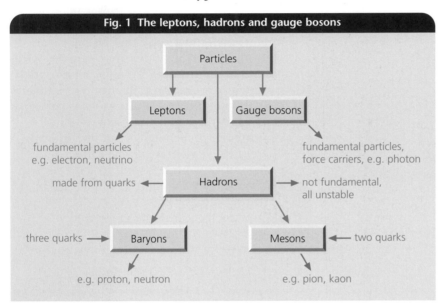

Fig. 1 The leptons, hadrons and gauge bosons

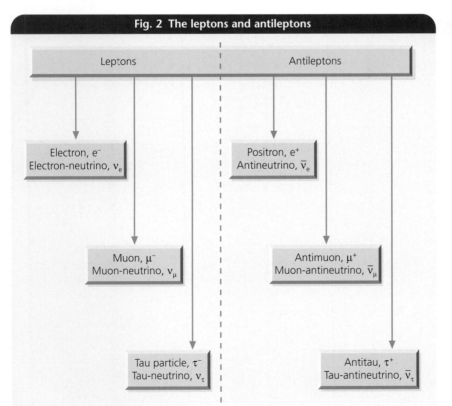

Fig. 2 The leptons and antileptons

Table 2 Hadron data					
Name	**Symbol**	**Rest mass (GeV/c^2)**	**Q**	**B**	**S**
K minus	K^-	0.4937	−1	0	−1
K plus	K^+	0.4937	1	0	1
K zero	K^0	0.4977	0	0	1
K zero bar	$\overline{K}^0$	0.4977	0	0	−1
lambda	Λ	1.116	0	1	−1
neutron	n	0.9396	0	1	0
phi	ϕ	1.020	0	0	0
pi minus	π^-	0.1396	−1	0	0
pi plus	π^+	0.1396	1	0	0
pi zero	π^0	0.1350	0	0	0
proton	p	0.9383	1	1	0
sigma minus	Σ^-	1.197	−1	1	−1
sigma plus	Σ^+	1.189	1	1	−1
sigma zero	Σ^0	1.192	0	1	−1
xi minus	Ξ^-	1.315	−1	1	−2
xi zero	Ξ^0	1.321	0	1	−2

3.2 Hadron reactions and conservation laws

A large number of hadron reactions and decays have now been studied. Most of the results are from particle accelerators where protons, or other charged particles, are made to collide with a target material at high energies. It soon became apparent that some reactions could, and did, happen whereas other reactions never actually took place. It seems as if some reactions are forbidden.

Our first ideas about charge come from experiments on electrostatics. We know that charged objects exert a force on each other. We also know that there are two 'types' of charge, which we call positive and negative. Positively charged bodies attract negatively charged ones, but repel other positive charges. Similarly two negatively charged bodies repel each other, so two electrons exert a force on each other that pushes them apart.

particles are denoted using a symbol, often a Greek letter such as π, Δ or Σ. A superscript is used to denote charge, e.g. π^+ carries a single positive charge, π^- carries a single negative charge and π^0 is uncharged.

One of the rules that governs the interactions between particles is the **conservation of charge**. In all the charged particle reactions that have been studied, the total charge of the particles has always been conserved. That means that the total charge after the reaction is always the same as the total charge before the reaction takes place. No reactions that contravene this rule have ever been observed.

> **1** Which of these reactions is forbidden because it contravenes the conservation of charge?
> **a** $\Sigma^+ \rightarrow \Lambda + \pi^-$
> **b** $\pi^- + p \rightarrow \Sigma^- + K^+$
> **c** $\pi^- + p \rightarrow \Sigma^- + K^+ + \pi^-$

Charge conservation

Many hadrons, and leptons, carry a charge. We define the charge on the proton to be +1. The charge carried by other particles is related to that. The charge on the electron is therefore equal to –1, the positron charge is +1, and the neutron has a charge of 0. Other

Conservation of baryon number

There are some reactions, allowed by charge conservation, which have never been detected. This is because there are conservation laws which apply to quantities other than charge. These place new restrictions on which reactions can take place. One of these is the conservation of **baryon number**, B.

Example: Particle interactions and conservation of charge, Q			
	Before	**After**	
Reaction	$p + p$ $\longrightarrow$	$p + p + \pi^- + \pi^+$	
Q	$1 + 1 = 2$	$1 + 1 + (-1) + 1 = 2$	Allowed
Reaction	$p + \pi^-$ $\longrightarrow$	$p + \pi^+$	
Q	$1 + (-1) = 0$	$1 + 1 = 2$	Not allowed

Example: Particle interactions and conservation of baryon number, B			
	Before	**After**	
Reaction	$p + p$ $\longrightarrow$	$p - p + n$	
B	$1 + 1 = 2$	$1 - 1 + 1 = 3$	Not allowed
Reaction	$p + p$ $\longrightarrow$	$p - p + \pi^0$	
B	$1 + 1 = 2$	$1 - 1 + 0 = 2$	Allowed

Table 3 Hadrons: baryons, antibaryons and mesons		
Baryons	**Antibaryons**	**Mesons**
B = baryon number = 1	B = baryon number = −1	B = baryon number = 0
Proton, p and neutron, n	Antiproton, $\bar{p}$	Pi-mesons (pions), π^+, π^-, π^0
Sigma particles, Σ^+, Σ^-, Σ^0	Antineutron, $\bar{n}$	K-mesons (kaons), K^+, K^-, K^0

N.B. All particles which are not hadrons, the leptons and bosons (to be discussed later), have a baryon number of 0.

The hadrons can be divided into two groups, the **mesons** and the **baryons**; both groups have their antiparticles. Baryons are named from the Greek word *barus* meaning heavy as they were thought to be heavier than mesons. We now know that this is not always true. Mesons and antimesons have a baryon number, $B = 0$, baryons have $B = 1$ and the antibaryons have $B = -1$ (Table 3). Reactions between any of these hadrons can only occur if the baryon number is conserved. Just like charge, the total baryon number before the collision has to be the same as the total baryon number afterwards.

2 Which of these reactions is forbidden because it contravenes the conservation of baryon number?

a $\Sigma^+ \rightarrow p + \pi^0$

b $p + p \rightarrow p + p + n$

c $p + p \rightarrow p + p + \pi^0 + \pi^0$

Strangeness

Both conservation of charge and conservation of baryon number have to be satisfied if a reaction is to take place. But some reactions which satisfy these two rules and seem to be perfectly possible have never been observed.

The particles called K-mesons, or kaons, caused particular problems to particle physicists. Kaons appear as the decay products of some neutral particles, but they always seemed to turn up in pairs. Kaons didn't appear individually, although there was nothing in charge or baryon number conservation that would prevent this. The kaons also had an unusually long lifetime, 10^{-10} s, compared to other, apparently similar, hadrons which have typical lifetimes of the order of 10^{-23} s.

Murray Gell-Mann, a physicist at Caltech, suggested that there was yet another property, like charge and baryon number, that had to be conserved in hadron reactions. He called this property **strangeness**. All hadrons are given a strangeness number, S (Table 4). Strangeness has to be conserved in a reaction, just like charge and baryon number.

In these 'production' reactions, where two or more particles combine, strangeness is always conserved. However, sometimes when strange particles decay, their strangeness changes (see 'The weak interaction', p. 48).

3 Which of these reactions is forbidden because it contravenes the conservation of strangeness?

a $p + \pi^- \rightarrow K^- + \Sigma^+$

b $\pi^- + p \rightarrow K^+ + \Sigma^-$

c $K^+ + p \rightarrow \pi^+ + \Sigma^+$

Table 4 Strangeness, S, for some hadrons			
S = Strangeness = −2	S = −1	S = 0	S = +1
Ξ^- (xi minus)	Λ (lambda)	Proton, p	Kaons, K^+ and K^0
Ξ^0 (xi zero)	K^- (K-minus)	Neutron, n	
	Sigma particles, Σ^+, Σ^-, Σ^0	Pions, π^+, π^-, π^0	

N.B. All particles which are not hadrons, the leptons and bosons (to be discussed later), have zero strangeness.

Example: Particle interactions and conservation of strangeness, S	Before		After	
Reaction	$p + \pi^-$	$\rightarrow$	$K^0 + \Lambda^0$	
S	$0 + 0 = 0$		$1 + (-1) = 0$	Allowed
Reaction	$p + \pi^-$	$\rightarrow$	$K^- + \Sigma^+$	
S	$0 + 0 = 0$		$(-1) - (-1) = -2$	Not allowed

An experiment deep within an old zinc mine in Japan is looking for evidence of proton decays. The proton is now thought to be unstable, though its lifetime may be of the order of 10^{32} years, much longer than the life of the Universe so far.

4 For a reaction to take place it must satisfy conservation of charge, baryon number and strangeness. Say which of these reactions could not take place and give the reason (see Table 2).

a $\pi^+ + n \rightarrow \pi^+ + \Lambda$

b $n \rightarrow \pi^+ + e^-$

c $K^+ + K^- \rightarrow \pi^0$

d $\pi^+ + p \rightarrow \Sigma^+ + K^+$

e $p + \pi^- \rightarrow K^+ + K^-$

f $p + \pi^- \rightarrow K^0$

KEY FACTS

- All sub-atomic particles are classified as leptons, hadrons or bosons.

- There are three groups of leptons; the electron, muon and tau particle and their neutrinos and antiparticles. All leptons are fundamental particles.

- Hadrons can be classified as baryons or mesons. Hadrons are not fundamental and all of them are unstable (though the proton has a very long lifetime).

- Hadrons have a fixed value for charge, Q, baryon number, B, and strangeness, S. Reactions between hadrons can only take place if the reaction conserves charge, Q, baryon number, B, and strangeness, S.

- Decays of strange particles that take place by the weak interaction do not conserve strangeness.

More about leptons

Lepton conservation

It is not only baryon number that must be conserved in a particle reaction. The total number of leptons after any reaction must be the same as the number of leptons before the reaction. In fact the conservation law is even more constraining than that. Each branch of the lepton family, the electron, the muon and the tau particle, have their own lepton number which must be conserved separately (Table 5).

For example the decay of a muon, $\mu^- \rightarrow e^- + v_\mu + \bar{v}_e$, satisfies all of these criteria, as well as charge conservation.

Before the reaction: $L_e = 0$
$L_\mu = 1$
$L_\tau = 0.$

After the reaction: $L_e = 1 + (-1) = 0$
$L_\mu = 1$
$L_\tau = 0.$

Leptons and spin

One way of studying electrons in atoms is to look at the spectrum of light emitted by an element (see Chapter 5).

Studies of the spectra produced by atoms in a magnetic field led scientists to believe that

The spectrum of mercury vapour tells us something about the way that electrons are arranged in a mercury atom.

electrons have a property now known as **spin**. Although the spin of an electron is a complicated concept it can be thought of as a tiny ball spinning about an axis through its centre. Electrons, and all the leptons, have a spin of $^1/_2$. Any particle which has half-integer spin ($^1/_2$, $^3/_2$, $^5/_2$, ... etc.) is known as a **fermion**. Fermions obey the Pauli exclusion principle which says that any two identical particles in the same system cannot have identical values for energy, momentum and spin. Because electrons are fermions there are strict rules about how many electrons can occupy each energy level within an atom. This governs how many electrons occupy each shell in an atom and leads to the enormous range of different atoms with different chemical properties.

The concept of spin also points to the existence of the neutrino. The decay of the neutron that leads to beta radiation can be written $n \rightarrow p + e^- + \bar{v}_e$. Spin is another conserved quantity. Since the spin of the neutron, proton and electron are all equal to $^1/_2$, there had to be another particle, the neutrino, to 'balance the books' and account for the missing spin.

Particles with integer values of spin (0, 1, 2, 3, ...) are called **bosons**. Mesons and antimesons are bosons. Baryons have spin $^1/_2$ and are therefore **fermions**. Photons, and the other force-carrying particles, are also bosons.

5 A positive pion decays into a muon and a third particle X, $\pi^+ \rightarrow \mu^+ + X$. Suggest what the third particle could be. Explain what conservation rules this has to obey.

Table 5 Leptons												
			Particle					Antiparticle				
Name	Rest mass (MeV/c^2)	Spin	Symbol	Charge	L_e	L_μ	L_τ	Symbol	Charge	L_e	L_μ	L_τ
Electron	0.511	1/2	e^-	−1	1	0	0	e^+	1	−1	0	0
Electron-neutrino	Probably zero	1/2	v_e	0	1	0	0	$\bar{v}_e$	0	−1	0	0
Muon*	105.7	1/2	μ^-	−1	0	1	0	μ^+	1	0	−1	0
Muon-neutrino	Probably zero	1/2	v_μ	0	0	1	0	$\bar{v}_\mu$	0	0	−1	0
Tau*	1784	1/2	τ^-	−1	0	0	1	τ^+	1	0	0	−1
Tau-neutrino	Probably zero	1/2	v_τ	0	0	0	1	$\bar{v}_\tau$	0	0	0	−1

* These are unstable with mean lifetimes of 2.2×10^{-6} s (muon) and 3×10^{-13} s (tau). The muon is sometimes referred to as a μ meson but it should not be. The old term is now obsolete.

3.3 The three quark theory

The number and properties of all the different hadrons is rather confusing. The crucial question for physics in the 1960s was, were all these different particles actually fundamental? Or was there a simpler, underlying structure that would explain the composition and properties of these particles? At the turn of the century when scientists were faced with almost a hundred different types of atom, Rutherford's scattering experiments had helped to show that there was an underlying structure that explained the variety of atoms. This structure turned out to depend on just three particles; protons, electrons and neutrons. In the 1960s it was another scattering experiment, this time carried out at Stanford in the USA, that revealed the structure inside hadrons (Fig. 3).

The Stanford Linear Accelerator Center (SLAC) in California accelerated electrons to an energy of around 6 GeV, high enough to probe inside protons and neutrons. The SLAC experiment found that a significant proportion of the high energy electrons were scattered through a large angle. These results indicated that the neutrons and protons are not particles of uniform density, but have point-like charged particles within them.

The SLAC results confirmed the theory put forward by Murray Gell-Mann and George Zweig a few years earlier. Gell-Mann had grouped the hadrons together in families (Fig 4), rather as Mendeleev had grouped the elements together in the periodic table about 100 years before. The patterns that he and others created could be explained by supposing that all hadrons were composed of smaller constituents which Gell-Mann christened **quarks**. The SLAC experiments confirmed that hadrons are not fundamental particles at all, but were composed of combinations of the different types of quark.

Gell-Mann suggested that there were three different quarks which he labelled **up, u, down, d,** and **strange, s.** Each of these quarks has a specified mass and values for charge,

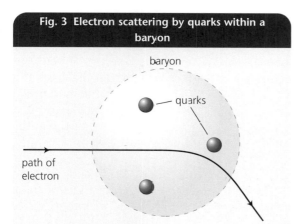

Fig. 3 Electron scattering by quarks within a baryon

baryon

quarks

path of electron

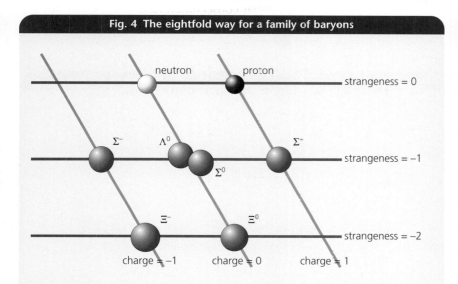

Fig. 4 The eightfold way for a family of baryons

neutron   proton
strangeness = 0

Σ⁻   Λ⁰   Σ⁺
Σ⁰
strangeness = –1

Ξ⁻   Ξ⁰
strangeness = –2

charge = –1   charge = 0   charge = 1

These eight baryons all have a baryon number of 1. There is a similar grid for the antiparticles (baryon number –1). The Λ^0 and Σ^0 differ only in their energy. Gell-Mann called these patterns the 'eightfold way', a term which came from Buddhism.

The term 'quark' was given to these particles by Murray Gell-Mann. He took the term from 'Three quarks for Muster Mark', a quotation from *Finnegans Wake* by James Joyce.

Table 6 Properties of quarks and antiquarks								
Quark	Baryon number B	Charge Q	Strangeness S	Antiquark	Baryon number B	Charge Q	Strangeness S	Mass (GeV/c^2)
up, u	1/3	2/3	0	$\bar{u}$	−1/3	−2/3	0	0.005
down, d	1/3	−1/3	0	$\bar{d}$	−1/3	1/3	0	0.01
strange, s	1/3	−1/3	−1	$\bar{s}$	−1/3	1/3	+1	0.2

N.B. Note that the strange quark is defined to have a strangeness of −1. Its antiparticle, the antistrange quark, has a strangeness of 1.

baryon number and strangeness (Table 6). Each quark has a corresponding antiquark of exactly equal mass but opposite values for charge, baryon number and strangeness.

Using the quark model it is possible to describe all hadrons in terms of combinations of quarks and antiquarks. Baryons are always combinations of three quarks, not necessarily the same type. Antibaryons are combinations of three antiquarks. Mesons are always composed of a quark and an antiquark, again not necessarily the same type.

The properties of each hadron can now be explained in terms of the quarks that it is made from. The total charge on the hadron is the sum of the quark charges. The same can be said for the total baryon number and strangeness. The quark model is surprisingly simple. Only two types of quark, the up and the down, are needed to account for the properties of neutrons and protons which together make up almost all of everyday, observable matter (Table 7). The two antiquarks, $\bar{u}$ and $\bar{d}$, are needed to explain the existence of the antiproton and the antineutron.

Table 7 Quark structure of proton and antiproton				
A proton is composed of two up quarks and a down quark				
	Up, u	Up, u	Down, d	Proton, p
Charge, Q	2/3	2/3	−1/3	1
Baryon number, B	1/3	1/3	1/3	1
Strangeness, S	0	0	0	0
Antiproton: $\bar{p} = \bar{u} + \bar{u} + \bar{d}$				
	$\bar{u}$	$\bar{u}$	$\bar{d}$	Antiproton, $\bar{p}$
Charge, Q	−2/3	−2/3	1/3	−1
Baryon number, B	−1/3	−1/3	−1/3	−1
Strangeness, S	0	0	0	0

6 A neutron is composed of two down quarks and an up quark. An antineutron is an anti-up and two anti-down quarks, $\bar{n} = \bar{u} + \bar{d} + \bar{d}$. Construct tables (as in Table 7) for the neutron and antineutron that show how their properties are the sum of the quark properties.

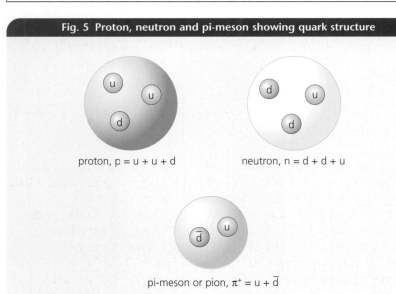

Fig. 5 Proton, neutron and pi-meson showing quark structure

proton, p = u + u + d

neutron, n = d + d + u

pi-meson or pion, π^+ = u + $\bar{d}$

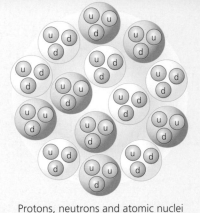

Fig. 6 The quark structure of a nucleus

Protons, neutrons and atomic nuclei are constructed entirely from up quarks and down quarks.

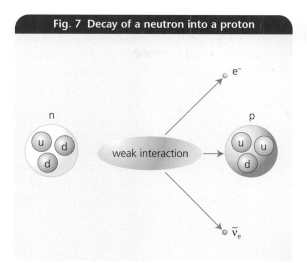

Fig. 7 Decay of a neutron into a proton

Table 8 Simple quark model description of pions and kaons

π^-	$u\bar{d}$
π^-	$\bar{u}d$
π^0	$u\bar{u}$ or $d\bar{d}$
K^-	$u\bar{s}$
K^-	$\bar{u}s$
K^0	$d\bar{s}$
$\overline{K}^0$	$\bar{d}s$

Table 9 Quark structure of a K$^+$ meson

	u	$\bar{s}$	K$^+$
Charge, Q	2/3	1/3	1
Baryon number, B	1/3	−1/3	−1
Strangeness, S	0	1	1

Mesons are always quark–antiquark pairs. The properties of a meson are just the sum of the properties of its constituent quarks. A meson's antiparticle is the opposite combination of quark–antiquark. For example the pi-plus meson is formed from the two quarks, $u\bar{d}$, whilst its antiparticle, the pi-minus, is formed from the opposite combination of $\bar{u}d$ (Table 8).

The quark model has been extraordinarily successful in describing and predicting the properties of hadrons. It can be used to understand what is happening in nuclear reactions or decays, for example during a beta particle emission. In beta-minus emission a neutron decays to a proton, emitting an electron and an antineutrino in the process. The quark theory tells us that inside the neutron a down quark has changed into an up quark, emitting an electron and an antineutrino.

7 Why is it that mesons can only have strangeness ±1 or 0, whereas a baryon may have strangeness of ±3, ±2, ±1 or 0?

KEY FACTS

■ Hadrons are composed of particles called quarks.

■ Quarks have antiparticles, known as antiquarks. Antiquarks have the same mass but opposite values of charge, baryon number and strangeness.

■ Baryons are composed of three quarks or three antiquarks.

■ Mesons are composed of a quark and an antiquark.

■ Three types (or flavours) of quark, up, down and strange, were sufficient to describe all the hadrons that were known up to 1970.

Difficulties with the three quark model

There are some problems with the simple quark model. The main difficulty is that no-one has been able to isolate a quark. A solitary quark has never been seen. The masses and properties of the quarks have to be inferred from those of the hadrons that they make up. The reason why an individual quark has never been observed is due to the enormous amount of energy that would be needed to rip it from within a hadron. Relatively speaking, splitting the atom is easy: it takes only a few electronvolts to tear an electron away and ionise the atom. Breaking up a nucleus requires more energy, in the region of millions of electronvolts. To separate a single quark from a proton by only a centimetre or two would require 10^{13} eV. This amount of energy is more than enough to create a new quark–antiquark pair. Rather than tear the quarks apart, new quarks would be created which would replace the one you were trying to remove. All this would achieve would be the creation of a new meson. It seems unlikely that we will ever be able to observe an unconfined quark.

A fourth quark

The three quark model was initially very successful, but several arguments suggested that there should be a fourth quark. One of these arguments was quark–lepton symmetry. In the early 1970s four leptons had been discovered (eight counting the antiparticles). These four leptons could be grouped as follows:

Leptons e^- μ $Q = -1$
ν_e ν_μ $Q = 0$

Only three quarks had been identified. These were grouped:

Quarks u ??? $Q = +2/3$
d s $Q = -1/3$

Symmetry suggests that there should be another quark with charge +2/3. The quark was expected to have a larger mass than the other three and to carry zero strangeness. It was expected to have a new conserved property of its own. This property became known as **charm**. In November 1974 two independent teams of experimenters in the USA discovered a new massive meson which became known as the J/ψ particle. It had zero strangeness and zero charm and was eventually identified as being composed of a charm quark and an anticharm quark pair, $c\bar{c}$. Because the particle had no overall charm it was referred to as having 'hidden charm'. Later particles containing a single charm quark together with other quarks were discovered; these particles were said to have naked charm.

8 Is it possible to have a particle with hidden charge, or hidden strangeness?

3.4 The standard model

The top quark was revealed by the pattern of its decay products in this collision at Fermilab. One of the decay products is a muon (in the yellow rectangle)

We now know that protons and neutrons, as well as the other baryons and mesons, are not fundamental particles. They are made up of quarks in different combinations. It seems that quarks are fundamental particles and it is at least possible that there isn't another layer of structure beneath the quarks.

Not all particles are composed of quarks though. The lepton family, i.e. the electron, the muon and the tau particle and their associated neutrinos, are fundamental particles in their own right.

There is a symmetry between the leptons and the quarks in that there are three families of each. This symmetry isn't just satisfying, it is essential for the theory which explains quark behaviour (quantum chromodynamics, QCD) to work properly. The number of pairs of leptons, one with charge –1 and the other with charge 0, must be matched by the number of pairs of quarks, one with charge +2/3, the other with charge –1/3.

Leptons e^- μ τ
ν_e ν_μ ν_τ

Quarks u c t
d s b

Until the discovery of the tau particle both families, leptons and quarks, only had four members. After the tau particle turned up, the final column in the quark table was added to

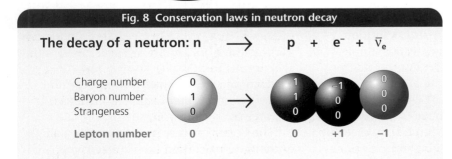

Fig. 8 Conservation laws in neutron decay

The decay of a neutron: n $\longrightarrow$ **p + e⁻ + $\bar{\nu}_e$**

	n		p	e⁻	$\bar{\nu}_e$
Charge number	0		1	–1	0
Baryon number	1		1	0	0
Strangeness	0		0	0	0
Lepton number	0		0	+1	–1

Table 10 Properties of the six quarks						
Type of quark	Charge Q	Baryon number B	Strangeness S	Charm C	Bottomness B	Topness T
u	+2/3	1/3	0	0	0	0
d	−1/3	1/3	0	0	0	0
c	+2/3	1/3	0	1	0	0
s	−1/3	1/3	−1	0	0	0
t	+2/3	1/3	0	0	0	1
b	−1/3	1/3	0	0	−1	0

preserve the symmetry. This suggested that there should be two 'new' quarks, both considerably heavier than those previously discovered. The two new quarks were given the names **top** and **bottom**. They were expected to have zero strangeness and charm but they should each have a new conserved property of their own, namely topness, T, and bottomness, B.

In 1977 a new, heavy meson was discovered at Fermilab in Chicago. This new meson was christened Y, and it had all the right characteristics to be composed of a bottom–antibottom pair, b$\overline{\text{b}}$. Following the case of the charmed quark, this was referred to as having hidden bottom. It wasn't long before a hadron was found which had non-zero bottomness; naturally these hadrons are referred to as **naked bottoms**.

In 1995, a team of scientists at Fermilab completed the set: a hadron containing the predicted top quark was discovered. The top quark took such a long time to find because it was much more massive than anticipated, over 40 times heavier than the bottom quark and 35 000 times heavier than the up and down quarks that make up ordinary nuclear matter.

3.5 Exchange particles or gauge bosons

There is one final group of fundamental particles known as **exchange particles** or **gauge bosons**. On a sub-atomic scale these particles are responsible for transmitting the fundamental forces that hold nuclei and atoms together. On a larger scale they are responsible for the everyday forces which affect our lives.

Exchange particles and Feynman diagrams
When two bodies exert a force on each other, perhaps the floor exerting a force on your shoes, what is it that happens between the two bodies? What happens to make the two objects repel each other? The Japanese physicist Hidewa Yukawa suggested that when two particles, A and B, exert a force on each other a **virtual particle** is created. This virtual particle can travel between particles A and B and affect their motion. The virtual particle, which may exist for only a short time, is referred to as an exchange particle and it is the mediator of the force.

The idea of a force being carried by an exchange particle can be pictured by considering two people on ice skates (Fig. 9).

If one of them throws a ball to the other one both the skaters' motion will be affected, in fact they will be repelled away from each other. We have to stretch the analogy a bit to understand attraction, but if you imagine a boomerang being thrown, rather than a ball,

then the two skaters will be drawn together.

The exchange particles which are transferred between fundamental particles are known as **gauge bosons** and each fundamental force has its own boson or bosons.

The electrostatic force

The electrostatic force is carried between charged particles by the **photon, γ**. When two charged particles, say two electrons, exert a force on each other, a photon is exchanged between them. We use Feynman diagrams to represent what happens (Fig. 10).

The photon is a massless, chargeless particle. In fact it is its own antiparticle: a photon is identical to an antiphoton. The photon is a boson, since it has spin of 1.

The strong interaction

It was the strong interaction, the force that acts between nucleons, that Yukawa was working on when he proposed the idea of exchange particles. He suggested that these exchange particles could be travelling at close to the speed of light across the nucleus. An exchange particle moving at close to the speed of light has to exist for about 10^{-23} s if it is to have time to travel across the nucleus. This enabled Yukawa to predict a maximum mass for the particle, which became known as the pi-meson or pion.

At a deeper level the strong interaction is mediated by gauge bosons called **gluons** that pass between quarks. The pion is simply a vehicle carrying gluons between hadrons. There are eight different gluons, none of which have ever been detected as an individual particle, though scattering experiments have given a strong indication that the theory is correct.

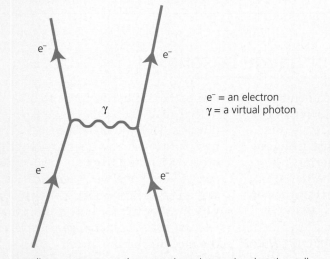

Fig. 9 Analogy of particle interactions

(a) Exchanging a heavy object

A   B   A   B

(b) Exchanging a boomerang

A   B   A   B

Fig. 10 Feynman diagram of photon exchange

This Feynman diagram shows two electrons feeling the electric force as a result of a photon being exchanged between them.

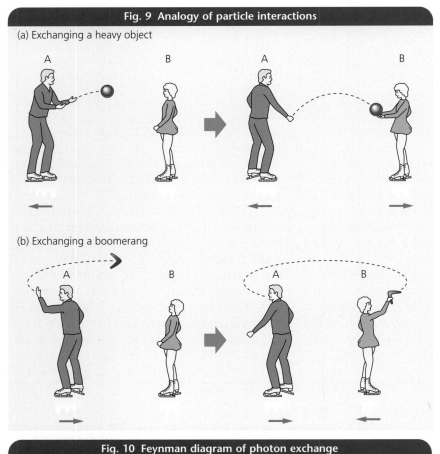

e^- e^-

γ e^- = an electron
                         γ = a virtual photon

e^- e^-

Feynman diagrams represent the events in an interaction, but they tell us nothing about the actual paths of the two particles. The angles in the diagrams have no significance.

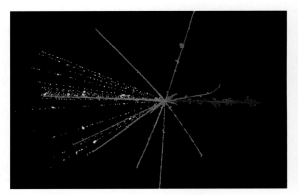

Yukawa's predicted pion was discovered in 1947 in cosmic ray experiments. This cosmic ray collision produces a spray of particles including 16 pions, shown in yellow.

Fig. 11 Feynman diagram of pion exchange

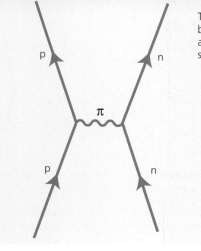

This Feynman diagram shows a pion being exchanged between a proton and a neutron. This exchange is the source of the strong nuclear force.

p = a proton
n = a neutron
π = a pion

Fig. 12 Feynman diagram of beta decay

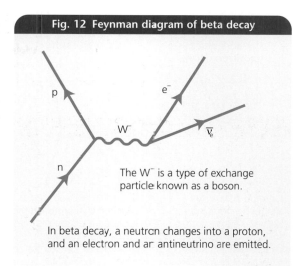

The W^- is a type of exchange particle known as a boson.

In beta decay, a neutron changes into a proton, and an electron and an antineutrino are emitted.

The weak interaction

The weak interaction has a very short range. This suggests that its gauge bosons are relatively massive, since a large mass/energy would mean a short lifetime and therefore the exchange particles could only travel a short distance. The weak interaction has three gauge bosons, known as **intermediate vector bosons**, W^+, W^- and Z. These bosons were eventually discovered in 1983 at CERN in Geneva.

The weak interaction acts on both leptons and hadrons. In fact it is the only force, other than gravity, which acts on neutrinos. This explains the fact that they are so reluctant to interact with anything. The weak interaction can alter the 'flavour' of a quark. Since W bosons carry charge, the weak interaction may lead to an up quark being changed into a down quark. When the weak interaction acts on hadrons it may change the strangeness of the particles, so that strangeness is not conserved in reactions that take place via the weak interaction.

9 Positron emission happens when a proton is transformed into a neutron. A positron and a neutrino are emitted. Draw a diagram (similar to Fig. 13) to show what happens to the quarks.

Fig. 13 Changes in quarks due to weak interaction

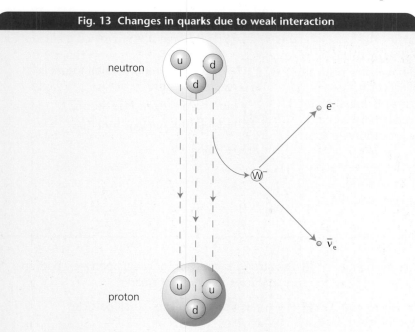

The exchange of a W^- boson changes a neutron into a proton by changing the 'flavour' of a quark. A down quark is transformed into an up quark. The W^- then decays, via the weak force, into an electron and an antineutrino.

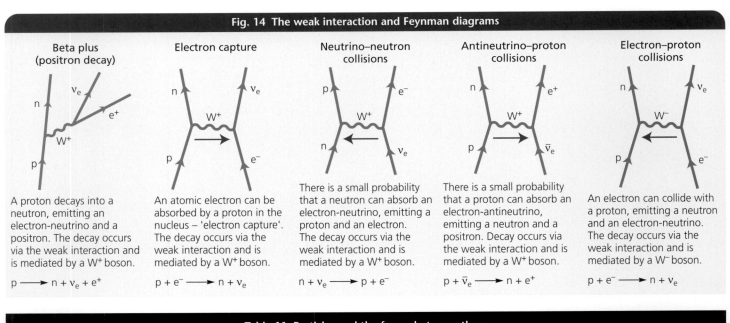

Fig. 14 The weak interaction and Feynman diagrams

Beta plus (positron decay)

A proton decays into a neutron, emitting an electron-neutrino and a positron. The decay occurs via the weak interaction and is mediated by a W^+ boson.

$$p \longrightarrow n + \nu_e + e^+$$

Electron capture

An atomic electron can be absorbed by a proton in the nucleus – 'electron capture'. The decay occurs via the weak interaction and is mediated by a W^+ boson.

$$p + e^- \longrightarrow n + \nu_e$$

Neutrino–neutron collisions

There is a small probability that a neutron can absorb an electron-neutrino, emitting a proton and an electron. The decay occurs via the weak interaction and is mediated by a W^+ boson.

$$n + \nu_e \longrightarrow p + e^-$$

Antineutrino–proton collisions

There is a small probability that a proton can absorb an electron-antineutrino, emitting a neutron and a positron. Decay occurs via the weak interaction and is mediated by a W^+ boson.

$$p + \bar{\nu}_e \longrightarrow n + e^+$$

Electron–proton collisions

An electron can collide with a proton, emitting a neutron and an electron-neutrino. The decay occurs via the weak interaction and is mediated by a W^- boson.

$$p + e^- \longrightarrow n + \nu_e$$

Table 11 Particles and the forces between them

Force		Strong	Weak	Electromagnetic	Gravity
Carried by		Gluons	W^+, W^- and Z bosons	Photons	Gravitons?
Particle family	*Particles*				
Leptons	Electrons, muons	✗	✓	✓	✓
	Neutrinos (e, μ, τ)	✗	✓	✗	✓
Hadrons	Mesons	✓	✓	✓ (if charged)	✓
	Baryons	✓	✓	✓ (if charged)	✓

Gravity

The gauge boson which carries the gravitational force has been named the graviton. It is predicted to have zero rest mass and zero charge, but it has never been detected. Because the graviton is massless it has infinite range. Gravity acts between all particles, but it is the weakest of all the four forces.

10 What are the differences and the similarities between gravity and the electromagnetic interaction?

11 Why do neutrinos interact so weakly with other forms of matter?

12 Which of the fundamental forces is responsible for:

a binding electrons into atoms;

b holding the nucleus together;

c beta decay?

Fig. 15 Quark colour

Quarks have been given one more property – colour or 'colour charge'.
Quarks can have red, green or blue colour and only exist together in 'colourless' mixes:

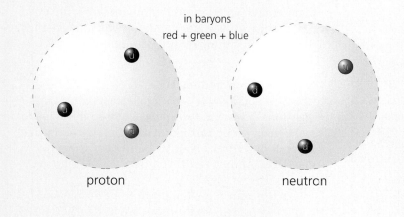

in baryons
red + green + blue

proton

neutron

in mesons
blue + antiblue
red + antired
green + antigreen

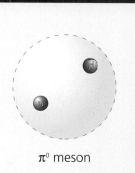

π^0 meson

The standard model is becoming more and more complex. It now seems that every quark has to carry a colour charge, so that an up quark can be red, blue or green. This multiplies the number of quarks by three. If we believe that the Universe has only a few basic building blocks we may need to look deeper for the underlying structure.

The final picture?

The list of fundamental particles now includes 24 matter particles (six leptons and six quarks and their antiparticles) and five force particles (gluons, photons, W's, Z's and the graviton). Amongst these only the graviton has yet to make an appearance. No-one has yet been able to explain why we need three lepton and quark families, when it seems that we could manage quite well with only one. Neither has anyone been able to explain why the particles have the mass values that they do, why for example is the top quark so massive? Scientists at CERN are searching for one more exotic particle, the Higgs boson, which is supposed to be instrumental in giving the other particles their masses. New theories like supersymmetry and string theory are making predictions which have yet to be tested. The story of particle physics is far from over.

Fig. 16 The constituents of matter

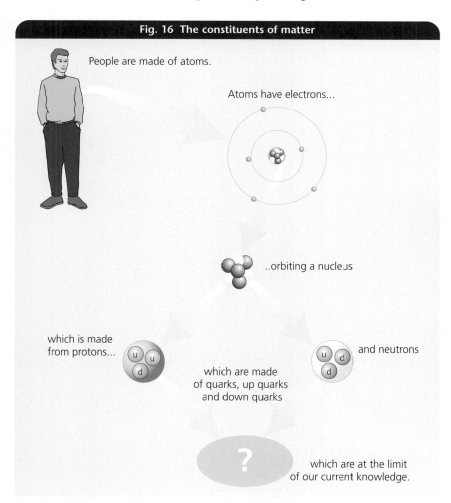

People are made of atoms.

Atoms have electrons...

...orbiting a nucleus

which is made from protons...

which are made of quarks, up quarks and down quarks

and neutrons

?

which are at the limit of our current knowledge.

Dirac meets anti-Dirac

The fundamental particles

Sub-atomic physics is 'hot'. There are a number of books written for the general public which cover this ground. Stephen Hawkings' *A Brief History of Time* sold millions of copies even though it was a theoretical treatment of some very difficult modern physics. This branch of physics is fascinating because it contains surprises – little seems to follow sensible rules in the sub-atomic world.

1 Prepare a presentation entitled '*The fundamental particles*' for a GCSE science class. The idea is to show how exciting and interesting modern physics can be and so encourage students to take up physics at Advanced Level.

Preparing your presentation

Think about your 'audience' – in this case you will practise your presentation with your teaching group. They will already be familiar with much of the physics and the use of scientific conventions and symbols. Since you know the group you can make certain assumptions about their background knowledge – but remember that your eventual aim is to give this same presentation to a younger group.

Visual interest

Choose your images carefully – are they simply there to add interest or do they carry important information? If they carry information think about how you can make sure your audience takes time to study the images and extract the relevant material.

How will you display your images – OHT slides, handouts, video or computer screen?

Emphasising the main points

How will you help your listeners to remember your main points? Will you use summaries on a flip chart or handouts? If you use handouts will you give them out at the beginning or at the end of your presentation?

Involving your audience

How will you involve your audience? Asking questions is a useful technique – but do not hope to make them up on the spot. Plan your questions in advance and think about the kind of answers you might get. And how will you treat people who get the answers wrong?

Practise your presentation in front of someone you know to help you sort out any little problems. This is a very good way to prepare for the real thing.

Finally, keep everything you use to develop your presentation – this will help to form the evidence of your efforts.

After the presentation

2 Once you have completed your presentation, ask for some feedback. Note down your group's comments – they will be useful when you prepare for another presentation.

3 Now make a list of the ways you would modify your presentation so that it would be suitable for your target group – the GCSE class.

1 a State which interaction, strong or weak, is experienced by each of the following particles: hadrons and leptons.

b Give one example of a hadron and one example of a lepton.

c Hadrons are classified as either baryons or mesons. How many quarks are there in a baryon and in a meson?

d (i) State the quark composition of a neutron.

(ii) Describe, in terms of quarks, the process of ß⁻ decay when a neutron changes into a proton.

(iii) Sketch a Feynman diagram to represent ß⁻ decay.

4 Waves, refraction and optical fibres

Keeping in touch wherever you are seems to be increasingly important. With a satellite phone and a laptop you can take your office to the ends of the Earth! A satellite phone offers 24-hour access by voice, fax or data (e-mail and Internet) to anywhere else in the world.

Video conferencing is also becoming increasingly common. Faster communications systems based on satellite transmissions and optical fibre links mean that it is possible to send good quality pictures at frame rates of 15 frames per second, fast enough so that the images seem continuous. New applications for video transmissions include transmitting live pictures of rare surgical operations for training purposes and allowing specialist surgeons to supervise or perform operations at remote sites.

The communication revolution depends crucially on the physics of radio waves travelling in air and of light travelling through glass.

The world's smallest satellite telephone weighs less than 2 kg and will run from batteries or the cigar lighter in a car.

A Belgian surgeon created medical history by using robotics and computer technology to lead an operation on a patient in a different country. Dr Luc Vanderheyden, a surgeon at St Lucas hospital in Bruges, Belgium, took charge of diagnostic stomach surgery on a patient at Nieuwegein in the Netherlands, over 125 miles away. 'The operation went very well', said Vanderheyden, who diagnosed a hernia.

The procedure, known as telerobotic laparoscopic surgery, took about half an hour. Surgeons have been using computers and robotics for over a decade, but this was the first time the technology had been used on a patient in a different country.

During the operation, Vanderheyden controlled a computer linked by digital telephone line to one in the Netherlands, which controlled the robot arm holding a surgical camera.

Both sites could see one another and the patient's stomach as cameras beamed pictures down an enhanced telephone line.

The procedure is currently expensive – the operation cost about $200 000 – but officials said the technology could eventually save money. 'In the future you could have a team of the very best surgeons, all located centrally, and have remote-controlled theatres scattered around the country', said Vanderheyden.

4.1 Moving waves

The vibrations of the strings are passed to our ears by oscillations of the air molecules.

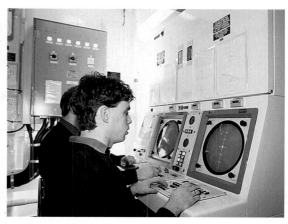

SONAR uses high frequency longitudinal pressure waves to locate objects (fish) in the sea.

A wave is caused by something which oscillates. For example, sound waves can be created by any object which vibrates. The vibrations are passed on to molecules of the air in a process called propagation. As a wave propagates, energy from the oscillator is transferred to different regions of space. Electromagnetic waves can be thought of as an oscillation of electric and magnetic fields in space (Fig. 1). Unlike sound waves, they do not need a medium: electromagnetic waves can travel through a vacuum.

Longitudinal and transverse waves

Although sound waves and electromagnetic waves have a lot in common, they have one important difference. Electromagnetic waves are **transverse**, whereas sound waves are **longitudinal.** In sound waves, air particles are pushed and pulled by the vibrations along the line of the wave (Fig. 2). The wave spreads as

Fig. 1 An electromagnetic wave

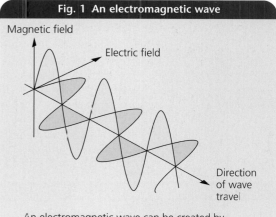

An electromagnetic wave can be created by an oscillating electric charge.

a pressure wave made up of **compressions** and **rarefactions** of the air. The air particles vibrate in the same direction that the wave propagates (along the wave). These types of waves are called longitudinal waves.

In transverse waves, the vibrations are at right angles to the direction of propagation. This can be demonstrated using a wave travelling along a spring (Fig. 3).

Fig. 2 Longitudinal waves

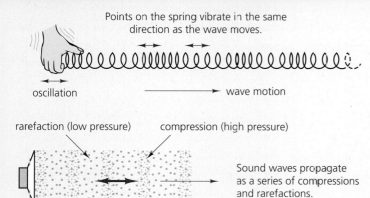

Points on the spring vibrate in the same direction as the wave moves.

oscillation   wave motion

rarefaction (low pressure)   compression (high pressure)

Sound waves propagate as a series of compressions and rarefactions.

Fig. 3 Transverse waves in a spring

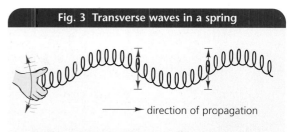

direction of propagation

Points on the spring vibrate at right angles to the direction of propagation.

When a news reporter speaks, energy and information from the reporter's voice is carried along waves: initially as sound waves, then as electrical waves from the microphone and finally as radio waves from the outside broadcast unit.

Electromagnetic waves, like light or radio, are transverse waves. All electromagnetic waves exchange energy between electric fields and magnetic fields. These fields are perpendicular to each other (Fig. 1). Other examples of transverse wave motion include earthquake s-waves, water ripples and waves on the strings of musical instruments.

Progressive waves

The ability of waves to transfer energy makes them ideal for transmitting information from one place to another. Waves that can transfer energy in this way are called **progressive**. Radio waves from a transmitter or light waves from a laser are progressive waves.

EXTENSION

Standing waves

Not all waves are progressive. If a guitar string is plucked at its centre, the disturbance makes the whole string vibrate. This certainly has the appearance of a wave motion, but it is not a progressive wave: there is no transfer of energy from one place on the string to another. Because the wave stands still, we call it a standing wave or stationary wave (Fig. 4).

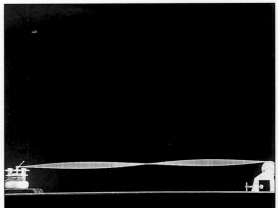

Fig. 4 Nodes and antinodes on a standing wave

Antinodes (A) are positions of maximum displacement.

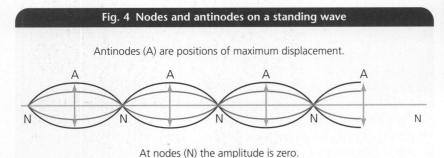

At nodes (N) the amplitude is zero.

There are some important differences between progressive and standing waves (Table 1). Standing waves in a system can set up progressive waves. For example, a standing wave on a guitar string makes air molecules vibrate, causing a progressive sound wave at the same frequency to

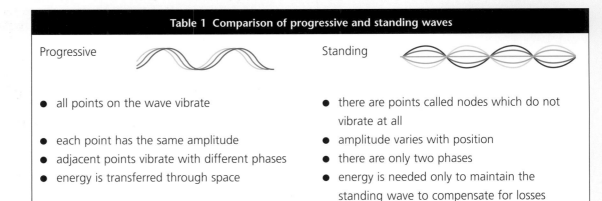

Table 1 Comparison of progressive and standing waves	
Progressive	Standing
• all points on the wave vibrate	• there are points called nodes which do not vibrate at all
• each point has the same amplitude	• amplitude varies with position
• adjacent points vibrate with different phases	• there are only two phases
• energy is transferred through space	• energy is needed only to maintain the standing wave to compensate for losses

travel through the air. The standing wave gradually dies out as its energy transfers to the progressive wave.

Musical instruments often rely on standing waves on strings, as in a guitar, or in columns of air, like a clarinet, as the source of vibration to generate sound waves. For waves on strings the simplest standing wave, known as the **fundamental**, occurs when the length of the string is equal to half a wavelength (Fig. 5). Only certain standing wave patterns can appear on a string; they are always an integral number of half wavelengths. On a guitar or violin string these patterns give rise to notes whose frequency is an exact multiple of the fundamental frequency. These notes are known as **harmonics** or **overtones**.

It is the mixture of harmonics that is emitted by a particular instrument that gives it its distinctive sound, and makes a Stradivarius worth so much money.

Fig. 5 The fundamental

Only certain wave patterns will fit on a fixed string:

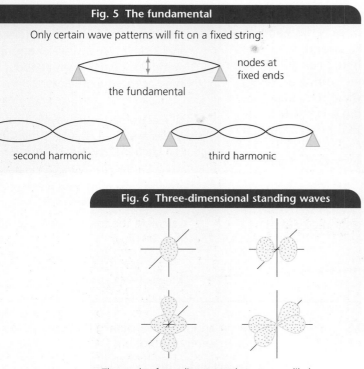

nodes at fixed ends

the fundamental

second harmonic

third harmonic

Fig. 6 Three-dimensional standing waves

The study of standing waves has some unlikely applications, like describing the orbits of electrons in atoms. Quantum mechanics treats particles as though they have wave-like properties and the 'orbits' are linked with three-dimensional standing waves.

Television and radio signals are transmitted and received by aerials. An electrical standing wave in the aerial gives rise to a progressive radio wave which radiates into space. The length of the aerial is very important: it is linked to the frequency of the radio wave in the air. These long aerials transmit long-wave radio signals.

1 When a guitar string is plucked a wave is set up on the string. Give two differences between this wave and the sound wave that it causes.

2 Why does shortening a guitar string, by pressing on one of the frets, make the note higher pitched?

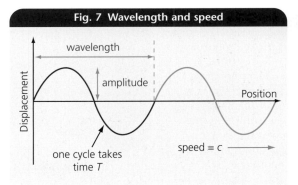

Fig. 7 Wavelength and speed

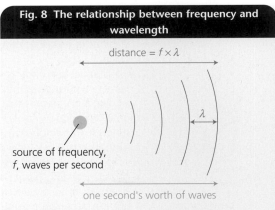

Fig. 8 The relationship between frequency and wavelength

If there are f waves every second and each wave is λ metres long, then the distance travelled by any wave in one second must be $f \times \lambda$. Therefore, the wave speed $c = f\lambda$.

Defining waves

The length of one complete wave is called the **wavelength**, λ. This is the distance between any two consecutive identical points on the wave. For a sinusoidal wave this is the distance between two adjacent peaks.

The **frequency**, f, of a wave is the number of complete wave cycles per second. Frequency is measured in hertz, Hz. A frequency of 1 Hz means one complete wave every second. The frequency of the radio waves used to transmit Radio 1 is 98 MHz; the frequency of the light emitted by a red laser is around 5×10^{14} Hz.

The time for one complete wave cycle is known as the **period**, T. This is linked to the frequency by $f = 1/T$.

The speed of a wave, c, its wavelength, λ, and frequency, f, are linked by the equation $c = f\lambda$ (see Fig. 8).

3 Most young, healthy ears can detect sounds with a frequency between 20 Hz and 20 kHz. What wavelengths are these sounds? (Sound travels at about 340 m s^{-1} in air at room temperature.)

4 All electromagnetic waves, including radio waves and light, travel at the same speed in a vacuum, $c = 3 \times 10^8$ m s^{-1}.

a Calculate the frequency of the radio waves used to transmit Radio 4 (long wave) radio signals, $\lambda = 1500$ m.

b Calculate the frequency of red light, $\lambda = 700$ nm.

KEY FACTS

■ Longitudinal waves (e.g. sound) oscillate in the direction of propagation. Transverse waves (e.g. electromagnetic) oscillate at right angles to the direction of propagation.

■ Waves may be progressive (energy transmitting) or stationary (standing).

■ The frequency, f, is the number of complete wave cycles per second. It is measured in Hz.

■ Wavelength is the distance the wave propagates in one period of vibration.

■ For all waves, the wave speed, c, is related to wavelength and frequency by the equation $c = f\lambda$.

APPLICATION

Radio aerials

The size of the transmitting or receiving aerial depends on the wavelength of radio waves used.

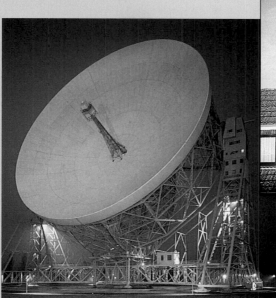

Fig. 9 Half wave dipole

signal cable

$\frac{\lambda}{2}$

A wide range of frequencies of electromagnetic waves are used for communication. The low frequency (LF) band (around 200 kHz) gives poor sound quality, but long range. Ground-based TV broadcasts use frequencies around 500 MHz, and satellite broadcasts in the region of 10 GHz. The aerial lengths needed to pick up each of these signals varies enormously. The ideal aerial is a **half wave dipole**, an aerial that is half a wavelength long, with a central feeder cable (Fig. 9).

At high frequencies, the wavelength is small. This tends to make the aerial a more practicable length. Signals transmitted at lower frequencies can rarely use a half wave dipole aerial: the aerial would simply be too long. We can calculate the length of aerial required for common broadcasting frequencies by rearranging the equation $c = f\lambda$. For a 200 kHz radio transmission on the LF band:

$$\lambda = \frac{c}{f} = \frac{3.0 \times 10^8 \text{ m s}^{-1}}{200\,000 \text{ Hz}} = 1500 \text{ m},$$

so the aerial length $= \frac{\lambda}{2} = 750$ m

Using this method, a 500 MHz ground-based television broadcast would need a 30 cm aerial and a 1.9 GHz cordless phone would require a 16 cm aerial. These two aerial lengths are practicable, but a LF radio receiver with an aerial 750 metres long would not be. Electromagnetic waves have an electric and a magnetic component. Most receivers of low frequencies pick up the magnetic component of radio waves. This is done with a ferrite rod.

Ferrite is a magnetic ceramic material which is able to respond to the alternating magnetic field of the radio wave. This induces a current in the coils which can be amplified and decoded.

If you open a radio receiver, you will usually be able to see a ferrite rod with coils around it

5a Sketch the standing wave patterns possible on a dipole aerial 10 cm long.

b What frequencies could the aerial transmit? (Note: the current must be zero at the ends of the aerial and a maximum at the central feeder cable.)

APPLICATION   **Phase**

'I live on a farm which is a long way from the nearest TV transmitter. The signal I receive is very weak. I'm wondering if I can join together several aerials to make a stronger signal.'

Arrays of aerials can be used to boost signals in the fields of radar and radio astronomy. However, the exact positioning of the aerials is critical. This can be understood by considering the link between the position of an aerial and the **phase** of waves.

As a wave moves, each point in its path oscillates. At any given time different points along the wave have different displacements and velocities. We say that they are oscillating with different phases. This phase difference arises because the vibration takes time to travel from one place to another. Oscillations are in phase if they differ by a whole number of wavelengths. Oscillations are in antiphase if there is a half wavelength difference (Fig. 10).

Other phase differences can be calculated by taking a simple ratio. A distance of one wavelength, λ, is equivalent to one complete cycle. For points separated by a distance x, the phase difference is therefore x/λ. This is often stated as an angle, in which case the phase difference is $x/\lambda \times 360°$, or $x/\lambda \times 2\pi$ **radians**.

The wavelength of waves used for TV broadcasts is around 0.6 m, so in theory we could put several aerials 0.6 m apart and add the signals. However, exact alignment and spacing of the aerials would require a high degree of accuracy. An electronic amplifier for an existing aerial would be a far more practical solution.

6   Study Fig. 11. Sketch how the amplitude varies with time at point D.

Fig. 10 Boats on sea

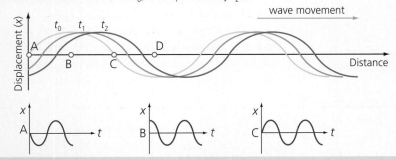

The position of the boat affects the timing of its oscillations; in other words the phase is different. Boats B and C will oscillate *in antiphase*, boats B and D are *in phase*.

Fig. 11 Position and phase

The diagram shows the effect of a wave passing points A, B, C and D. The wave is drawn at time t_0, then t_1 and finally t_2.

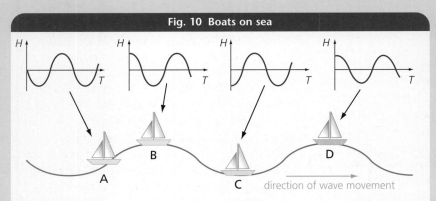

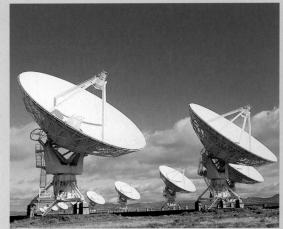

The world's largest radio telescope is the Very Large Array in New Mexico, USA. It uses 27 radio dishes connected together so as to take account of the different phase that each dish receives.

WAVES, REFRACTION AND OPTICAL FIBRES

4.2 Diffraction

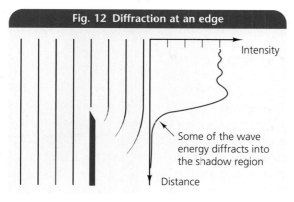

Fig. 12 Diffraction at an edge

Intensity

Some of the wave energy diffracts into the shadow region

Distance

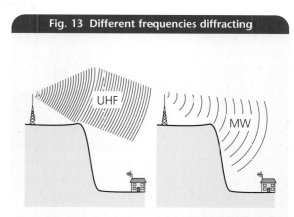

Fig. 13 Different frequencies diffracting

UHF

MW

High frequencies diffract very little so reception of TV is poor in valleys...

... but longer wavelength radio waves are easier to receive.

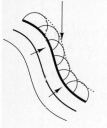

Fig. 14 Huygens' construction

The envelope of the 'secondary wavelets' shows the position of the wavefront.

People who live in valleys often have poor reception of television and VHF radio, but good reception of long wave and medium wave radio broadcasts. This can be partly explained by the way in which radio waves bounce off the upper layers of the atmosphere. Another reason is the diffraction of waves. Diffraction is the name for the way in which waves spread out as they pass an obstacle. As well as spreading out, the waves vary in intensity at different positions (Figs. 12 and 13). Waves of different frequencies diffract by different amounts. High frequency waves, such as visible light, undergo very little diffraction. In everyday life we never notice diffraction of light around corners.

Diffraction can be understood by considering the way in which waves spread. When a vibration sets up a wave, it disturbs the medium. Each point on a wavefront is itself a place where the medium is no longer in equilibrium. Therefore, each point can act as a source of disturbance, or secondary wavelets. The position of the next wavefront can be found by taking the envelope of these secondary wavelets using Huygens' principle. Huygens' construction (Fig. 14) can be used to show the position of successive wavefronts. The principle can be extended to show that waves passing through gaps tend to curve at the edges. Very narrow gaps (of width $\approx \lambda$) give almost circular wavefronts: a narrow gap acts as a point source of waves (Fig. 15).

Waves at low frequencies, when the obstacle size and wavelength are comparable, will diffract well around the obstacle, but short wavelengths tend to give a geometrical shadow with little diffraction.

The short wavelengths used by mobile phones show little diffraction around hills and so there is a need for repeater aerials.

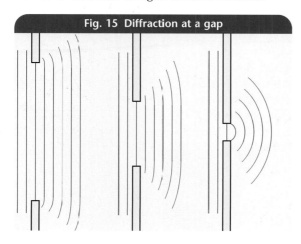

Fig. 15 Diffraction at a gap

KEY FACTS

- Diffraction is the spreading of waves into the region of geometrical shadow.

- Diffraction at a gap is greater when the gap is smaller.

- Diffraction is greatest when the wavelength is similar to the gap size.

61

4.3 Transmitting signals with light

'I work on commercial projects for a large telecommunications company. I think the days of the video shop are numbered. People don't always want to collect a video from the shop, then take it back the next day. That's why we're working on ways to transmit video pictures over high speed telephone networks. At our end, there are a few big problems to crack, like storing thousands of videos on a central computer data bank and sending them out on demand. But the potential turnover is enormous.'

The demands for rapid, on-line information transfer are increasing. A page of text is made up of about 10 000 bits of information, but takes us only a minute or so to read. Direct conversion from a television camera to binary code would generate over 200 million bits every second!

Ordinary twisted pairs of copper wires, used in standard computer networks and in the connection between telephones and the local exchanges, are not able to cope with these transmission demands. The signal becomes unintelligible over distances of only a few hundred metres. To meet the need for high speed transmission of information, network designers have developed systems which carry signals by light. Light waves have a frequency of around

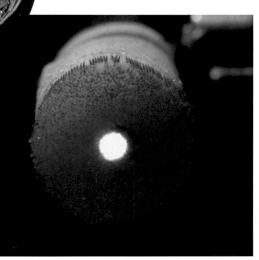

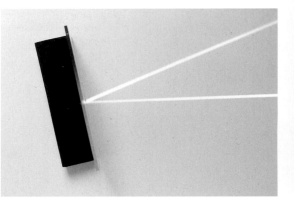

10^{14} Hz, far higher than any electronic circuit could use. The capability of optical fibres is limited only by the speed at which you can transmit and receive binary pulses. Optical fibres are potentially millions of times faster than copper wire.

Reflection of light

The laws of reflection and refraction govern the path of light down an optical fibre. We can illustrate this using ray diagrams. A ray diagram shows the paths taken by light wavefronts. Each ray is drawn perpendicular to the wavefront it represents.

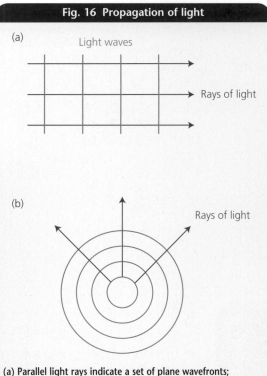

Fig. 16 Propagation of light

(a) Light waves
Rays of light

(b) Rays of light

(a) Parallel light rays indicate a set of plane wavefronts;
(b) diverging rays can be traced back to a point source of light.

Reflection at a plane mirror

Optical fibres work by repeatedly reflecting the light inside the fibre. The inner walls behave as perfect mirrors. Light reflects from a plane mirror at the same angle at which it approaches.

Angles of incidence and reflection are usually measured from the normal, a line at right angles to the surface (Fig. 17).

The laws of reflection:

- For any reflecting surface, the angle of incidence and the angle of reflection, both measured from the normal, are equal.
- The incident ray, reflected ray and normal lie in the same plane.

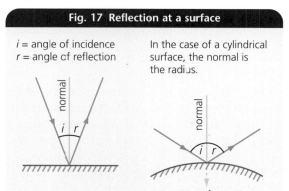

Fig. 17 Reflection at a surface

i = angle of incidence
r = angle of reflection

In the case of a cylindrical surface, the normal is the radius.

normal

i r

normal

i r

to centre of curvature

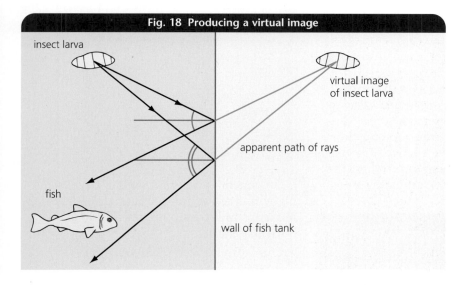

Fig. 18 Producing a virtual image

insect larva

virtual image of insect larva

apparent path of rays

fish

wall of fish tank

Fig. 19 Using 'no parallax'

If the pin is correctly positioned at the image point, the image of pin A and the top of pin B will stay together even if you change your viewing position.

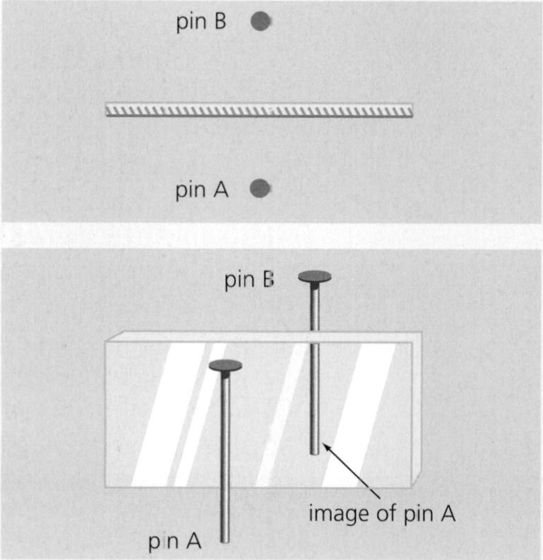

pin B

pin A

pin B

image of pin A

pin A

In the case of the plane mirror, we can use the rule with several rays to construct a theoretical ray diagram (Fig. 18). From that, we can predict the type and position of the image.

The reflected rays diverge. The brain interprets the image as a set of rays diverging from a point behind the mirror surface. Images that can be projected onto a screen, as in a slide projector, are called **real images**. No light rays are actually present at the position of the image in a mirror (Fig. 18), so it is called a **virtual image.**

The position of an object's virtual image can be found using the **no parallax** technique (Fig. 19). The experimental results confirm the predictions of the ray diagrams: the image is erect (upright), laterally inverted (left to right) and the same distance from the reflecting surface as the object.

7 The image in a plane mirror appears laterally inverted (i.e. left and right are swapped). Why isn't the image vertically inverted (i.e. top and bottom swapped)?

- For reflection at a plane mirror, the angle of incidence is equal to the angle of reflection. The incident ray, reflected ray and normal lie in the same plane.

- The image and object are the same distance from the reflecting surface and lie on a line normal to the surface. The image is virtual, erect and laterally inverted.

4.4 Refraction at a plane surface

Most optical fibres consist of two layers of glass: an inner core and an outer cladding. The difference between the two types of glass gives rise to **refraction** at the interface surface. This property is used to give the inside of the fibre its perfect reflecting properties.

Refraction means the change of direction of waves when they move from one medium to another. Refraction occurs because of a difference of wave speed in the two media. If a wavefront approaches at an angle to the surface separating the media, the edge which hits first will slow down first, causing a change of direction of the wavefront.

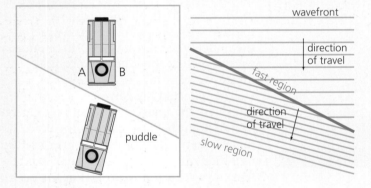

Fig. 20 A change of speed

When a car hits a puddle it will change direction. This is because wheel A hits the puddle first and slows down. This causes the car to swerve into the puddle.

A zig-zag effect takes place as the waves first slow down and then speed up as they re-enter the first medium (see below).

You can work out the angle of refraction by thinking about how the change of speed affects wavefronts. A ray refracts towards the normal when it slows down and away from the normal when it speeds up. The degree of deflection of the light ray depends on the change of speed.

8 Sketch a ray diagram to show why objects under water appear nearer the surface than the true depth of the water.

Refractive index

Electromagnetic waves all travel at the same speed, c, in a vacuum ($c = 299\,792\,458\,\mathrm{m\,s^{-1}}$). When they pass through matter, the waves slow down. We define the refractive index of a material, n, as the ratio of the wave's velocity in a vacuum, c, to the velocity in a material, v:

$$n = \frac{c}{v}$$

Since the speed of light in a vacuum is higher than in any material, the refractive index is always greater than 1 (Table 2). The higher its value, the more the rays are deflected. Air has a refractive index of around 1.0003 (we usually take it as 1).

Table 2 Refractive indexes	
Diamond	2.42
Glass	1.5 to 2.0
Perspex	1.50
Water	1.33
Sea water	1.34
Ice	1.31

In general, denser substances have a higher refractive index. Materials with a high refractive index are often referred to as **optically dense**.

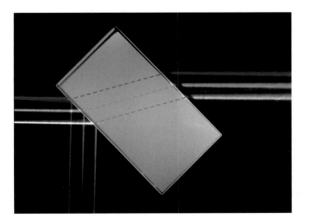

The dotted lines show the path of the light rays through the glass block.

APPLICATION   ## Chromatic dispersion

For some materials, the refractive index varies with wavelength. The values quoted in Table 2 are for a standard colour of light: the 589 nm bright orange light which you get from sodium street lamps. For almost all materials, refractive index increases with frequency, so blue light is refracted more than red light. For flint glass, for example, the typical refractive indexes are: red light = 1.640, yellow = 1.646, blue = 1.660. This variation of refractive index is the reason that white light beams are split up into different colours by prisms. The separation of different colours is called chromatic dispersion.

It is important to avoid chromatic dispersion in optical fibres, because a range of wavelengths transmitted as a sharp pulse would spread out as it travelled along the fibre (Fig. 22).

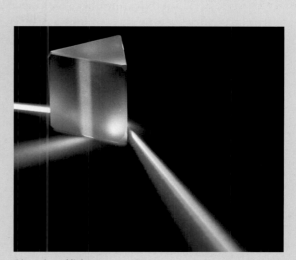

Dispersion of light.

Fig. 21 Illustrating chromatic dispersion

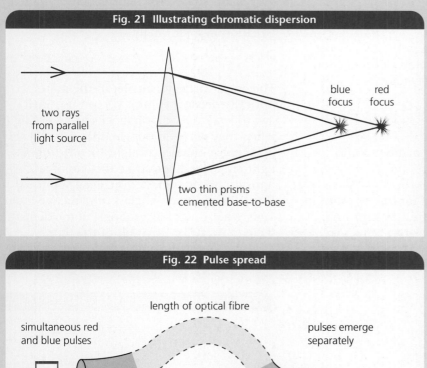

two rays from parallel light source

blue focus   red focus

two thin prisms cemented base-to-base

Fig. 22 Pulse spread

length of optical fibre

simultaneous red and blue pulses

pulses emerge separately

It is difficult to make glass which has no chromatic dispersion. Instead, light with a very narrow wavelength band is used. Lasers make ideal light sources for optical fibres because they are monochromatic – the light is just one colour. Other sources include light-emitting diodes (LEDs). These are much cheaper but they do transmit light over a wider band of wavelengths. Chromatic dispersion also depends on wavelength; for glass, there is very little chromatic dispersion at wavelengths in the infrared at around 1300 nm. Most telecommunications systems use infrared transmitters.

9 A semiconductor light transmitter has a wavelength range from 750 nm to 790 nm. At these wavelengths, the glass of an optical fibre has refractive index 1.6404 and 1.6400 respectively. The light transmitter is switched on for 100 ns. How long would it take for light at the extremes of the wavelength range to travel 30 km along the optical fibre? What is the time difference (in nanoseconds) between the arrival of the two colours? (Take $c = 3 \times 10^8$ m s^{-1}.)

Relative refractive index

Most optical fibres are made up of two layers of glass of different refractive index. The signal is transmitted along the inner layer which has a higher refractive index. The boundary between the two layers is important. To work out what happens at such a boundary, it is easier to think in terms of a flat surface between two media.

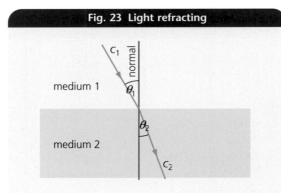

Fig. 23 Light refracting

It is the relative speed in the two media which determines the amount of refraction. We can define the relative refractive index to be:

$$_1n_2 = \frac{c_1}{c_2}$$

for a ray travelling from medium 1 into medium 2.

Suppose we know that the refractive indexes (measured in air) for the two sorts of glass in an optical fibre are 1.50 and 1.60. How could we find the relative refractive index? Both are related to the speed of waves in a vacuum, c. We need to re-introduce this to the equation:

$$_1n_2 = \frac{c_1}{c_2}$$

$$= \frac{c}{c_2} \times \frac{c_1}{c}$$

$$= n_2 \times \frac{1}{n_1}$$

or, $_1n_2 = \frac{n_2}{n_1}$

Relative refractive index can be less than 1; for the ray of light in the central core of the fibre, the glass of the cladding has a refractive index of $1.50/1.60 = 0.938$. It is this low refractive index that leads to the perfect reflections inside the optical fibre. The refractive index can be linked to the angles of the rays to predict the way that rays will travel along the fibre.

Snell's law

The refractive index affects the angles of the ray at a boundary (Fig. 23).

For a particular wavelength or colour of light, the link is surprisingly simple:

$$\text{refractive index} = \frac{\sin (\text{angle of incidence})}{\sin (\text{angle of refraction})}$$

$$= \frac{\sin i}{\sin r}$$

The incident and refracted rays and the normal all lie in the same plane.

This is called Snell's law (Fig. 24). Note that you cannot just cancel the sines, although $n = i/r$ is a fair approximation for very small angles. For light travelling from one medium to another, we can restate the equation more formally as:

$$_1n_2 = \frac{\sin \theta_1}{\sin \theta_2}$$

The angle is always smaller in the more optically dense medium. We can use Snell's law to work out what happens to rays of light when they enter an optical fibre (Fig. 25).

Suppose the rays of light (in air) from a light-emitting diode strike the end of an optical fibre at angles of incidence up to 30°. If the fibre is made of glass of refractive index 1.60, what is the biggest angle of incidence at which rays strike the walls of the fibre?

If the end is flat and at right angles to the fibre, then the biggest angle of incidence at

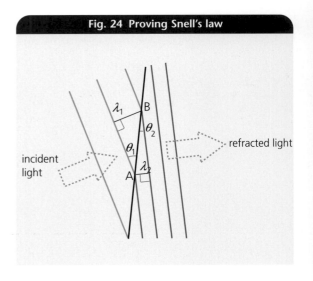

Fig. 24 Proving Snell's law

WAVES, REFRACTION AND OPTICAL FIBRES

the wall of the fibre will be for a ray from the edge of the beam, when $i = 30°$.

$$n = \frac{\sin i}{\sin r}$$

Therefore, $\sin r = \dfrac{\sin 30°}{1.6}$

$$= \frac{0.5}{1.6}$$

$r = 18.2°$

From the right-angled triangle:

$$90° + I + r = 180°$$

$$I = 90° - r$$

$$= 71.8°$$

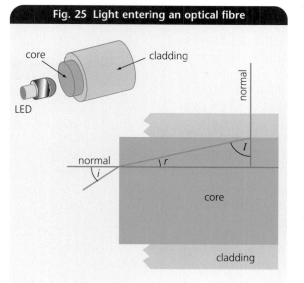

Fig. 25 Light entering an optical fibre

core   cladding

LED

normal

normal

i r I

core

cladding

What will happen to the rays when they meet the interface between the layers? Suppose the outer layer of glass has a refractive index of 1.50.

Using $_1n_2 = \dfrac{n_2}{n_1}$

$$= \frac{1.50}{1.60} = 0.9375$$

From $_1n_2 = \dfrac{\sin \theta_1}{\sin \theta_2}$

$$\sin \theta_2 = \frac{\sin 71.8°}{0.9375} = 1.013$$

If you try to find the inverse sine of 1.013 on your calculator, it will tell you have made an error. This does not mean that the calculation is wrong, only that the mathematics has not kept up with the physics of refraction. Snell's law only works if the ray actually crosses the boundary. At high angles of incidence the rays cannot cross over: they reflect instead.

10 To reduce light loss, an LED is stuck onto an optical fibre with a transparent glue. The refractive indexes of the glue and fibre are 1.40 and 1.60.

a Calculate the relative refractive index.

b If a ray of light from the LED hits the end of the fibre at 30° to the normal, at what angle will it strike the wall of the fibre?

■ Refracted rays deflect towards the normal when they slow down.

■ The refractive index is

$$n = \frac{\text{speed of light in a vacuum}}{\text{speed of light in material}}$$

■ For a ray travelling from medium 1 into medium 2, the relative refractive index is

$$_1n_2 = \frac{n_2}{n_1} = \frac{c_1}{c_2}$$

■ Snell's law says that the refractive index

$$n = \frac{\sin i}{\sin r} \quad \text{or} \quad _1n_2 = \frac{\sin \theta_1}{\sin \theta_2}$$

4.5 Total internal reflection

Fig. 26 Refraction and reflection

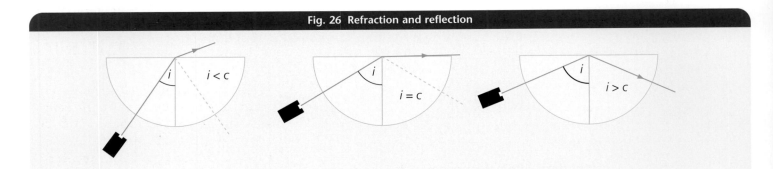

Optical fibres work using internal reflection of light rays. This is what allows the light to go around corners when the fibre is bent. The phenomenon occurs when light travels from one medium to another, less optically dense, medium (Fig. 26).

Light refracts as expected at low angles of incidence, but at higher angles reflection increases until the internal surface acts as a perfect mirror. This is called **total internal reflection**, because all of the incident light energy is reflected.

The change to reflection is not sudden; there is always partial reflection inside the block. This effect gets stronger as the angle of incidence rises. However, at one particular angle, the **critical angle**, c, the refracted ray disappears. At this angle, the refracted ray is trying to travel along the boundary between the media ($r = 90°$). Beyond the critical angle ($i > c$) the internal reflection is total.

The critical angle depends on the refractive index of the media. At the critical angle, the ray travels at 90° from the normal in the less dense medium 2, so:

$$_1n_2 = \frac{\sin c}{\sin 90°} = \sin c$$

$$_1n_2 = \frac{n_2}{n_1}$$

so, $\sin c = \dfrac{n_2}{n_1}$

In the case of rays travelling in a medium of refractive index n where the less dense medium is air, we have $n_2 \approx 1$, so

$$\sin c = \frac{1}{n}$$

A single pure glass fibre could be used to carry light pulses, but its surface is easily scratched, allowing some light to leak out (Fig. 27). One way to avoid this is to use an outer layer of less pure glass to protect the light-carrying fibre. What effect will this have on total internal reflection?

Fig. 27 Light leakage

Surface scratches lead to light leakage in a single fibre. Scratches in the outer cladding do not matter because it does not carry a light signal.

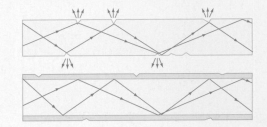

Suppose the core of an optical fibre has a refractive index of 1.60. In air, the critical angle of the glass is given by

$$\sin c = \frac{1}{n} = \frac{1}{1.60} = 0.625$$

$$c = 39°$$

If the cladding is made of less optically dense glass, the critical angle becomes much larger. Suppose the cladding has refractive index 1.50. The critical angle is now given by:

$$\sin c = \frac{n_2}{n_1} = \frac{1.50}{1.60} = 0.9375$$

$$c = 69.6°$$

Fig. 28 The longest path

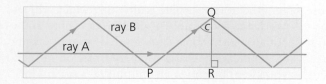

Ray B has the longest possible path with an angle of incidence equal to the critical angle. The ratio of the length of ray B's journey to the length of ray A's journey is $\dfrac{PQ}{PR} = \dfrac{1}{\sin c} = \dfrac{1}{0.9375} = 1.0667$

Along 1 km of fibre the maximum path is 1.0667 km.

ray B

ray A

Q

C

P   R

This X-ray shows an endoscope winding through a patient's colon after being passed through the rectum.

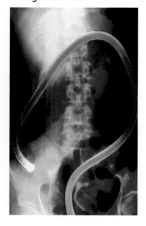

The protected fibre only reflects light rays with a very high angle of incidence. This increase of critical angle for the cladded fibre might seem to be a disadvantage, because fewer rays will reflect inside. However, it turns out to be an advantage because the rays that are internally reflected will travel by a more direct route and suffer less relative time delay. When only large angles of incidence are allowed, the zig-zag ray is almost the same length as the direct ray (Fig. 28).

Rays taking different paths along an optical fibre will take different amounts of time to reach the end. This is called **multimode dispersion**, because the different modes of travel are dispersed in terms of their time of arrival. It is important to keep multimode dispersion as small as possible. One way of doing this is to use core and cladding of almost identical refractive index.

Fig. 29 Coherent and incoherent bundles

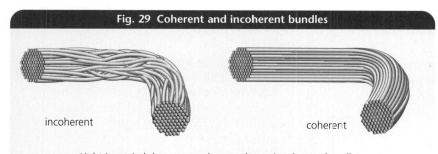

incoherent

coherent

Light is carried down an endoscope by an incoherent bundle and back up in a coherent bundle.

Another way is to keep the core of the fibre so small that only one pattern of electromagnetic wave motion is possible inside the fibre. This is called a monomode fibre. The core of such a fibre is only a few micrometres in diameter – about a hundred times thinner than a human hair!

11 What is the time delay between the straight path and the critical angle path for 1 km of the optical fibre with refractive indexes of 1.50 and 1.60?

12 What would be the maximum frequency of transmission of pulses among 10 km of this cable?

Endoscopes

Endoscopes are commonly used to examine the upper digestive tract (gastroscopy) or the rectum and colon (colonoscopy). Light is carried to the site of the examination through an **incoherent bundle** of glass fibres. As many as 30 000 individual fibres make up the bundle. An incoherent bundle cannot be used to form an image because the ends of the individual fibres are arranged randomly.

In a **coherent bundle**, the fibres have the same spatial position at each end of the bundle. The light emitted from the end of the bundle is an exact copy of the incident light and an image can be reproduced. Coherent bundles are expensive to manufacture, so incoherent bundles are used for illumination.

13 The diameter of each fibre in an incoherent bundle is about 50 μm. Fibres in a coherent bundle are much thinner, with a diameter of only 5 μm. Why do you think this is?

The laparoscope, a rigid form of endoscope, is used for examining the body through the small incisions made in keyhole surgery. It has often an extra optical fibre used for transmitting laser light.

KEY FACTS

■ Total internal reflection occurs at angles of incidence greater than the critical angle. For refraction into air, the critical angle is given by:
$$\sin c = \frac{1}{n}$$

■ Optical fibres rely on repeated total internal reflection to transmit light pulses.

■ Endoscopy is used to examine patients without the need for extensive surgery.

■ Incoherent bundles of optical fibres carry light for illumination, and coherent bundles carry image information.

Optical fibres in engineering, medicine and chemistry

Aircraft safety

The crew inside a modern aircraft need to monitor the stresses and strains on their plane and gain information in advance of any possible structural problems. One way of achieving this could be to use optical fibres. When an optical fibre is stretched or bent, the range of frequencies of the light in the fibre change. So any bending in the structure of an aircraft with a fibre optic cable attached to it can be detected by the change in the light travelling along the fibre. Light carried by fibres is not affected by magnetic fields so this method avoids any possible interference problems created by electrical cables lying nearby.

Optical fibres can also carry information in a more secure and efficient way than through copper wires, so security of data in the air transport business is improved.

Medical applications

The cost of surgery is affected by the amount of time that a patient has to spend in bed recovering. In the past, many operations involved opening up the patient and exploring to find out what was wrong. This was called exploratory surgery and was always a last resort because it was so disruptive. The cuts tended to be large as surgeons did not know exactly which structure they were investigating. Exploration is inevitably more disruptive than a quick in-and-out procedure.

Modern X-ray, nuclear magnetic resonance and body scanning techniques have drastically reduced the need for exploratory surgery. However, in some instances nothing can replace the chance to take a good look inside an organ. Doctors can now take advantage of **endoscopes** instead of more intrusive exploration – sometimes without anaesthetic. An endoscope is a thin, flexible tubular structure containing a cluster of optical fibres. Some of the fibres carry light down into the patient, others carry reflected light back out of the patient to a television camera. This allows the surgeon to see inside the body through a tiny hole made to insert the endoscope. This tiny hole gives the technique its name – keyhole surgery. The most recent developments allow surgeons not just to look but actually to carry out operations through this keyhole. Tiny tools are mounted on the endoscope to let the surgeon cut and seal wounds deep inside the body. Recovery from the procedure takes days rather than the weeks needed for traditional surgery.

Optical fibres in industry

Many chemical engineering plants use quite dangerous chemicals which can be corrosive or explosive. Monitoring the levels of liquids like these is a difficult task if there is anything which will react with the chemicals. Fortunately glass fibre in the form of an optical fibre is not affected by most chemicals.

Optical fibres also carry information in the form of a light beam which will not be a hazard. In contrast, a copper wire carrying an electric current may react with the chemicals or could cause a spark. Copper wire is also more expensive than the raw materials for optical fibre.

As the level of a liquid changes, the optical properties of the air–liquid interface change. Detectors have now been developed which can monitor mixtures of liquids and gases in pipes. This is particularly useful in pipelines, which can contain several types of liquid being pumped along one after the other, e.g. petrol followed by kerosene followed by lubricating oil. One pipeline which can be used for a range of liquids is much cheaper to build than a cluster of different pipes for different liquids. Detectors using optical fibres can monitor the movement of the junction between petrol and kerosene along a pipe.

1 List the advantages and disadvantages of sending information down fibre optic cable compared with using traditional cable such as copper.

2 Plan, research and produce an extended essay considering the physics which allows monomode optical fibre (also called **single mode optical fibre**) to send a light beam straight down the middle of the fibre.

You should consider the physical effects of **diffraction** and **refraction** in your account and use diagrams wherever possible to aid your explanation.

You should consider using the Internet to search for information as well as in your resources centre or library. Remember to keep a record of all of your resources.

Your essay should not exceed 350 words (diagrams do not count in the word limit).

Hint: Most modern fibre optic cable is monomode. The light beam doesn't bounce off the sides of the fibre as in multimode fibre optic cable. Single mode fibre optic cable is made so thin that only a fundamental mode of light intensity can fit across its diameter. The fibre is also made with a high refractive index in the middle, decreasing towards the edges.

1 A small intense light source is 1.5 m below the surface of the water in a large swimming pool, as shown in the diagram.

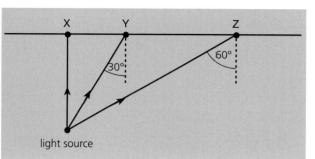

(i) Complete the paths of rays from the light source which strike the water surface at X, Y and Z.

(ii) Calculate the diameter of the disc through which the light emerges from the surface of the water. (7)

speed of light in water = $2.25 \times 10^8 \, \text{m s}^{-1}$

speed of light in air = $3.00 \times 10^8 \, \text{m s}^{-1}$

5 Atomic spectra and photons

Until about 40 years ago, all the information that we had about the Universe was carried to us by light. Although light is just a tiny part of the electromagnetic spectrum, it can penetrate our atmosphere more effectively than most other types of radiation and our eyes have evolved to respond to these wavelengths. Although we now have huge radio telescopes and satellites that can 'see' the Universe at X-ray and infra-red wavelengths, optical telescopes still provide enormous amounts of information. By studying the light from distant stars or galaxies we can tell what elements they are composed of and even at what speed they are moving.

Light is absorbed by the large dust and gas clouds in space, like the Horsehead Nebula. Even our atmosphere stops some light, so our biggest telescopes are put on top of mountains like the extinct volcano Mauna Kea in Hawaii.

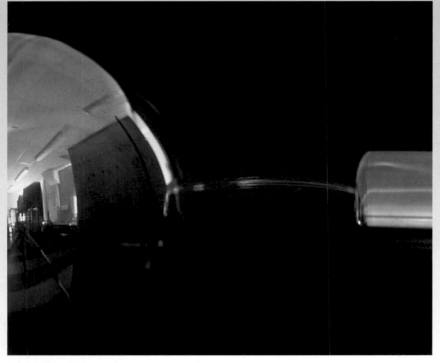

The study of light spectra has also given us vital insights into the workings of atoms. Passing a high voltage between two sample electrodes produces a spark. The spectrum of the emitted light provides information on the composition of elements in the samples.

5.1 Atomic fingerprints

Light is an electromagnetic wave (see Chapter 4). Electromagnetic waves cover an enormous range of wavelengths (Fig. 1) from radio waves, which can be hundreds of kilometres long, to very short X- and gamma radiation, which may have a wavelength of 10^{-12} m. Our eyes only respond to the very small part of this wavelength range which lies between

Fig. 1 The electromagnetic spectrum

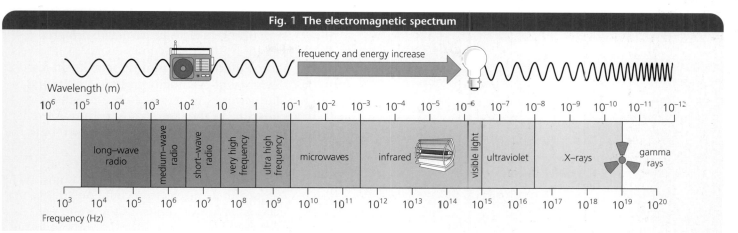

frequency and energy increase

Wavelength (m)

| 10^6 | 10^5 | 10^4 | 10^3 | 10^2 | 10 | 1 | 10^{-1} | 10^{-2} | 10^{-3} | 10^{-4} | 10^{-5} | 10^{-6} | 10^{-7} | 10^{-8} | 10^{-9} | 10^{-10} | 10^{-11} | 10^{-12} |

| long–wave radio | medium–wave radio | short–wave radio | very high frequency | ultra high frequency | microwaves | infrared | visible light | ultraviolet | X–rays | gamma rays |

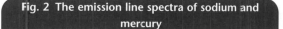

| 10^3 | 10^4 | 10^5 | 10^6 | 10^7 | 10^8 | 10^9 | 10^{10} | 10^{11} | 10^{12} | 10^{13} | 10^{14} | 10^{15} | 10^{16} | 10^{17} | 10^{18} | 10^{19} | 10^{20} |

Frequency (Hz)

400 nm and 700 nm. This is the part of the electromagnetic spectrum that we call light.

All objects emit electromagnetic radiation. This is due to the random vibrations of their molecules and it is known as **thermal radiation**. When an object is heated, its molecules vibrate faster and the object emits radiation of higher frequency. Objects emit light at relatively high temperatures. A star like our Sun, with a surface temperature of around 6000 K, emits most of its radiation in the visible part of the spectrum.

Humans are not hot enough to glow in the dark. We have a surface temperature of around 27 °C (300 K) and we emit radiation in the infra-red part of the spectrum. This infra-red image shows the cool parts of the face as blue and the hotter parts as red and yellow.

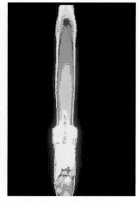

This thermograph shows the variation of temperature in a Bunsen burner flame.

Line spectra

The colour of light can tell us about the temperature of its source, but it also holds information on the composition of the source. Light can be analysed by using a prism, or a **diffraction grating**, to disperse it into its separate colours. This produces an **emission spectrum** which appears as a series of bright lines against a darker background (Fig. 2). The combination of colours are a 'fingerprint', revealing exactly which elements are present in the source.

The simplest emission spectra come from low-pressure monatomic gases, such as sodium vapour in a street light. Experiments on these gases have shown that each element produces a unique set of sharp lines.

Fig. 2 The emission line spectra of sodium and mercury

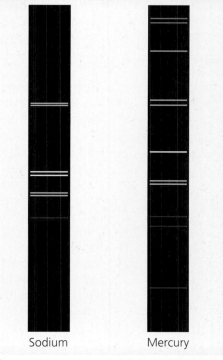

Sodium   Mercury

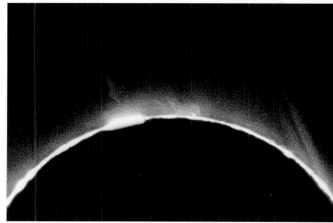

The red colour of the flare seen during a solar eclipse is due to emission from hydrogen atoms.

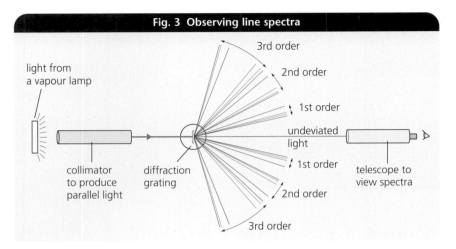

Fig. 3 Observing line spectra

light from a vapour lamp

collimator to produce parallel light

diffraction grating

3rd order
2nd order
1st order
undeviated light
1st order
2nd order
3rd order

telescope to view spectra

The line spectrum of hydrogen was first observed in 1853. It couldn't be explained satisfactorily until the early 20th century when Niels Bohr and Max Planck made advances critical to our understanding of spectra and atoms.

Bohr's hydrogen atom

Niels Bohr built on Rutherford's vision of the nuclear atom (see Chapter 1). He thought it was likely that the hydrogen atom contained only one electron orbiting around a positively charged nucleus.

But there was a major problem. All charged particles emit radiation when they accelerate. Because an atomic electron is moving in a circle it is constantly changing its velocity. An electron orbiting a nucleus is accelerating towards the centre of its orbit. According to the laws of classical physics, the electron should be radiating, and so losing energy.

Niels Bohr said that the spectrum was like a stained glass window looking into the heart of the atom.

In Rutherford's model of the atom, the electron is rather like a satellite orbiting Earth. If the satellite loses energy as it travels through the upper atmosphere, it will lose height and eventually crash to the ground. Rutherford's hydrogen atom would be unstable in the same way – as the electron radiated energy it would spiral down onto the nucleus.

Bohr made the bold suggestion that classical physics did not apply to atoms. He argued that the electron could only move in certain 'allowed' orbits. In these allowed orbits the electron could exist without losing energy. Bohr called these orbits 'stationary' states (Fig. 4).

Bohr said that electrons can only transfer energy when they move from one allowed orbit to another. This energy is emitted as electromagnetic radiation. The line spectrum of an element is caused by electrons making transitions between allowed atomic orbits. Each allowed orbit corresponds to a certain energy. The energy values of these orbits is defined as being negative. This is because the electron is in a **bound state**, so it would need to gain energy to free it from the atom. An orbit that is nearer to the nucleus has a higher negative value because more energy is required to free an electron from this orbit. An electron that is *just* free of the atom has zero energy and an electron with positive energy is free of the atom and has some kinetic energy.

Because each orbit represents a given energy value, and because atomic electrons cannot exist in any intermediate orbit between stationary states, Bohr's theory only allows atomic electrons to gain or lose energy in steps of a given size. In other words, an atomic electron's energy is **quantised**. This was one of the first steps in developing the **quantum theory**.

There is only one electron in the hydrogen atom. When the electron is in the lowest possible energy level, the hydrogen atom is said to be in the **ground state**. In this orbit, the electron cannot lose any more energy. This is the most stable state of the hydrogen atom.

Electrons can move to a higher energy level. This process is called **excitation**. Energy can be transferred to electrons when atoms collide with other particles, such as free electrons. When the electron is in a higher level, it can drop to a lower level, emitting

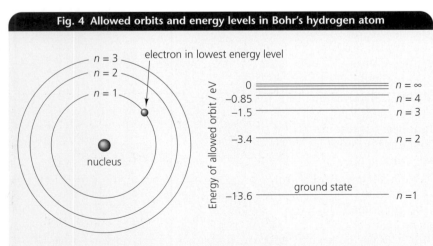

Fig. 4 Allowed orbits and energy levels in Bohr's hydrogen atom

$n = 3$
$n = 2$
$n = 1$

electron in lowest energy level

nucleus

Energy of allowed orbit / eV

0 — $n = \infty$
−0.85 — $n = 4$
−1.5 — $n = 3$
−3.4 — $n = 2$
ground state
−13.6 — $n = 1$

The ground state, $n = 1$, is the lowest energy level. An electron in this level needs an energy transfer of 13.6 eV to free it from the atom.

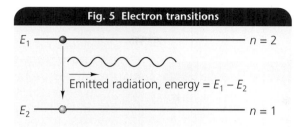

Fig. 5 Electron transitions

E_1 ———————●———————— $n = 2$

Emitted radiation, energy = $E_1 - E_2$

E_2 ———————●———————— $n = 1$

radiation (Fig. 5). The energy of the emitted radiation is equal to that transferred by the electron, i.e. the energy difference between the two states.

Fig. 6 Excitation and ionisation caused by an electron colliding with an atom

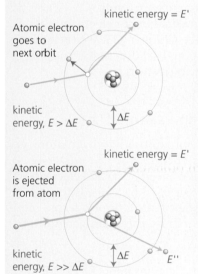

kinetic energy = E'

Incident electron

nucleus

kinetic energy, $E < \Delta E$

ΔE

Elastic scattering:
The energy of the incident electron is not enough to lift the atomic electron to the next allowed orbit. The atomic electron cannot absorb any of the incident electron's kinetic energy. The incident electron is elastically scattered, i.e. it loses no kinetic energy: $E = E'$

kinetic energy = E'

Atomic electron goes to next orbit

kinetic energy, $E > \Delta E$

ΔE

Inelastic scattering:
The energy of the incident electron is greater than the energy gap between allowed orbits. Some of the energy of the incident electron transfers to the atomic electron, raising it to a higher energy level. The atom is said to be in an excited state. Later, the atomic electron falls back to its original orbit, emitting radiation in the process. The incident electron is scattered, losing kinetic energy in the collision: $E' = E - \Delta E$

kinetic energy = E'

Atomic electron is ejected from atom

kinetic energy, $E \gg \Delta E$

ΔE E''

Ionisation:
The kinetic energy of the incident electron is greater than the negative energy of the atomic electron's orbit. The atomic electron is knocked completely out of orbit, and becomes a free electron. Any excess energy will appear as kinetic energy of the two electrons:
$$E - \Delta E = E' + E''$$

Sometimes the energy transferred to an atomic electron during a collision is so great that it is completely knocked out of the atom. This process is called **ionisation**.

The crucial thing about Bohr's model is that an atomic electron can only move from one allowed state to another by gaining or losing *exactly* the right amount of energy. No intermediate steps are allowed. That is why only certain frequencies appear in the line spectrum. Bohr predicted that the energy levels would become closer together as the energy values approached zero. His theory was in excellent agreement with the spectrum emitted by hydrogen atoms.

1 A TV emits light when free electrons accelerate across the tube and collide with atoms in the fluorescent coating on the inside of the screen. Use the ideas of excitation and energy levels to explain why this happens.

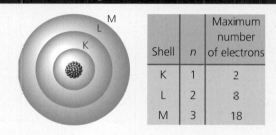

Fig. 7 Atomic shells

Shell	n	Maximum number of electrons
K	1	2
L	2	8
M	3	18

Bohr's model didn't work well for atoms other than hydrogen. The next model, wave mechanics, kept the idea of allowed energy levels. Each level, or shell, has a principal quantum number $n = 1, 2, 3$, etc. The number of electrons that can occupy each shell is given by $2n^2$.

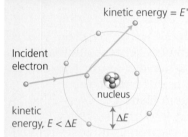

KEY FACTS

■ Light is an electromagnetic wave.

■ All objects emit electromagnetic waves due to the thermal motion of their atoms. The hotter the object the higher the frequency of radiation that it emits.

■ Low-pressure gases or vapours emit lines of coloured light with precisely defined frequencies. This is known as an emission spectrum.

■ Bohr's theory of the atom explained line spectra by suggesting that, in any atom, electrons can only occupy certain energy levels or orbits.

■ Electrons can be excited to a higher energy orbit by absorbing energy.

■ When electrons move to a lower orbit they emit radiation.

■ Electrons require an exact amount of energy to move between allowed orbits.

5.2 The photon

Fig. 8 A black body radiation curve and the Rayleigh–Jeans curve

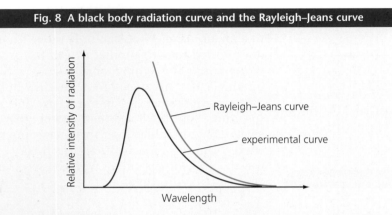

The experimental curves fall to zero at short wavelengths, but those based on classical theory head off towards infinity. This became known as the ultraviolet catastrophe.

At the start of the twentieth century there was a crisis in the physics of radiation. The current theories, now known as 'Classical Physics', could not explain the spectrum of radiation emitted from a hot object (Fig. 8).

Max Planck managed to resolve the problem by suggesting that energy, like matter, comes in 'lumps'. Planck said that radiation could be treated as if it consisted of 'parcels' of energy. The energy of these parcels, ΔE, was related to the frequency, f, of the radiation by:

$$\Delta E = hf$$

where h is a constant known as the Planck constant, $h = 6.626 \times 10^{-34}$ J s.

Fig. 9 Line series in the hydrogen spectrum

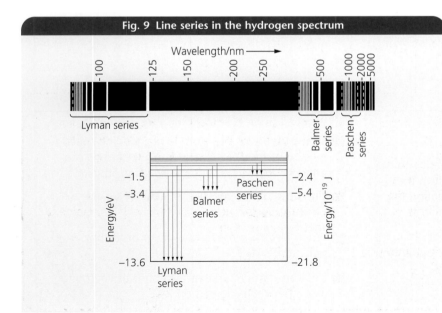

This idea was the beginning of the quantum theory. Quantum theory says that energy, like charge, is quantised; only certain discrete units of energy (quanta) are 'allowed'. By 1926, the quantum of radiation had been named the **photon**.

By combining the ideas of Planck's photons and Bohr's energy levels we can explain the origin of line spectra. Each time an electron falls to a lower energy level a photon of energy ΔE is emitted. So:

$$\Delta E = E_1 - E_2 = hf$$

The electronvolt

The energy differences between allowed orbits are very small in everyday terms. The joule is too large to be a useful unit, so the **electronvolt** is used instead.

One electronvolt, eV, is the energy transferred to an electron as it moves through a potential difference of 1 volt.

The charge carried by an electron, e, is 1.6×10^{-19} C (see Chapter 11). When it moves through a 1 V potential difference, the energy transferred to the electron is:

$$E = eV = 1.6 \times 10^{-19} \text{ C} \times 1 \text{ V}$$

so 1 electronvolt = 1.6×10^{-19} J

In the ground state of the hydrogen atom, an electron has an energy of -13.6 eV (see Fig. 4). The negative sign means that the electron is in a bound state, i.e. 13.6 eV needs to be transferred to the electron to pull it free of the atom and so cause the hydrogen atom to become ionised.

2a How many different frequencies of light could be emitted by an electron moving between the lowest three energy levels in hydrogen (see Fig. 4)?

b Calculate those frequencies.

3 What is the shortest wavelength of light that can be emitted by an electron transition in a hydrogen atom?

In a hydrogen atom, small energy changes cause infra-red emission. Larger energy changes emit visible light (the Balmer series, Fig. 9). The largest energy changes, where an electron falls back to the ground state, emit ultraviolet radiation.

Hydrogen is the simplest atom. It has only one electron. Although the energy level diagrams for other atoms are more complicated, the same principles apply. The atoms of each element have their own set of allowed energy levels. Each element has a unique line spectrum that identifies it. The starlight that reaches us on Earth carries a record of the elements that made it.

Absorption spectra

Superimposed on the continuous spectrum from the Sun are a large number of dark lines. This is the **absorption spectrum** of the Sun.

The solar absorption spectrum.

The lines represent the wavelengths at which photons have been absorbed by cooler gases in the outer regions of the Sun. Only radiation which has exactly the right amount of energy to lift an electron in the cooler gases' atoms from one allowed energy level to another will be absorbed.

When the atoms in the cooler gases return to their ground state, they may do so via intermediate energy levels, emitting radiation of other frequencies. The atoms also emit radiation in all directions. These effects reduce the intensity of the absorbed frequency travelling towards Earth, so producing dark lines in the spectra.

4 Explain why absorption lines come from the cooler outer atmospheres of the stars and not the hotter centres.

Absorption lines can also be observed in the laboratory by shining a strong white light through a vapour. In 1859, Kirchhoff related the dark lines to particular elements. He observed the Sun's spectrum through a flame into which he sprinkled some kitchen salt (sodium chloride). He found that some of the lines in the Sun's spectrum darkened. Kirchhoff concluded that there must be sodium in the Sun. Just as in emission, each element has its own unique absorption spectrum. Helium was discovered on the Sun, using absorption spectra, before it was found on Earth.

5 When Kirchhoff observed the Sun's light through a sodium flame he noticed that, 'If the sunlight is sufficiently damped, then two luminous lines appear at the position of the two dark lines'. Explain why this happens.

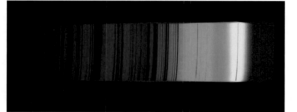

Fig. 10 The absorption of photons

energy levels of atoms in vapour

Only a photon with precisely the right energy will be absorbed. Other wavelengths pass through unaffected.

EXTENSION · The X-ray spectrum

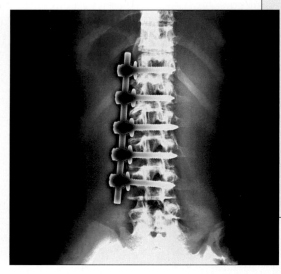

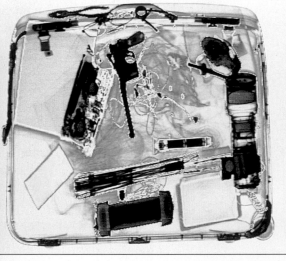

X-rays are used in a wide range of situations. Their penetrating power enables them to pass where light rays cannot, allowing us to look for a fracture in a patient's leg or for weapons at airport security.

X-rays are produced by making high-speed electrons collide with a metal target. The electrons slow down rapidly and so they emit electromagnetic radiation of a short wavelength (high frequency). These X-rays are emitted with a range of frequencies as a continuous spectrum, known as Bremsstrahlung or 'braking' radiation. Increasing the voltage across the X-ray tube accelerates the electrons to higher speeds. The electrons then emit more radiation as they decelerate.

Superimposed on this continuous spectrum is a **line spectrum** known as **characteristic lines**.

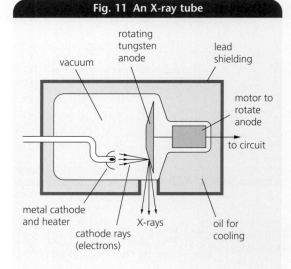

Fig. 11 An X-ray tube

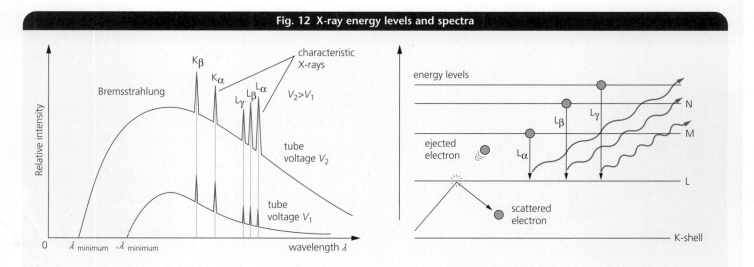

Fig. 12 X-ray energy levels and spectra

This characteristic X-ray spectrum is caused when high-energy electrons collide with atoms in the target material. The incident electrons have enough energy to remove electrons from atoms in the target. These atomic electrons may be removed from lower energy levels, leaving a vacancy for other atomic electrons – from higher energy levels – to fall into. As the electrons fall to the lower energy level they emit radiation. In a metal target, such as tungsten, the energy gap between the higher and lower levels may be large, so the radiation is emitted as a high-energy X-ray photon. Electrons may fall into the vacant energy level from one of a number of different orbits. This gives rise to a series of X-ray wavelengths being emitted.

The wavelength of the peaks in an X-ray spectrum does not change as the tube voltage is increased, but changing the target material would affect the line spectrum, since each metal has its own set of allowed electron orbits. These characteristic lines are due to energy changes in the target atoms.

Finding the shortest wavelength emitted by an X-ray tube

An electron gains kinetic energy as it is accelerated across the tube. When it hits the target, the most energetic X-ray (minimum wavelength) is produced if the electron loses all of its energy in just one direct collision with a target atom.

What is this minimum wavelength for a dental X-ray set, with a tube voltage of 60 kV?

For a tube voltage of 60 kV the electron gains an energy of 60 keV. In joules this is:

$$\text{energy} = 1.6 \times 10^{-19}\,C \times 60 \times 10^3\,V$$
$$= 9.60 \times 10^{-15}\,J$$

Since the energy of a photon is given by $E = hf$, the highest frequency that this X-ray tube can produce is:

$$f = \frac{E}{h} = \frac{9.60 \times 10^{-15}\,mJ}{6.63 \times 10^{-34}\,Js} = 1.54 \times 10^{19}\,Hz$$

So the minimum wavelength is:

$$\lambda = \frac{c}{f} = \frac{3.00 \times 10^8\,m\,s^{-1}}{1.54 \times 10^{19}\,Hz} = 1.95 \times 10^{-19}\,m$$

6 When the voltage across an X-ray tube is increased, the minimum wavelength at which X-rays are emitted goes down and more characteristic lines may appear in the spectrum. Explain why.

7 An X-ray tube uses a target metal with a higher atomic number, i.e. the target atoms have more electrons. We find that the minimum wavelength of X-rays stays the same but the characteristic lines move to shorter wavelengths. Explain why this occurs.

5.3   The photoelectric effect

At the beginning of the twentieth century, Planck's view of light as a stream of photons cast the first doubts about the wave theory of light. Another discovery, the **photoelectric effect**, was also making physicists re-examine their theories on the nature of light.

The photoelectric effect occurs when light knocks electrons out of the surface of a metal.

Not all wavelengths of light give rise to the effect. For electrons to be emitted from a metal surface, the frequency has to be above a certain minimum value, called the **threshold frequency**. If the frequency of the light is below the threshold, the electrons remain bound to the metal surface. Each metal has a different threshold frequency. For sodium, it is 5.5×10^{14} Hz, which is in the yellow part of

the spectrum. Blue or violet light can eject electrons from sodium, whereas red or orange light cannot. The light has to provide enough energy to rip an electron free from the metal's surface. This energy is known as the work function, ϕ, of the metal.

The discovery of the photoelectric effect in 1887 seemed to contradict the theory that light was a wave. The energy carried by a wave depends on its amplitude. A more energetic wave has a larger amplitude. This means a brighter light. However, light below the threshold frequency cannot dislodge electrons no matter how bright it is. Several intense red lasers will not prise a single electron from zinc, whereas a feeble UV glow does so easily (Fig. 13).

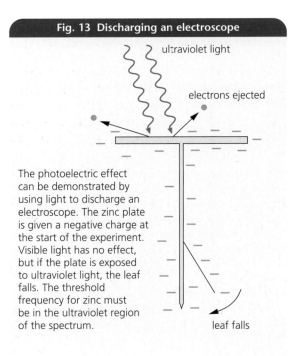

Fig. 13 Discharging an electroscope

ultraviolet light

electrons ejected

leaf falls

The photoelectric effect can be demonstrated by using light to discharge an electroscope. The zinc plate is given a negative charge at the start of the experiment. Visible light has no effect, but if the plate is exposed to ultraviolet light, the leaf falls. The threshold frequency for zinc must be in the ultraviolet region of the spectrum.

In 1905, Einstein extended Planck's theory of photons and derived an equation which describes the photoelectric effect. Einstein realised that light is not only *emitted* in discrete chunks or **quanta**, but it is *absorbed* in them too. When a photon strikes a metal surface either all or none of its energy is absorbed. It is not possible to absorb part of a photon.

Below the threshold frequency, the photon does not have enough energy to free an electron. At the threshold frequency there is just enough energy to free the electron. Above the threshold frequency all of the photon's energy is absorbed. Some of this energy is used to liberate the electron from the surface and any energy left over goes into the kinetic energy of the electron.

Einstein expressed this in terms of energy conservation:

photon energy in = energy needed to remove the electron (work function) + kinetic energy of emitted electron

$$hf = \phi + E_k$$

The observed kinetic energy of an emitted electron may be less than E_k if it has come from below the surface of the metal.

8 A particular metal surface has a threshold frequency in the blue part of the spectrum. Suppose you can measure the number of electrons emitted. What would you notice when the metal is exposed to:

a Faint red light? Bright red light?

b Faint blue light? Bright blue light?

c How would the maximum kinetic energy of the electrons alter in each case?

APPLICATION **The gamma camera**

The gamma scan (scintigram, above) of a healthy person injected with a bone-seeking radioisotope (right).

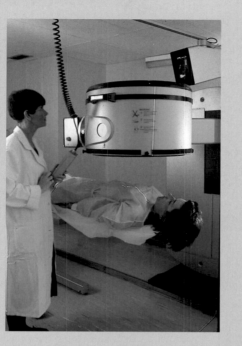

The gamma camera is an essential tool in the diagnosis of many conditions. The patient is injected with a small amount of a radioisotope which emits gamma radiation. The gamma camera detects the gamma radiation as it is emitted from the patient and uses the information to construct an image of the patient.

The gamma camera uses a crystal of sodium iodide as a scintillator. The scintillator emits a brief flash of light when a gamma ray passes through it. The flash of light is detected by photomultiplier tubes which use the photoelectric effect to cause a pulse of electric current. These pulses are analysed by a computer to reconstruct an image of the source of the radiation coming from the patient.

9 A gamma camera uses a sodium iodide scintillator to detect gamma rays. Technetium-99 emits gamma rays of frequency 3.4×10^{19} Hz. Sodium iodide absorbs these gamma rays and emits blue-green light of wavelength 415 nm. Calculate the energy of absorbed and emitted photons.

10 The photocathode in the photomultiplier tubes is made of a bi-alkali material, such as an alloy of caesium and potassium. What is the maximum possible value for the work function of this metal if it is to be used with a sodium iodide scintillator?

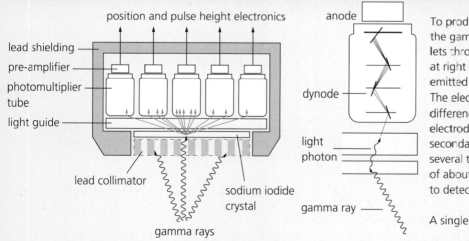

Fig. 14 The gamma camera

position and pulse height electronics

lead shielding
pre-amplifier
photomultiplier tube
light guide

lead collimator

sodium iodide crystal

gamma rays

anode

dynode

light photon

gamma ray

To produce an image we need to know where the gamma ray came from. The collimator only lets through gamma rays which are travelling at right angles to the crystal. An electron is emitted by the photoelectric effect at the cathode. The electron is accelerated through a potential difference and made to collide with another electrode where it knocks off a shower of secondary electrons. This process is repeated several times, amplifying the current by a factor of about 10^9, until the pulse is large enough to detect.

A single gamma ray has been detected.

EXTENSION

The stopping voltage

When electrons are emitted from a metal by the photoelectric effect they have a range of kinetic energies up to a maximum value. This value depends on the frequency of light.

Robert Millikan devised an ingenious way of finding the maximum kinetic energy of the electrons (Fig. 15). If the collecting electrode of a photocell is made slightly negative with respect to the photocathode it will repel the emitted electrons. Only the most energetic will reach the collecting electrode. The potential difference between the cathode and the collecting electrode

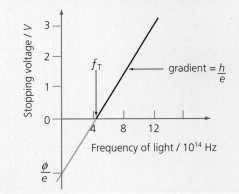

Fig. 16 Stopping voltage

Graph of stopping voltage versus frequency of incident light in Millikan's photoelectric experiment.

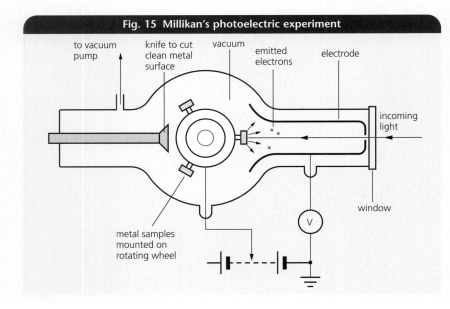

Fig. 15 Millikan's photoelectric experiment

to vacuum pump

knife to cut clean metal surface

vacuum

emitted electrons

electrode

incoming light

window

metal samples mounted on rotating wheel

V

can be gradually increased until all the electrons are stopped and the current drops to zero. The value of the p.d. when this happens is called the **stopping voltage**.

work done = charge × potential difference

The maximum kinetic energy of an electron = electron charge × stopping voltage

$$E = eV_{stop} = E_k$$
$$\text{and } hf = \phi + E_k$$
$$\text{so, } eV_{stop} = hf - \phi$$
$$V_{stop} = \frac{h}{e}f - \frac{\phi}{e}$$

A graph of V_{stop} versus f is a straight line of gradient h/e with a y-axis intercept of $-\phi/e$ (Fig. 16).

5.4 Seeing with particles

Fig. 17 Wave–particle duality experiment

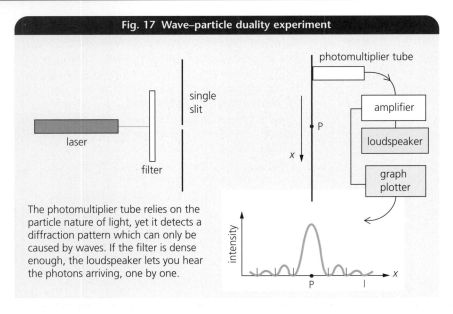

photomultiplier tube

single slit

amplifier

P

loudspeaker

laser

graph plotter

filter

x

intensity

x

P

l

The photomultiplier tube relies on the particle nature of light, yet it detects a diffraction pattern which can only be caused by waves. If the filter is dense enough, the loudspeaker lets you hear the photons arriving, one by one.

Wave–particle duality

The photoelectric effect suggests that light behaves as a particle. However, effects such as diffraction (page 61) show that light can also behave like a wave. It is possible to carry out an experiment in which light behaves as a wave in one part of the apparatus and as a particle in another (Fig. 17). This seemingly contradictory behaviour is an example of what is called **wave–particle duality**. This 'double-nature' is not just restricted to light; things like electrons and protons which we have traditionally pictured as particles turn out to have wave-like characteristics as well.

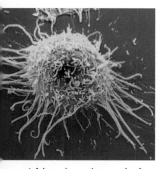

A false-colour micrograph of a human cancer cell.

De Broglie waves

In 1924, the young prince Louis de Broglie wrote in his PhD thesis, 'all material particles have a wave nature'. He predicted that a particle of momentum p would have a wavelength λ given by:

$$\lambda = \frac{h}{p}$$

where h = Planck's constant.

De Broglie suggested that it should be possible to diffract electrons. Davisson and Germer confirmed this theory four years later when they successfully diffracted electrons through a crystal. Today this principle is used in electron microscopes.

An electron diffraction tube is a primitive form of electron microscope. The tube lacks focusing coils, so it just produces a diffraction pattern on the fluorescent screen (Fig. 18).

If we know the potential difference across the tube (in this case 5 kV), we can work out the de Broglie wavelength of the electrons. The energy gained by the electron is:

$$E = q_e V$$
$$= 1.6 \times 10^{-19} \text{ C} \times 5000 \text{ V}$$
$$= 8 \times 10^{-16} \text{ J}$$

This is the electron's kinetic energy, so its velocity is approximately:

$$\tfrac{1}{2} m_e v^2 = 8 \times 10^{-16} \text{ J}$$
$$v^2 = \frac{2 \times 8 \times 10^{-16} \text{ J}}{9.1 \times 10^{-31} \text{ kg}}$$
$$v = 4.2 \times 10^7 \text{ m s}^{-1}$$

The momentum of the electron is:

$$p = m_e v$$
$$= 9.1 \times 10^{-31} \text{ kg} \times 4.2 \times 10^7 \text{ m s}^{-1}$$
$$= 3.8 \times 10^{-23} \text{ kg m s}^{-1}$$

So the de Broglie wavelength of the electron is:

$$\lambda = \frac{h}{p}$$
$$= \frac{6.6 \times 10^{-34} \text{ Js}}{3.8 \times 10^{-23} \text{ kg m s}^{-1}}$$
$$= 1.7 \times 10^{-11} \text{ m}$$

The de Broglie wavelength of a particle decreases as its momentum increases. An electron which is accelerated through a potential difference of 60 kV gains a momentum of about 1.3×10^{-22} kg m s^{-1}. This gives it a wavelength of about 0.005 nm, compared with an average value for visible light of about 500 nm. By looking at something with electrons, rather than light, we can improve the detail of the image 100 000 times.

11 All matter can show wave-like properties, duality isn't confined to just electrons and protons, but everyday objects tend to have rather short de Broglie wavelengths. Estimate your de Broglie wavelength when you are walking and hence explain why you don't get diffracted when you pass through a doorway!

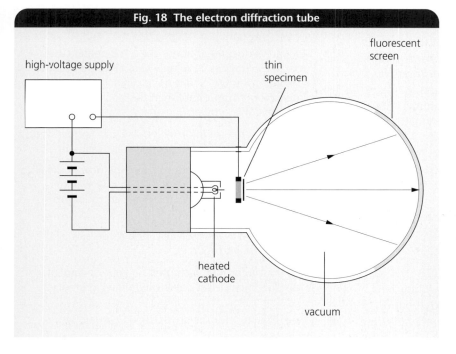

Fig. 18 The electron diffraction tube

high-voltage supply

thin specimen

fluorescent screen

heated cathode

vacuum

■ Diffraction suggests that light is a wave, and the photoelectric effect suggests that light also behaves as a particle.

■ Electrons and protons can be diffracted as if they were waves. All particles have a wavelength associated with them; the de Broglie wavelength is given by:

$$\lambda = \frac{h}{p}$$

Lighting the way

The further away a bright object is, the dimmer it appears, so making it more difficult to see. Astronomers have been trying to push back the boundaries of what we can 'see' for hundreds of years. Firstly we used our eyes, then came photographic plates which could allow longer exposure times to look at the stars and increase our field of view. Even the photographic plate has its limitations though, as its sensitivity to light is typically only around 2%. Then came photocathode-type detectors which used the **photoelectric effect**. In these detectors, photons from space fall on a cathode which releases electrons to give a current. The output was viewed on monitors rather than with the naked eye. This allowed astronomers to store and process information easily on computer disks. But even these have been superseded by two other devices: charge coupled devices (CCDs) and superconducting tunnel junctions (STJs).

Charge coupled devices

CCDs use the fact that the surface of a silicon chip can produce an electric charge when photons of light strike them. The CCD has many individual picture elements or *pixels* on its surface, e.g. a 12 mm × 8 mm CCD can have 576 × 385 pixels. Each of these pixels transfers charge from the chip which is used to build up an image. There are now many applications of CCDs, such as cameras, TVs, fax machines, dental X-ray equipment and spectroscopic equipment, but the whole interest in these devices started with astronomy.

However, CCDs have some drawbacks for astronomers. For example, data is needed about the arrival times of photons from rapidly changing stellar objects such as pulsars or oscillating white dwarfs. Also, the wavelength is difficult to measure without the use of filters and gratings. Hence the arrival of STJs.

Superconducting tunnel junctions (STJs)

At very low temperatures (just above absolute zero, –273 °C), electrons move about in weakly bound pairs called *Cooper pairs*. The binding energy of these Cooper pairs is only a few millielectronvolts. Photons on the other hand can have an energy of about 3 eV, so thousands of Cooper pairs can be broken up by an individual photon. The number of free electrons produced can give a measure of the energy of the photon and so allow us to calculate its wavelength. The counting is done using an STJ chip and an image is built up from the charge collected. The Cooper pairs recombine within microseconds, so are

available to receive more photons. The first small camera using this technology was produced in 1999 and used on the UK's 4.2 metre William Herschel Telescope on La Palma in the Canaries. A sapphire substrate fitted with a sandwich of lead, aluminium oxide and layers of tantalum is used in the device developed at the European Space Agency's centre at Noordwijk in Holland. Each STJ is only 25 mm^2.

1 The argument has sometimes been made that astronomy uses up a great deal of public money, constructing telescopes in far off countries, with little benefit to most people (except astronomers who enjoy holidays in the sun!)

Prepare for a group discussion on this topic. Some people in your teaching group should be prepared to support the idea that the money has been wasted and the government grants should stop. Others should argue the opposite view. You may need to agree before you start who will take up each viewpoint. Do not worry if you have to argue for a viewpoint you do not agree with. Sometimes arguing against a particular viewpoint will allow you to understand just how reasonable that position is and can strengthen and focus your original opinions.

2 Prepare a document about the STJ camera. Given that these devices have only very recently become available, you will find it quite difficult to get information from established textbooks. How can you solve this problem?

a List the sources of information likely to contain the most recent data.

b For each information source describe how you will search it. There may be more than one way to carry out the search so rank them according to expected usefulness.

c Now carry out your search. Keep records of all information and sources.

d Use your information to prepare your document. The document must cover the following points:

- a brief explanation of how the STJ camera works (include a diagram);
- examples of areas where STJ cameras are currently being used;
- a comparison of STJ cameras with older imaging techniques;
- suggestions for other areas of science and technology where STJ cameras might be used to improve on current equipment.

1 a Calculate the wavelength of a gamma-ray photon which has an energy of 1.6×10^{-15} J. (2)

b An X-ray photon is generated which has the same energy as the gamma-ray described in part (a). Compare these two photons in respect of their

(i) speed of transmission in a vacuum,

(ii) ability to penetrate a given material. (2)

2 One of the spectral lines of hydrogen has a wavelength of 435 nm. The energy level diagram below represents the first five energy levels for hydrogen. Determine which of the energy level transitions will give this spectral line. (4)

level 4 ——————— −0.54 eV
level 3 ——————— −0.85 eV

level 2 ——————— −1.51 eV

level 1 ——————— −3.4 eV

ground ——————— −13.6 eV
state

3 The Einstein photoelectric equation is

$$hf = \phi + E_k$$

a State the meaning of each of the terms in the equation.
hf
ϕ
E_k (3)

b In a laboratory demonstration of the photoelectric effect, a metal plate is given an electric charge and light of various wavelengths is shone onto the surface of the plate in turn. It is found that the plate loses its electric charge when the plate is given a negative charge **and** when ultraviolet light is shone onto the plate.

Explain why the plate does not lose its charge when

(i) The plate is given a positive charge and illuminated by ultraviolet light,

(ii) The plate is given a negative charge and illuminated by visible light. (4)

4 The spacing of atoms in a crystal is 1.0×10^{-10} m.

mass of the electron = 9.1×10^{-31} kg

the Planck constant = 6.6×10^{-34} J s

a Estimate the speed of electrons which would give detectable diffraction effects with such crystals. (3)

b State and explain how the speed of electrons would have to be different in an experiment to observe their diffraction by atomic nuclei. (2)

c Give **two** pieces of evidence to demonstrate that electrons have particle properties. (2)

5 Use data from a Data booklet in this question.

a (i) Define the *electronvolt*.

(ii) Show that the speed of an electron accelerated through a potential difference of 6.0 kV is 4.6×10^7 m s^{-1}. (4)

b State what is meant by the duality of the nature of electrons. (1)

c In a demonstration of electron diffraction, a narrow beam of electrons is accelerated through 6.0 kV and passes normally through a thin film of graphite mounted in a vacuum tube. Concentric rings appear on a fluorescent screen at the end of the tube.

(i) Calculate the wavelength associated with the electrons.

(ii) What information does your answer to part (c) (i) suggest about the spacing of carbon atoms in graphite? (4)

6 Dynamics

'Citius, Altius, Fortius' is the motto of the Olympic games. It means 'Swifter, Higher, Stronger', a challenge which athletes have tried to meet since the modern Olympic games began in 1896.

In the last 10 years, world records have been set for all the major athletic disciplines. What has given modern athletes the edge over their predecessors?

One answer is the increasing impact of science. Teams of scientists advise modern athletes. Physiologists design training routines, nutritionists plan special diets and psychologists work on an athlete's state of mind. Electronic measurements of heart-rate, temperature and even brain activity, are used to monitor performance.

The influence of biochemistry has been more controversial. The first evidence of systematic drug use came during the 1950s when athletes began using anabolic steroids to build muscle. This has had most impact in disciplines which rely on strength, such as sprinting, weightlifting or the throwing events.

Science has also played a part in the measurement of achievement. Electronic timing now allows records to be broken by one-hundredth of a second. Wind speed is measured using an ultrasonic device, and displayed alongside the winning times. Any records that are set with a strong wind in the athletes' favour will not stand.

Research in biomechanics now uses computer simulation to analyse athletic performance. These computer models use the laws of motion, and accurate data about the athlete, to suggest slight changes in style which could make that vital millisecond of difference.

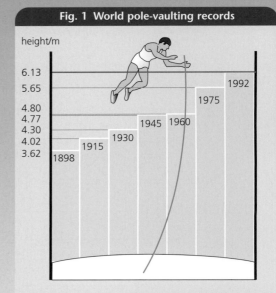

Fig. 1 World pole-vaulting records

Improvements in pole-vault heights owe more to material science than athletic coaching. Poles have progressed from bamboo, through metal, to glass-fibre reinforced plastic.

Chris Boardman used the psychological technique of 'visualisation' – the mental action-replay of a good performance – to help him win a gold medal. His racing was also helped by the engineers who designed his bike, his clothes and his helmet.

6.1 Setting the pace

Vectors and scalars

In 1985 Marita Koch ran 400 m in a record-breaking time of 47.60 s. Her average speed during the race was:

$$\text{average speed (m s}^{-1}) = \frac{\text{distance moved (m)}}{\text{time taken (s)}}$$

$$= \frac{400 \text{ m}}{47.6 \text{ s}}$$

$$= 8.40 \text{ m s}^{-1}$$

The 400 m race is run over one complete lap of a running track. At the end of the race, the runner in the inside lane will be back where she started. We say that her **displacement** is zero. Displacement describes the *effect* of a journey, rather than distance travelled. Displacement and distance have the same units, but displacement, *s*, is defined as the distance covered *in a certain direction*. (Do not confuse with seconds, s.) Displacement is a **vector** quantity. It has a magnitude (size) and a direction. A vector needs two numbers to describe it (Fig. 2).

Distance is a **scalar** quantity. It has magnitude only, so it can be described by just one number. **Velocity** is speed in a given direction, so it is a vector quantity.

$$\text{velocity (m s}^{-1}) = \frac{\text{displacement (m)}}{\text{time (s)}}, \quad v = \frac{\Delta s}{\Delta t}$$

The delta symbol, Δ, represents a change in a quantity. Speed is a scalar quantity. For motion in a straight line (linear motion), velocity and speed have the same magnitude. For non-linear motion, velocity can change even if the speed stays the same.

1. Athletes in a 1500 m race can run a lap at a steady speed, but their velocity changes. Explain why this is so.

2. In 1986, Ingrid Kristiansen of Norway won a women's 10 000 m race (25 laps of a 400 m track) in a record time of 30 minutes 13.74 s.

a. What was her average speed during the race?

b. What was her average velocity?

Average and instantaneous values

A 100 m race is run in a straight line, so the speed and the magnitude of the velocity are

Fig. 2 Displacement and distance

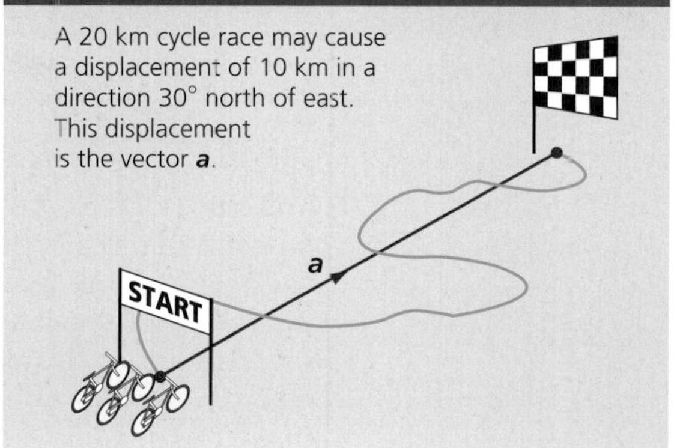

A 20 km cycle race may cause a displacement of 10 km in a direction 30° north of east. This displacement is the vector **a**.

the same. In the Barcelona Olympics in 1992, Linford Christie ran this distance in 9.96 s. His average velocity for the race was:

$$v = \frac{s}{t} = \frac{100.0 \text{ m}}{9.96 \text{ s}} = 10.04 \text{ m s}^{-1}$$

Linford ran the first 10 m in 1.87 seconds, a velocity of just over 5 m s^{-1}. He ran the last 10 m at a velocity of 11.36 m s^{-1}.

In reality, velocity is measured as an average. It is a measurement of displacement over a certain time. If that time interval is very small, we are close to measuring the **instantaneous velocity** (Fig. 3). If the time interval Δt is very small, any motion will be approximately linear so the magnitude of the instantaneous velocity is also its instantaneous speed.

Florence Griffith-Joyner was timed at 0.91 s over each 10 m from 60 m to 90 m in the 1988 100 m final. If the instantaneous velocity of an athlete is the same in successive time intervals they are running at constant or uniform velocity. Uniform velocity means that equal distances are covered in equal times, in a straight line.

3. Does the highest average speed or the highest instantaneous speed win races? Explain your answer.

4. Is it the average speed or the instantaneous speed which is more important in a long jumper's run up? Explain your answer.

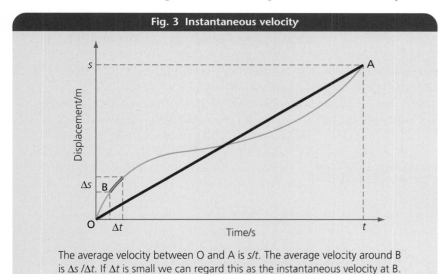

Fig. 3 Instantaneous velocity

The average velocity between O and A is s/t. The average velocity around B is $\Delta s / \Delta t$. If Δt is small we can regard this as the instantaneous velocity at B.

6.2 Components of velocity

Relative motion

Velocity is always measured relative to an observer. Two athletes running together at uniform velocity appear stationary *relative* to one another, while the track appears to move backwards. Every measurement of velocity depends on the relative motion, or the frame of reference, of the observer. Each time you record a velocity, you should specify the frame of reference. In practice, we rarely do this because most measurements are made with respect to the surface of the Earth.

5 Is there such a thing as a 'stationary' object? Explain your answer.

6 The equator moves at a speed of 465 m s^{-1} relative to the Earth's axis. Olympic high jumpers can stay in the air for up to 1 second. Why don't they land up to 465 m from their take-off point?

Resolving vectors

In 1986, Fatima Whitbread broke the UK women's javelin record when she threw the javelin a distance of 77.44 m. The release speed for the javelin was about 27 m s^{-1}. Its *horizontal* speed was only about 23 m s^{-1}. This is because the javelin is thrown at an angle of about 30° to the ground.

The javelin's velocity can be thought of as having two parts, or **components**; a horizontal component and a vertical component (Fig. 4). All vectors can be divided up into two components by a process called resolving.

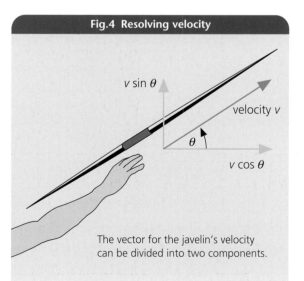

Fig.4 Resolving velocity

v sin *θ*

velocity *v*

θ

v cos *θ*

The vector for the javelin's velocity can be divided into two components.

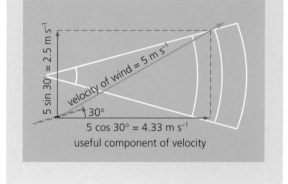

Fig. 5 Worked example of resolving

Records in events such as the javelin are not recognised if a wind speed greater than 2 m s^{-1} is blowing in the competitor's favour. If the wind is blowing at an angle to the event we can calculate how much it helps the athlete.

A wind blows at 5 m s^{-1} at an angle of 30° to the throwing direction. The component in the direction of the throw is 5 cos 30° = 4.33 m s^{-1}.

5 sin 30° = 2.5 m s^{-1}

velocity of wind = 5 m s^{-1}

30°

5 cos 30° = 4.33 m s^{-1}
useful component of velocity

Vector addition is more complicated than scalar addition. Adding together two *distances* of 3 m will always produce the answer 6 m. Adding together two *displacements* of 3 m could give a result from 0 to 6 m. This is because we have to take the direction of the displacements into account.

You can add vectors by drawing a scale diagram and measuring the length and direction of the **resultant** (Fig. 6). The resultant is the sum of any number of vectors. Vector additions can also be solved using trigonometry (Fig. 7).

7 A shot-putter releases the shot at a velocity of 12.5 m s^{-1} at an angle of 41° to the horizontal. What is the horizontal velocity of the shot?

Fig. 6 Adding vectors by scale drawing

The resultant, **a+b**, of adding two vectors, **a** and **b**, can be found by:

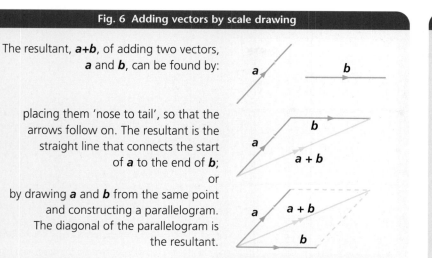

placing them 'nose to tail', so that the arrows follow on. The resultant is the straight line that connects the start of **a** to the end of **b**;

or

by drawing **a** and **b** from the same point and constructing a parallelogram. The diagonal of the parallelogram is the resultant.

Fig. 7 Adding vectors using trigonometry

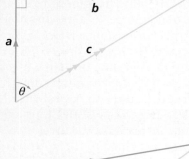

Vectors at right angles
Find the magnitude of c with Pythagoras' theorem:
$c^2 = a^2 + b^2$, so $c = \sqrt{(a^2 + b^2)}$.
Find the angle θ from
$\tan \theta = b/a$, so $\theta = \tan^{-1} b/a$.

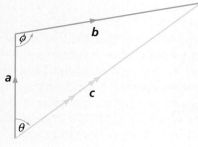

For two vectors at angle ϕ
Find the magnitude of c with the cosine rule: $c^2 = a^2 + b^2 - 2ab \cos \phi$
Find the angle θ from the sine rule:
$$\frac{\sin \theta}{b} = \frac{\sin \phi}{c}$$

Acceleration

In a 100 m race it is vital to get a good start. A sprinter needs to increase her velocity as quickly as possible. The rate at which velocity increases is called acceleration:

$$\text{acceleration} = \frac{\text{change in velocity}}{\text{time taken for change}}$$

Fig. 8 Velocity–time graph

A velocity–time graph can be used to find the acceleration at a given time. The instantaneous acceleration at any time is given by the slope of the tangent at that point. The tangent at a point is approximated by taking a small change in the velocity, Δv, over a small time interval, Δt. The average acceleration is then given by $\Delta v/\Delta t$. As Δt gets smaller $\Delta v/\Delta t$ gets closer to the instantaneous acceleration.

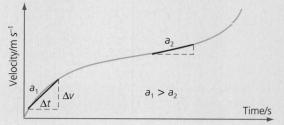

Since velocity is measured in m s^{-1} and time is in seconds, acceleration has units of m s^{-1}/s, written as m s^{-2}. Acceleration takes place in a certain direction and is therefore a vector quantity.

Any change in velocity, a change in speed *or* just a change in direction, constitutes an acceleration. If the acceleration is in the opposite direction to the velocity, it will act to reduce the velocity. This is often referred to as a deceleration or retardation.

Two seconds into a 100 m race a top sprinter reaches a speed of 10 m s^{-1}. The average acceleration is 5 m s^{-2}. A sprinter achieves a much higher acceleration at the instant she leaves the starting blocks. The acceleration at a particular moment is defined in a similar way to instantaneous velocity (Fig. 8). If we consider the change in velocity, Δv, in a very small interval of time, Δt, then:

$$\text{instantaneous acceleration} = \frac{\Delta v}{\Delta t}$$

8 A tennis ball is dropped and bounces up again. Sketch the ball:

a as it falls;

b as it bounces up.

Mark in the direction of the velocity and the acceleration in each case.

KEY FACTS

- A single vector may be resolved into two components.
- Vectors can be added and subtracted by scale drawing or by trigonometry.

- Acceleration is a vector quantity. It is the rate of change of velocity.

Free fall and terminal velocity

An object is said to be in free fall if the only force acting on it is gravity. Experiments show that on Earth the acceleration due to gravity, g, is about $9.8\,\text{m s}^{-2}$, though the exact value varies from place to place.

The acceleration due to gravity at a particular place is the same for all objects. The mass of a free-falling diver has no effect on her acceleration. Heavy or light, she would reach the water in the same time.

Sky divers reach their terminal velocity when the downward force of gravity is equal to the force of air resistance.

However, an object falling on Earth is never quite in free fall. The atmosphere always exerts a drag force on a moving object. The effect of this air resistance is negligible for sprinters, jumpers or even divers, but in some sports, such as cycling or skiing, it is a dominant factor. This is because the drag force due to **air resistance** increases with speed. For a sky diver, the resistive force due to air resistance increases as the diver accelerates until it is equal to the downward force of gravity.

When this happens, the sky diver stops accelerating and falls at a constant speed. We say the diver has reached **terminal velocity** (Fig. 9). For a sky diver in a head-down position the terminal velocity is about $82\,\text{m s}^{-1}$ (185 mph). In the upper atmosphere, where the air is less dense, speeds of up to $280\,\text{m s}^{-1}$ (625 mph) have been reached.

Air resistance also depends on the area and the mass of the object. In general, a dense object with a small surface area will experience a low air resistance, and have a higher terminal velocity.

Air resistance has little effect on compact objects that are moving slowly. Divers are effectively in free fall.

High-speed skiing is one of the fastest sports. Speed skiers wear streamlined clothes and adopt a crouching position to reduce air resistance. The record speed is over $230\,\text{km h}^{-1}$ ($65\,\text{m s}^{-1}$).

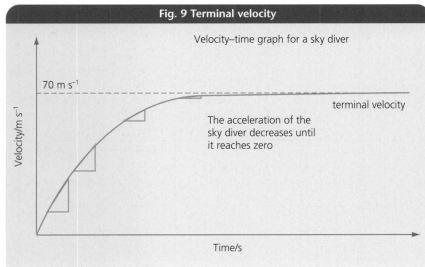

Fig. 9 Terminal velocity

Velocity–time graph for a sky diver

$70\,\text{m s}^{-1}$

terminal velocity

The acceleration of the sky diver decreases until it reaches zero

Velocity/m s^{-1}

Time/s

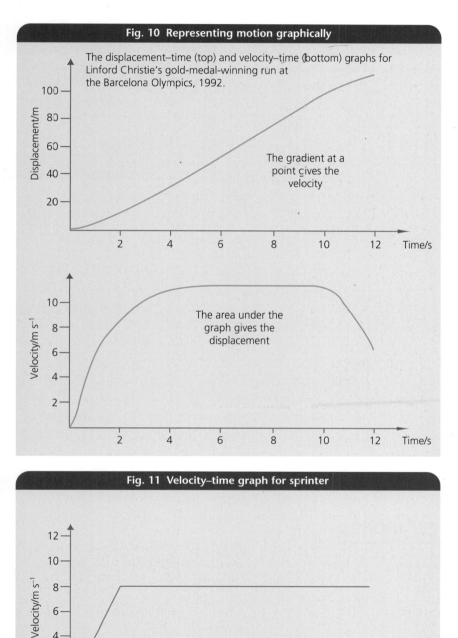

Fig. 10 Representing motion graphically

The displacement–time (top) and velocity–time (bottom) graphs for Linford Christie's gold-medal-winning run at the Barcelona Olympics, 1992.

The gradient at a point gives the velocity

The area under the graph gives the displacement

Fig. 11 Velocity–time graph for sprinter

Time and motion graphs

Graphs showing how the displacement, velocity and acceleration of an object vary with time are an excellent way of visualising motion. A displacement–time graph can provide us with information on velocity. The velocity at any given time is $\Delta s/\Delta t$. This is the same as the gradient of the graph in Fig. 10.

Another way of looking at an athlete's motion is to show how their velocity varies with time. The gradient of this graph is $\Delta v/\Delta t$, the acceleration. A straight line means that the velocity is changing by the same amount over equal time intervals. This is uniform acceleration.

A velocity–time graph can also give information about the displacement. For constant velocity:

displacement = velocity × time

If the velocity varies, the displacement at a certain time can be found by calculating the area under the line up to that point (Fig. 10).

9 Figure 11 shows an idealised velocity–time graph for a sprinter.

a Calculate the acceleration over the first 2 seconds.

b Calculate the distance covered in the first 8 seconds.

10 A diver jumps 1 m up from a 10 m high board, before diving into the pool below. Sketch graphs to show how her displacement, velocity and acceleration change with time. Take 'down' as negative and use the height of the board as zero displacement. (Assume the motion is all vertical and that air resistance can be ignored.)

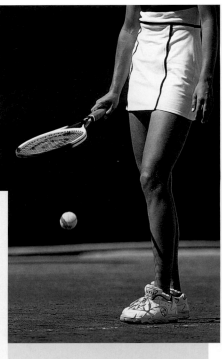

APPLICATION   Time and motion for a bouncing ball

We can see how acceleration, velocity and displacement are linked by plotting graphs which show how the motion of an object varies with time. Think about a tennis ball, dropped from a height of 1m, which bounces three times before being caught again. Because we are dealing with vector quantities we need to decide on a sign convention. In this case we will take 'down' as negative and treat ground level as zero displacement.

Acceleration. The ball is always accelerating under gravity, $a = -10 \, \text{m s}^{-2}$, except for the very brief time that it is touching the ground, when the acceleration will be upwards. As soon as the ball loses contact with the ground, its acceleration will be $-10 \, \text{m s}^{-2}$ once more. The ball will transfer some energy each time it hits the ground so each bounce will be lower than the previous one and the bounces will get closer together.

Velocity. The ball is dropped, so its initial velocity is zero. The gradient of the velocity–time graph is the instantaneous acceleration of the ball. The graph will be straight, with a gradient of $-10 \, \text{m s}^{-2}$, until the ball hits the ground. Then the ball rapidly slows to a halt and accelerates back up. After the ball has left the ground, the velocity will decrease as the ball rises, until it is zero again at the top of the bounce.

Displacement. The gradient of the displacement–time graph is the instantaneous velocity, so the slope starts at zero and becomes increasingly negative until the ball hits the ground. The displacement does not go negative because we have taken ground level to be zero.

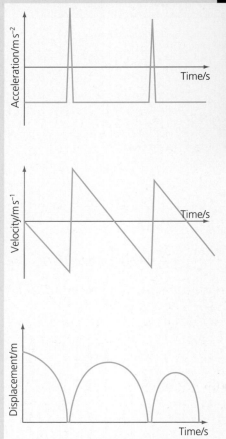

6.3   Equations of linear motion

There are five important variables that can be used to describe motion.

Quantity	Symbol
displacement	s
initial velocity	u
final velocity	v
acceleration	a
time	t

These quantities are linked by the equations of linear motion:

1 The definition of acceleration gives us the first equation:

$$\text{acceleration} = \frac{\text{change in velocity}}{\text{time taken}}$$

$$\text{or, } a = \frac{v - u}{t}$$

$$at = v - u$$

So, $v = u + at$ (Equation 1)

2 The definition of velocity leads to the second equation:

$$velocity = \frac{displacement}{time}$$

or, displacement = velocity × time

When the velocity changes at a constant rate, we take the average velocity as half-way between the initial and final values.

displacement = average velocity × t

$$s = \tfrac{1}{2}(u + v)t \quad \text{(Equation 2)}$$

3 It is possible to eliminate v from Equations 1 and 2 (Fig. 12):

$$s = \tfrac{1}{2}(u + u + at)t$$

$$s = ut + \tfrac{1}{2}at^2 \quad \text{(Equation 3)}$$

4 We can eliminate t from Equation 3 by substituting

$$t = \frac{v - u}{a} \quad \text{(from Equation 1)}$$

$$\text{So, } s = u\left(\frac{v-u}{a}\right) + \tfrac{1}{2}a\left(\frac{v-u}{a}\right)^2$$

This simplifies to: $v^2 = u^2 + 2as$ (Equation 4)

Each equation has one of the five variables missing. If you know any three of the five variables you should be able to calculate the other two. These equations only work for motion in a straight line, where the acceleration is constant.

If a 100 m sprinter initially accelerates at 2.0 m s⁻² and maintains this acceleration over the whole race, we can use the equations to calculate how fast he will cross the finishing line and how long he will take. To find the final velocity you could use:

$$v^2 = u^2 + 2as$$
$$= 0 + 2 \times 2.0 \times 100$$

The final velocity, $v = \sqrt{400} = 20$ m s⁻¹. The time taken for the race would be:

$$t = \frac{v - u}{a}$$
$$= \frac{20.0 \text{ m s}^{-1} - 0}{2.0 \text{ m s}^{-2}}$$
$$= 10.0 \text{ s}$$

In reality, sprinters achieve a higher acceleration than this at the start of the race, though it cannot be maintained throughout the race (Fig. 11).

11 When a golfer hits a ball the club only touches the ball for about 0.0005 s, but the ball leaves the tee at a speed of 75 m s⁻¹.

What is the average acceleration of the golf ball while it is in contact with the club?

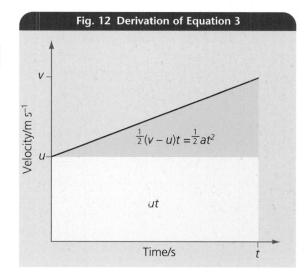

Fig. 12 Derivation of Equation 3

6.4 For a few centimetres more

Motion in two dimensions

In the 1968 Olympic games in Mexico City, the American Bob Beamon almost cleared the long jump pit! His jump of 8.90 m was 70 cm further than anyone had ever jumped at that time.

To understand a long jumper's motion we need to deal with movement in two dimensions. After take-off, the jumper moves horizontally *and* vertically. To complicate things still further, the velocity changes direction throughout the jump.

The motion seems complex, but we can simplify it. First we concentrate on the motion of just one point, the **centre of mass**. In the air, no matter how the jumper moves his arms or legs, his centre of mass will follow a symmetrical path, known as a parabola.

We can simplify things further by treating the two-dimensional movement as a combination of horizontal and vertical motion (Fig. 13). Vertical motion is totally independent of horizontal motion.

A record-breaking long jumper has to combine top-class sprinting with a high jumper's spring into the air. A good sprinter achieves a top speed of about 12 m s^{-1}; a high jumper leaves the ground with a vertical velocity of about 4.5 m s^{-1}. If a long jumper could combine these performances, how far would he be able to jump?

Strictly speaking, the equations of motion only apply to movement in a straight line, but we can use them to describe a long jump if we treat the vertical and horizontal velocities separately.

The **vertical** take-off velocity will determine the time of flight. We can use $v = u + at$ to find the time spent in the air:

$$t = \frac{v - u}{a}$$
$$= \frac{(-4.5 \text{ m s}^{-1}) - 4.5 \text{ m s}^{-1}}{-9.8 \text{ m s}^{-2}}$$
$$= 0.92 \text{ s}$$

The **horizontal** velocity can be used to find the length of the jump. We can use $s = ut + \frac{1}{2}at^2$, but $a = 0$, so this is just $s = ut$:

length of jump, $s = 12 \text{ m s}^{-1} \times 0.92 \text{ s} = 11 \text{ m}$

The world record for the long jump is about 2 m less than this theoretical result. There are a number of places where our simple model does not match the real event:

a A long jumper has to drop his horizontal speed so that he is in contact with the board long enough to gain some vertical speed;

b Air resistance can impose a horizontal retardation of up to 0.2 m s^{-2} (it has little affect on the vertical motion);

c We have treated the jumper as if he was a single point and the distance we have calculated is that travelled by the centre of mass. The actual jump may be longer than this because a good long jumper will have his centre of mass over the board at take-off and behind his heels on landing, thereby increasing the time of flight.

This approach to athletics is typical of the way physics works. We try to understand a complex system by identifying its essential features and creating a theoretical model. Experiments and measurements are used to check how closely our model reflects the real world.

12 The best high jumpers achieve a vertical take-off velocity of about 4.8 m s^{-1}. A typical high jumper's 'centre of mass' is 0.95 m above the ground. Use the equations of motion to estimate the height that this jumper can reach.

13 The divers of La Quebrada leap from the cliffs near Acapulco into the sea, 26.7 m below. They need a horizontal range of at least 8.22 m to clear the rocks at the foot of the cliff. Assuming they jump horizontally from the cliff-edge

a Estimate the horizontal velocity needed to clear the rocks.

b How fast do they hit the sea?

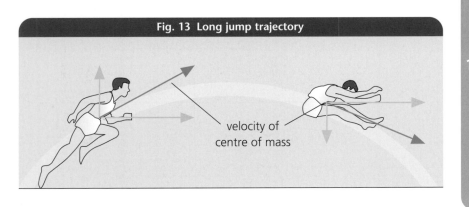

Fig. 13 Long jump trajectory

velocity of centre of mass

■ Horizontal motion does not affect vertical motion.

■ Problems of two-dimensional motion (projectiles) can be solved by resolving the initial velocity into vertical and horizontal components and applying the equations of linear motion to each component separately.

EXTENSION

Getting the right angle

Throwing the 'hammer' requires great strength. In 1986, the Russian Yuriy Sedykh set a world record with a throw of 86.74 m.

High-speed computers can be used to model athletes' performance and help improve their technique.

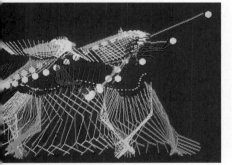

The 'hammer' is a small tungsten ball fastened to the end of a 1.22 m chain. It has a mass of 7.26 kg. The thrower whirls the hammer round three times before releasing it. The speed of release depends on how quickly the thrower can spin round in the 2 m circle, but the length of the throw also depends on the angle of release. A good thrower will release the hammer at a speed of about 26 m s^{-1}. We can use the equations of motion to find the best angle.

The distance thrown is determined by the horizontal speed and the time of flight. The time of flight depends on the vertical component of the velocity. The problem can be simplified by considering just the first half of the throw; from the moment of release to when the hammer reaches its highest point.

For the vertical motion, s is unknown, $u = 26 \sin \theta$ m s^{-1}, $v = 0$ m s^{-1}, $a = -9.8$ m s^{-2} and t is unknown. Using $v = u + at$:

$$t = \frac{v - u}{a}$$
$$= \frac{0 - 26 \sin \theta \text{ m s}^{-1}}{-9.8 \text{ m s}^{-2}}$$
$$= 2.65 \sin \theta \text{ seconds}$$

The time for the whole flight is:
$2 \times 2.65 \sin \theta = 5.30 \sin \theta$

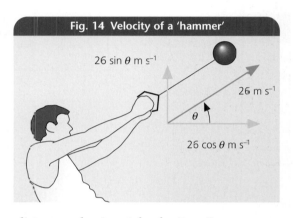

Fig. 14 Velocity of a 'hammer'

distance = horizontal velocity × time
$$= 26 \cos \theta \text{ m s}^{-1} \times 5.30 \sin \theta \text{ s}$$
$$= 138 \sin \theta \cos \theta \text{ metres}$$

But $\sin \theta \cos \theta = \frac{1}{2} \sin 2\theta$, so:
distance = $69 \sin 2\theta$ m

The greatest range will be achieved when $\sin 2\theta$ has its greatest value. The largest value of $\sin 2\theta$ is 1, so the hammer thrower has a maximum range of 69 m.

When $\sin 2\theta = 1$, $2\theta = 90°$ and $\theta = 45°$. Theoretically, the best angle at which to release the hammer is 45°. In fact, because the hammer is released from above ground level the best angle of release is slightly less than 45°.

14 Theoretically the optimum take-off angle for a projectile is 45°. Why don't long jumpers take off at this angle?

LAST NAME	FIRST NAME	CITY	AGE	SEX	TIME	SPLIT TIME
Mattern	Jan		28	M	2:07:25	
Bermudez	Ramiro		26	M	2:07:56	
Diaz	Joe	Haverfield	29	M	2:10:53	
Bensa	Janko	NM	22	M	2:14:10.1	1:04:10.0
Bekele	Tesfaye	NYC	29	M	2:14:46.0	1:06:18.6
Kirwa	Jacob	Chapel Hill	23	M	2:16:00.9	1:06:09.1
Mahon	Terrence	Haverfield	29	M	2:17:08.1	1:08:34.6
Chesang	Reuben	Chapel Hill	37	M	2:18:12.9	1:06:52.6
Dos Santos	Delmir	Tampa	33	M	2:18:19.6	1:06:17.2
Wilson	Steve	Clearwater	41	M	2:18:29.6	1:07:08.1
Randich	Julius		32	M	2:18:32.2	1:06:08.1
Klimes	Petr		41	M	2:18:56.0	1:08:34.3
Hernandez	Agustin	Dallas	27	M	2:19:07.1	1:08:35.1
Simonaitis	Dennis	Salt Lake City	37	M	2:19:12.9	1:08:50.3
Sepulveda	Rene		32	M	2:19:24.6	1:08:50.7
Sivou	Dzmitry	Libertyville	28	M	2:19:51.1	
Perez Rodriguez	Cesar	San Sebastian	42	M	2:20:07.5	1:08:53.5
Flores	Narciso	Tolvca	29	M	2:20:58.5	1:06:20.5
Karasev	Sergei	Austin	34	M	2:21:41.9	1:09:45.2
Lutz	Brantley	Albuquerque	24	M	2:21:46.4	1:09:38.5
Wharton	Phil		22	M	2:23:06.3	1:09:07.9
Yon	Jamey	Charlotte	33	M	2:23:13.4	1:10:53.1
Urbina	Jose		40	M	2:24:09.4	1:07:52.3
Hage	Jim		42	M	2:25:18.4	1:10:21.5
Halferty	Dave	Topeka	31	M	2:25:48.3	1:13:31.4
Rea	Peter	Atlanta	31	M	2:25:49.9	1:11:12.4
Wegenka	Matt		30	M	2:26:08.6	1:08:50.9
Hernandez	Juan	Dallas	42	M	2:26:20.5	1:09:08.5
Tilson	Alex	Mountain View	29	M	2:26:59.5	1:10:21.8
Skarpsno	Egil		37	M	2:27:18.9	1:10:16.9
Peters	Eric	Albuquerque	29	M	2:28:45.6	1:09:21.3
Kirk	Brad		31	M	2:28:55.2	1:11:37.8
Hunter	Katherine			F	2:30:34.0	
San Antonit	Gary			M	2:31:12.6	1:09:58.9
Burke	Edmund	Burtonsville	30	M	2:31:29.2	1:09:42.7
Schlesinger	Jonathan	Fairfax	27	M	2:31:49.7	1:11:01.6
Lawrence	James	Orange	30	M	2:32:35.0	1:13:56.1
Flores	Joe	Humble	40	M	2:33:09.3	1:12:47.2
Manz	Mark	Kiel	26	M	2:33:38.0	1:09:08.5
Titova	Tatiana	Tampa	34	F	2:34:01.9	1:15:54.1
Final ten runners to complete the race						
English	Bee	Lubbock	29	F	6:30:11.3	
Lenz	Tracey	Round Rock	40	F	6:36:00.4	3:04:35.7
Greenlee	Jackye	Buda	58	F	6:36:31.9	3:12:21.9
Mize	Matthew	Austin	21	M	6:38:29.2	2:57:15.3
Fest	Brenda	Pflugerville	50	F	6:43:56.8	3:05:38.7
Chatmon-Thomas	Socar	Austin	36	F	6:45:16.2	3:03:00.8
Garcia	Rudy	Poth	42	M	6:45:16.2	3:07:34.5
Finley	Sandra	Houston	50	F	6:54:15.0	2:59:56.4
Sifuentes	Rudy	San Antonio	64	M	6:54:35.2	2:48:06.8
Jones	Harold	Kettering	75	M	7:29:49.0	3:10:03.4

The Motorola Marathon is held in Austin, Texas every year over 42.2 km. The table here shows the results for the top 40 runners and the last 10.

1 What is the average speed in km h^{-1} for:

  a the top ten runners?

  b the last ten runners?

2 If the race starts and finishes at the same line what is the displacement for the complete race?

3 What is the average speed in m s^{-1} for the fastest woman?

4 What is the average velocity for the slowest male?

5 What is the average age for males completing the course in less than 2 hr 20 mins?

6 What is the average speed in m s^{-1} for the fastest person over the age of 35?

7 What is the percentage difference in the time for:

  a first and second places?

  b first and last places?

  c the fastest man and the fastest woman?

1 Throughout this question, neglect air resistance and take the value of the acceleration of free fall, g, as $10\,\text{m s}^{-2}$.

   (i) A ball is dropped from rest from a height of 80 m. Calculate the time taken to reach the ground.

   (ii) A ball is thrown horizontally at $20\,\text{m s}^{-1}$ from the top of a cliff 80 m high. It falls into the sea. Using the axes provided, and showing appropriate numerical values, draw graphs of

      (A) the horizontal component of velocity, v_H, against time, t,

      (B) the vertical component of velocity, v_V, against time, t,

      (C) the height of the ball above the sea, h, against time, t.   (6)

                  (AQA PH01 Jun 97 Q1)

2 a The table of results is taken from an experiment where the time taken for a ball to fall vertically through different distances is measured.

distance fallen/m	1.0	2.0	4.0	6.0	8.0	10.0
time/s	0.45	0.63	0.90	1.10	1.30	1.40

   (i) Plot a graph of distance fallen on the y-axis against time on the x-axis.

   (ii) Explain why your graph is not a straight line.

   (iii) Calculate the gradient of the graph at 0.70 s.

   (iv) State what your gradient represents and use it to determine a value for the acceleration of free fall, assuming that the ball started from rest.   (9)

  b A falling body experiences air resistance and this can result in it reaching a terminal speed. Explain, using Newton's laws of motion, why a terminal speed is reached.   *(3)*

                  (AQA PH01 Feb 97 Q4)

3 A dart is thrown at an angle of 20° above the horizontal and at a speed of $5.0\,\text{m s}^{-1}$. It strikes a dart board, situated a horizontal distance of 2.5 m from its point of projection.

  a Calculate

   (i) the horizontal component of the velocity of the dart,

   (ii) the time taken for the dart to reach the board.   *(3)*

  b If the dart is travelling horizontally at the time it strikes the board, calculate the vertical displacement of the dart.   *(3)*

                  (AQA PH01 Feb 97 Q6)

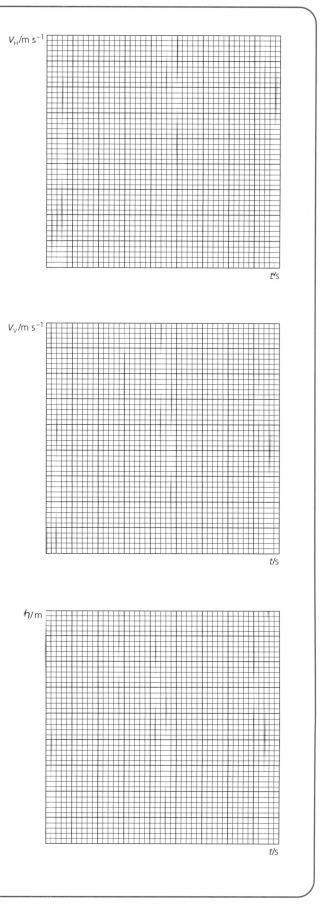

Civil engineers have occasionally underestimated the destructive force of the wind with catastrophic consequences. In 1879, a tornado wrecked the Tay railway bridge in Scotland, killing 71 people. Even relatively low wind speeds can be destructive. In 1940, the Tacoma Narrows bridge in the USA was brought down by a wind of only $18\,\mathrm{m\,s^{-1}}$.

In an attempt to avoid such disasters, engineers now subject their bridge designs to rigorous scrutiny. The Tokyo Bay suspension bridge was tested with gigantic hammers which delivered 100-tonne blows to the middle of the 600 m long central span. The bridge which connects Honshu and Shikoku includes the longest suspension bridge in the world. Before it was completed in 1998, wind tunnel tests were carried out on a 1:100 scale model. The results suggest that the 2 km central span will be stable at wind speeds of up to $90\,\mathrm{m\,s^{-1}}$.

Engineers and architects work to identify the forces and moments that will act on each part of the bridge in a variety of conditions in order to design and build stable structures.

The islands of Honshu and Shikoku are connected by 10 km of suspension and cable-stayed bridges.

The first step in analysing any problem is to identify the important forces that are involved. Most objects are subject to a range of different forces, such as:

● weight
● contact forces
● friction
● tension

Weight

Weight is the force that acts on a mass due to the **gravitational attraction** of the Earth. An object's weight depends on its mass, m, and the gravitational field strength, g. This is the gravitational force that acts on each kilogram of mass. The gravitational field strength is measured in newtons per kilogram, $\mathrm{N\,kg^{-1}}$.

The value of g at the Earth's surface is approximately $9.8\,\mathrm{N\,kg^{-1}}$. On Earth, a mass of 1 kg has a weight of 9.8 N.

weight (N) = mass (kg) × gravitational field strength ($\mathrm{N\,kg^{-1}}$)

$$W = mg$$

1a An astronaut has a mass of 80 kg. What is their weight on Earth?

b The same astronaut would weigh 128 N on the Moon. Calculate the gravitational field strength on the Moon.

The gravitational attraction of the Earth acts on every particle in an object. Adding up all these forces gives the total weight of the object. This **resultant force** can be thought of as acting at a single point. This point is called the **centre of gravity** of the object (Fig. 1). Because weight always acts vertically down, towards the centre of the Earth, we can represent this force by a single vertical arrow from the centre of gravity.

The **centre of mass** of an object is not exactly the same thing as its centre of gravity, though near the Earth's surface (where the force of gravitational attraction is almost constant) they can be regarded as the same point. The position of the centre of mass determines what happens to an object when a force is applied to it. If the resultant force acting on an object passes through its centre of mass, it will accelerate without rotating. Imagine trying to push a car that is parked on some extremely slippery ice. If you push through the centre of mass, the car will move forward without spinning. If the line of action of your force does not pass through the centre of mass, the car will rotate, as well as moving forward (Fig. 3).

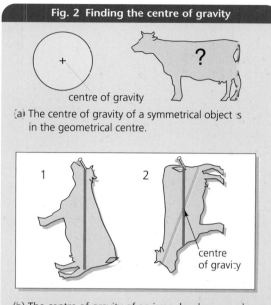

Fig. 2 Finding the centre of gravity

(a) The centre of gravity of a symmetrical object is in the geometrical centre.

(b) The centre of gravity of an irregular shape can be found by suspending it, so that it can hang freely.

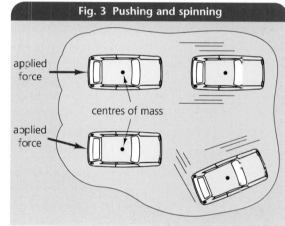

Fig. 3 Pushing and spinning

applied force

applied force

centres of mass

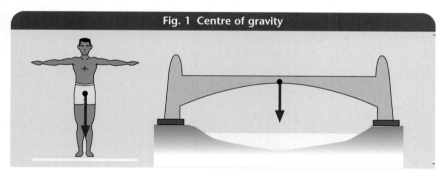

Fig. 1 Centre of gravity

■ The weight of a body = mass × gravitational field strength.

■ The centre of gravity is the point at which all the weight appears to act.

■ The centre of mass is the point through which an applied force causes no rotation.

Contact force

When two solid surfaces are touching, they exert a contact force on each other. This force is sometimes called the reaction. For example, it is the contact force between your feet and the ground that prevents the gravitational attraction of the Earth pulling you through the floor.

When two objects are pushed together, the atoms in each surface repel each other. Like compressed springs, the atoms exert a greater force as they are pushed closer together. The resultant force between the surfaces is the sum of all the inter-atomic repulsions. The component of this force which is at right angles to the surfaces is called the normal

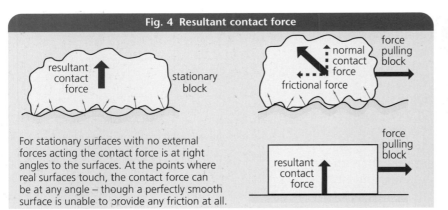

Fig. 4 Resultant contact force

For stationary surfaces with no external forces acting the contact force is at right angles to the surfaces. At the points where real surfaces touch, the contact force can be at any angle – though a perfectly smooth surface is unable to provide any friction at all.

A false-colour scanning electron micrograph of crystalline tungsten. Even the smoothest surfaces look like a mountain landscape at high magnifications.

contact force, or the perpendicular reaction (Fig. 4).

If the surfaces are in relative motion, or if an external horizontal force is acting, the resultant contact force will not be at right angles to the surface. We can treat the resultant as the combination of two forces. The component at right angles to the surface is the normal contact force. The component parallel to the surface is called the frictional force. For perfectly smooth surfaces there would be no friction and the only force would be the normal contact force.

2 Sketch the bridge shown in Fig. 5. Mark in the forces acting on the bridge.

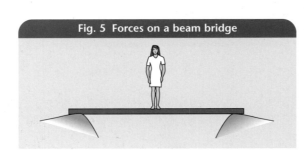

Fig. 5 Forces on a beam bridge

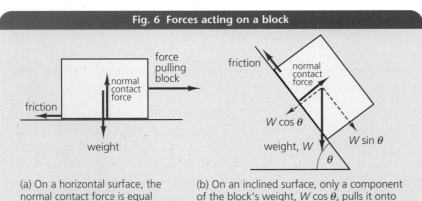

Fig. 6 Forces acting on a block

(a) On a horizontal surface, the normal contact force is equal to the weight of the block.

(b) On an inclined surface, only a component of the block's weight, $W \cos \theta$, pulls it onto the surface. The normal contact force is therefore less than the weight of the block.

Friction

A frictional force acts between two solid surfaces in contact when they are in relative motion, or if a force is trying to slide them across each other. Friction acts to oppose the sliding.

The actual area of contact between two surfaces can be as little as 0.01% of the full surface area. Since pressure at a point is the force per unit area, the pressure at these points is extremely high. The high pressure tends to join the two surfaces, actually 'welding' them together at these small points of contact.

Surfaces will not slide across each other unless an applied force breaks these 'welds'. At the point when the surfaces start to slide, the applied force is just sufficient to overcome the **limiting friction**. When the surfaces are moving, a frictional force acts against the relative motion. The size of this **dynamic friction** is usually less than the limiting friction. The relative speed of the two surfaces does not have very much effect on dynamic friction.

The area of the surfaces has no influence on the friction. The frictional force between two surfaces just depends on how hard they are pressed together, i.e. the normal contact force between them. The force due to friction, F, is proportional to the **normal** contact force, N.

$$F \propto N, \text{ or } F = \mu N$$

The constant of proportionality, μ, is known as the coefficient of friction. Its size depends on the nature of the surfaces. Rough surfaces, such as sandpaper, exert a large frictional force; the coefficient of friction between sandpaper and wood is high (Fig. 6).

Although frictional forces tend to prevent surfaces sliding over each other, they do not act to prevent all motion: imagine trying to cycle when the bicycle tyre has no grip on the road at all. Even when you walk it is the frictional force acting between the road and your shoe that allows you to move forward.

3 'On icy roads a car is more likely to skid if it is fully loaded.' Do you agree with this statement? Explain your answer.

4 Estimate the pressure at the points of contact for a 2 cm steel cube resting on a steel surface.
(Density of steel $\approx 8000 \, \text{kg m}^{-3}$)

5 The coefficient of friction between snow and skis is about 0.02.

a What limiting frictional force acts on a skier of mass 50 kg on horizontal ground?

b Why is the frictional force less than this when the skier is on a steep slope?

The tension in the tightrope is the same throughout its length, as its weight is small compared with the weight of the acrobat. The tension in the balloon cable changes along its length.

The force exerted by the rod is caused by the forces between its molecules. Like the force in a spring, these inter-molecular forces vary, depending on whether the rod is being stretched or compressed. When the rod is being stretched, the molecules are slightly further apart and an attractive force between the molecules tries to restore their original separation. When the molecules are pushed closer together, because the rod is being squashed, a repulsive force acts in a direction that would restore the equilibrium separation.

Tension

Tension is the force that tends to stretch a body. The cables in a cable-stayed bridge are in tension. We can assume that the tension is the same throughout a cable as long as the weight of the cable is small compared to the tension in it.

A solid object, like a metal rod, can act in tension, pulling on the objects that it is connected to. A rod may also act in compression, pushing outwards on the objects that are squashing it.

The cables exert a force on the bridge that acts in the same direction as the cable, along its length, pulling on the roadway and the pylon that it is attached to.

Fig. 7 Tension and compression

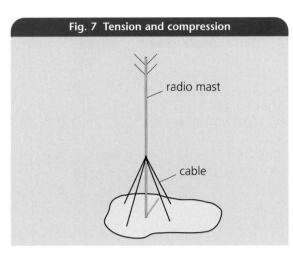

radio mast

cable

6 What are the forces acting on the radio mast (Fig. 7)? Which parts of the structure are in tension? Which are in compression?

Free-body diagrams

The forces acting on a real object, such as the central span of a bridge, are often complex. We can try to understand the situation by drawing a simplified picture of the situation, known as a free-body diagram (Fig. 8). There are several assumptions that engineers make when drawing a free-body diagram:

● Forces are vector quantities – they have a size and a direction. We represent forces on a diagram using arrows, pointing in the direction of the force and labelled with the magnitude. The examples in this chapter are restricted to systems of coplanar forces (two-dimensional problems).

● All the forces which do not act directly on an object are ignored; e.g. the reaction of the ground on the supports does not act directly on the central span of a bridge.

Fig. 8 Simple free-body diagram

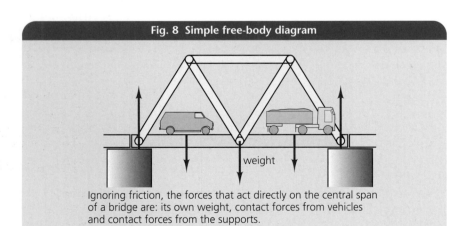

weight

Ignoring friction, the forces that act directly on the central span of a bridge are: its own weight, contact forces from vehicles and contact forces from the supports.

● We are not concerned with the set of balanced forces that are internal to the system; we can ignore any tension or compression in the span itself.

● We can sometimes combine several forces into one; although a vehicle on a bridge touches the road at several points, we need only consider a single contact force acting through the centre of mass of the vehicle.

7 Draw a free-body diagram for a child sliding down a playground slide. Label each of the forces.

The resultant force

Once we have identified all the forces which act on a structure, we can simplify the picture even further by combining them to form a single force. We add the vectors representing the individual forces to give the resultant force (Fig. 9).

Fig. 9 Polygon of forces

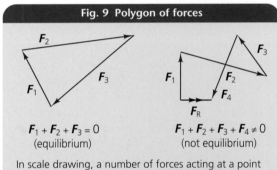

$F_1 + F_2 + F_3 = 0$
(equilibrium)

$F_1 + F_2 + F_3 + F_4 \neq 0$
(not equilibrium)

In scale drawing, a number of forces acting at a point can be added together by placing them 'nose to tail'. If the resulting polygon is closed, this means that the resultant force is zero and the point is in equilibrium.

An object is in equilibrium if it is stationary or if it moves at constant velocity. For equilibrium, the resultant force must be zero. This condition for equilibrium applies to the separate parts of a bridge, as well as to the whole structure.

8 The bridge in Fig. 8 is in equilibrium. Draw its 'polygon of forces'.

Suppose that an engineer suspects that a certain joint in the bridge may fail if the weight of traffic increases any further. When the bridge is not loaded with traffic, the joint is in equilibrium under the action of three forces. There is a contact force from the support, a tension in girder A and a compression from girder B (Fig. 10).

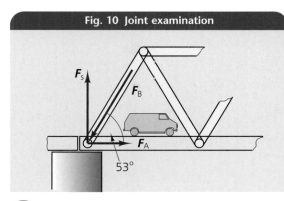

Fig. 10 Joint examination

9 Study Fig. 10. Given that F_A is 3000 N and F_B is 5000 N, what is the magnitude of F_S?

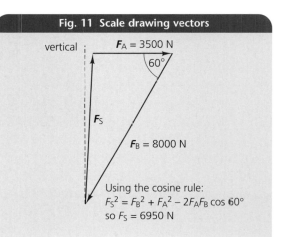

Fig. 11 Scale drawing vectors

vertical

F_A = 3500 N

60°

F_S

F_B = 8000 N

Using the cosine rule:
$F_S^2 = F_B^2 + F_A^2 - 2F_AF_B \cos 60°$
so F_S = 6950 N

In reality, friction will act at the joint, so F_S will not be vertical. Suppose that, with the bridge under load, F_B increases to 8000 N and F_A = 3500 N. In order to find the contact force required to maintain equilibrium, we can use a scale drawing or the cosine rule (Fig. 11). More complex problems can be simplified by resolving forces into horizontal and vertical components.

Resolving forces

It is often important to know the effect of a force in a certain direction. The tension in the cables of Tower Bridge has two effects:

(a) horizontally, which puts the road under compression;

(b) vertically, to lift the weight of the bridge section.

We find the size of these effects by splitting the tension into two **components**, at right angles to each other (Fig. 12). This process is called **resolving** the force (see p. 88). Resolving all the forces on a system can help us to calculate the forces needed to keep it in equilibrium. Suppose a car is unfortunate enough to be on Tower Bridge as it lifts. What frictional force is necessary to keep it in equilibrium and stop it sliding down?

First we draw a free-body diagram showing the forces on the car (Fig. 13).

Then we resolve the forces so that all the components are either parallel or perpendicular to each other. We often do this so that all the force components are horizontal or vertical, but in this case it makes more sense to resolve so that the forces act along the slope or at right angles to it.

For equilibrium the sum of the forces perpendicular to the slope must be zero:

Fig. 12 Resolving into components

$T_y = T \sin \theta$

Tension, T

θ

$T_x = T \cos \theta$

(a) Horizontal component, T_x: $\dfrac{T_x}{T} = \cos \theta$

So $T_x = T \cos \theta$

(b) Vertical component, T_y: $\dfrac{T_y}{T} = \sin \theta$

So $T_y = T \sin \theta$

103

$R = W \cos \theta$

and the sum of the forces along the slope must be zero:

$F = W \sin \theta$

For a car weighing 12 000 N, at an angle of 20°, the frictional force needs to be $12\,000 \times \sin 20° = 4100$ N, to keep the car in equilibrium.

At equilibrium, the sum of all the horizontal components must be zero, and the sum of all the vertical components must be zero (Fig. 14).

10 A car of mass 1000 kg is parked on a ramp inclined at 15° to the horizontal. If the car is in equilibrium, find the normal contact force and the frictional force between the car and the road.

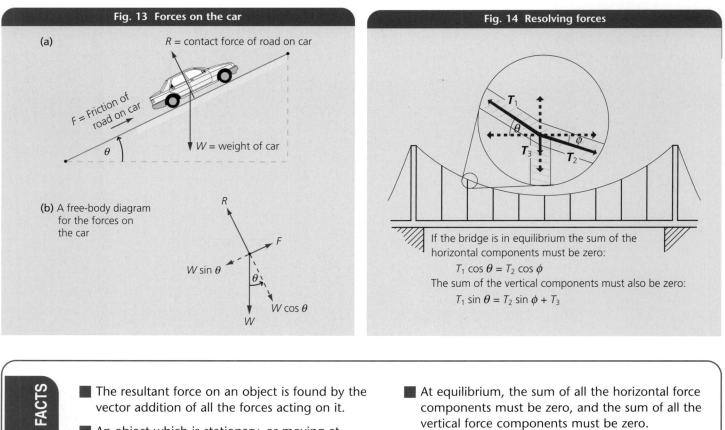

Fig. 13 Forces on the car

(a) R = contact force of road on car

F = Friction of road on car

W = weight of car

θ

(b) A free-body diagram for the forces on the car

R

F

$W \sin \theta$

θ

$W \cos \theta$

W

Fig. 14 Resolving forces

T_1

θ

ϕ

T_3

T_2

If the bridge is in equilibrium the sum of the horizontal components must be zero:

$T_1 \cos \theta = T_2 \cos \phi$

The sum of the vertical components must also be zero:

$T_1 \sin \theta = T_2 \sin \phi + T_3$

Adding forces

Sometimes we need to find the overall or **resultant** force on an object. Another way of adding the forces together is to resolve all the forces acting on an object into perpendicular components. Suppose a ship is being pulled by two tugs as shown in Fig. 15. What is the overall effect of these two forces?

If the two forces are resolved into perpendicular components, they can easily be added together.

In an easterly direction:
total force $= 3.2 \cos 10° + 2.8 \cos 8°$
$= 5.92$ MN

In a northerly direction:
total force $= 3.2 \sin 10° - 2.8 \sin 8°$
$= 0.17$ MN

To find the resultant force, these components must be combined (see Fig. 16).

To find the resultant force on the boat we need to add the forces from each tug.

11 Find the resultant force on the tug by an alternative method, either by scale drawing or by using the cosine rule (p. 89).

12 Draw a free-body diagram showing the forces on the skier in the photograph. Resolve the forces into components that are parallel or perpendicular to the slope. If the skier is being dragged at a steady speed up the slope, i.e. the skier is in equilibrium, write equations connecting the forces.

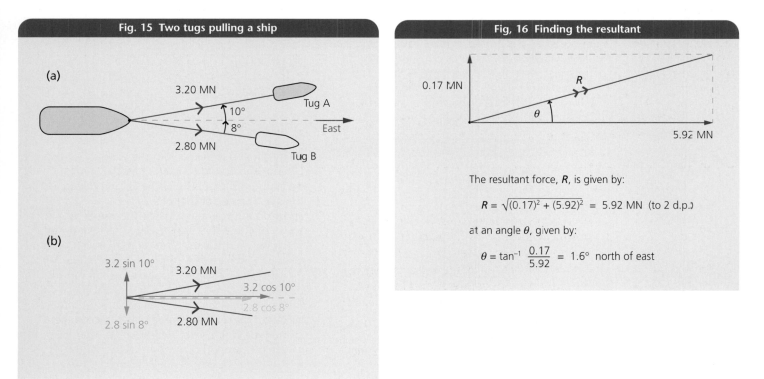

Fig. 15 Two tugs pulling a ship

(a)

3.20 MN — Tug A — 10°

East

8° — 2.80 MN — Tug B

(b)

3.2 sin 10° — 3.20 MN — 3.2 cos 10°

2.8 cos 8°

2.8 sin 8° — 2.80 MN

Fig, 16 Finding the resultant

0.17 MN — R — θ — 5.92 MN

The resultant force, R, is given by:

$$R = \sqrt{(0.17)^2 + (5.92)^2} = 5.92 \text{ MN (to 2 d.p.)}$$

at an angle θ, given by:

$$\theta = \tan^{-1}\frac{0.17}{5.92} = 1.6° \text{ north of east}$$

Forces in windsurfing

Sailboarding can be exhilarating. There is no rudder so you have to steer by tilting the sail. In very light winds you can stand upright, but when the wind gets stronger you have to lean into it. Then the sail tries to lift you and the board out of the water. This reduces the drag and the board gets faster. Speeds of up to 45 km h⁻¹ are possible.

Staying upright is a considerable challenge at first. You have to balance all the forces that are acting on you.

Some high-performance sailboards cannot displace enough water to float under the weight of a person. They can only 'float' when the board is moving, so they rely on a component of the wind's force to stop them from sinking.

Buoyancy

When a sailboard rests on the beach, its weight is opposed by the normal contact force from the sand. Once on the water, a buoyancy force, the **upthrust**, acts on the sailboard. All objects that are partly, or wholly, submerged in a fluid experience this force. Upthrust is caused by the pressure that the fluid exerts on the object.

Fig. 17 Origin of upthrust

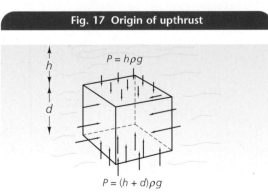

The pressure acting on each side of the object is the same, so the forces on the vertical faces cancel out. The pressure on the lower face is greater than that on the upper face.

Pressure is the average force per unit area. It is a **scalar** rather than a vector quantity. At a given depth it acts equally in all directions. The force acts at right angles to the surface of any object that is submerged in the fluid (Fig. 17).

Upthrust is due to the difference in fluid pressure between the top and bottom of an object. The fluid pressure at a depth of h metres in a fluid of density ρ kg m⁻³ is $h\rho g$.

If the object has a depth d, the extra pressure, P, on the lower surface, area A, is:

$$P = (h + d)\,\rho g - h\rho g = d\rho g$$

As force = pressure × area, the upthrust, U, is given by:

$$
\begin{aligned}
U &= P \times A \\
&= d\rho g \times A \\
&= dA\rho \times g \\
&= V\rho g
\end{aligned}
$$

The upthrust, which acts vertically upwards, is equal to the weight of the volume of fluid displaced by the object. If it is large enough, it will balance the weight of the object and the object will float (Fig. 18). A sailboard floats when it has displaced its own weight of water.

Fig. 18 Keeping afloat

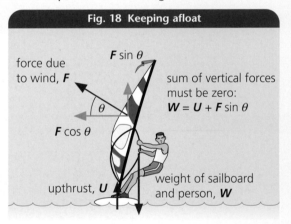

force due to wind, F

$F \sin \theta$

$F \cos \theta$

sum of vertical forces must be zero:

$$W = U + F \sin \theta$$

upthrust, U

weight of sailboard and person, W

Drag

Dead-running is sailing with the wind directly behind you. The force exerted by the wind depends on the density of the air and the area of the sail. The size of the force is also approximately proportional to the wind's velocity squared. The velocity is measured relative to the sailboard, so the faster the sailboard travels on a dead-run, the less force the wind exerts (Fig. 19).

The same principles apply to objects moving through still air. As a bicycle and cyclist move through the atmosphere they have to push the air out of the way. This produces a force known as drag, or in this case, air resistance. The size of the drag is proportional to the square of the relative velocity between bike and air.

Air resistance always acts to reduce the relative motion between the object and the air. The air will exert the same drag force on you whether you are cycling at $10\,\mathrm{m\,s^{-1}}$ on a still day, or if you are stationary in a $10\,\mathrm{m\,s^{-1}}$ wind. Air resistance is only zero when there is no relative motion between the object and the air.

Aerodynamic forces

A force caused by the air flow across the sail means that a sailboard can also move into the wind.

As a fluid flows over a surface it exerts a pressure on it. The pressure depends on the speed of the flow. The quicker the flow, the lower the pressure – this phenomenon is called the Bernoulli effect. Because a curved surface has a faster flow on one side than the other, the Bernoulli effect causes a force at right angles to the flow (Fig. 20). This force allows sailboards to move into the wind. The same effect is used to give aircraft lift and to make wind turbines rotate.

For a sailboard, the wind blowing over the curved surface of the sail creates a lower pressure on the convex side. The perpendicular force on the sail can be split into two components; a transverse force, F_T, and a driving force, F_D (Fig. 21).

13 Explain how a horizontal wind can lift the roof off a house.

Fig. 20 Aerodynamic lift

low pressure

air flow

high pressure

Fig. 19 Apparent wind

relative to sea

board velocity

wind velocity

relative to sailboarder

apparent wind velocity

wind velocity (relative to sea)

− board velocity

When the sailboard moves, the force due to air resistance is a combination of its movement through the air and the wind direction.

Fig. 21 Tacking into the wind

direction of travel

F

F_T

F_D

wind direction

It is possible to make progress into the wind by 'tacking'; steering a zig-zag course either side of the wind's direction.

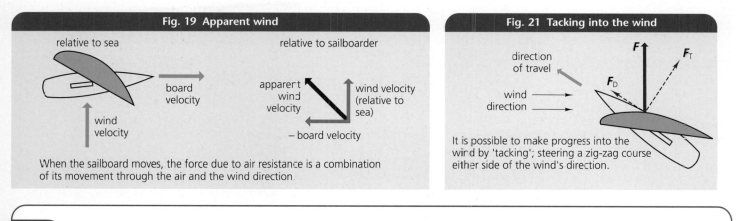

7.2 Forces in balance

Forces can cause objects to tip or rotate, as well as to accelerate in a straight line. For example, the transverse force acting on the sail (Fig. 22) tends to tip the sail and mast sideways. This turning effect of a force is called its moment.

The moment of a force

The moment of a force about a given point depends on the size of the force and the perpendicular distance between the point and the line of action of the force:

Moment (N m) = force (N) × perpendicular distance of point from line of action of force (m)

There may be several forces causing turning effects. If an object is to be in equilibrium, the total clockwise turning effect must be balanced by the total anticlockwise turning effect. This is known as the principle of moments:

For an object to be in equilibrium, the sum of the clockwise moments about any point must be equal to the sum of the anticlockwise moments about that point.

Fig. 22 The moment of a force

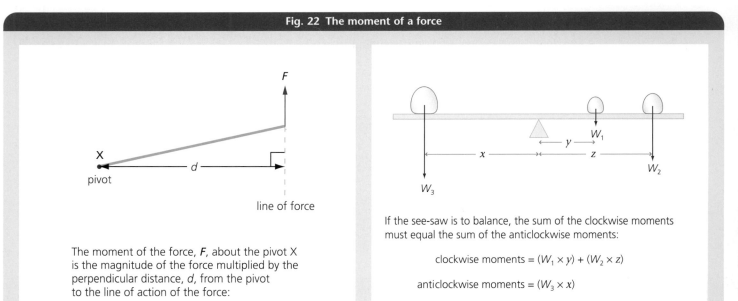

The moment of the force, **F**, about the pivot X is the magnitude of the force multiplied by the perpendicular distance, *d*, from the pivot to the line of action of the force:

$$\text{moment} = F\,d$$

If the see-saw is to balance, the sum of the clockwise moments must equal the sum of the anticlockwise moments:

clockwise moments = $(W_1 \times y) + (W_2 \times z)$

anticlockwise moments = $(W_3 \times x)$

So: $(W_1 \times y) + (W_2 \times z) = (W_3 \times x)$

The sailboarders lean out so that the turning effect of their weight balances the turning effect of the wind on the sail.

Torque and couples

Pivots and hinges, such as the flexible joint where a sailboard mast joins the board, are unlikely to be free of friction. The effect of this friction is to oppose rotation. It is known as a frictional torque. A torque may also cause rotation. When you grip a screwdriver to tighten a screw you are exerting a frictional torque on it. A torque produces or opposes rotation but does not cause any linear acceleration.

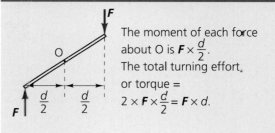

Fig. 23 Turning effect of a couple

The moment of each force about O is $F \times \dfrac{d}{2}$.
The total turning effort, or torque =
$$2 \times F \times \frac{d}{2} = F \times d.$$

Two equal forces that act in opposite directions do not cause any linear acceleration. However, if they do not pass through the same point they will cause rotation. A pair of forces like this is known as a couple. The torque produced by a couple is equal to the magnitude of the force multiplied by the distance between them. An important example of a couple is the turning effect produced in an electric motor (Fig. 24).

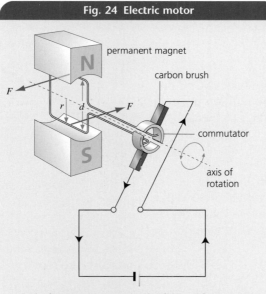

Fig. 24 Electric motor

permanent magnet

carbon brush

commutator

axis of rotation

The forces acting on each side of the coil form a couple which tends to make the coil spin. The couple on the coil of an electric motor is $F \times d$.

Staying upright

The transverse force of the wind, F_T, tends to tip the sailboard in an anticlockwise direction. If the sailboard is to stay upright, the windsurfer has to apply a force, F_S, that has a clockwise moment. The mast pivots freely

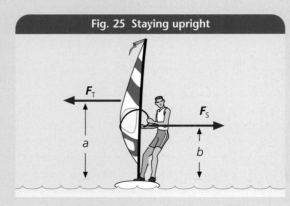

Fig. 25 Staying upright

where it joins the board. The moments acting about that point are:

anticlockwise moment = $F_T \times a$
clockwise moment = $F_S \times b$

For equilibrium, the moments must balance, so

$$F_T \times a = F_S \times b.$$

It is important to remember that the moment depends on the **perpendicular** distance from the force to the pivot. As the wind speed increases, the windsurfer needs to lean at an increasingly large angle into the wind. We can see why this is if we treat the board and the windsurfer as one object. The important external forces are the weight of the windsurfer, W_S, and the force of the wind on the sail, F_T.

As F_T gets larger, the anticlockwise turning moment increases (Fig. 26). To maintain balance, the windsurfer has to increase the clockwise turning moment by increasing the perpendicular distance, a, between the line of action of his weight and the pivot, by leaning out as far as possible.

The principle of moments can also be applied to the forces used in lifting the sailboard. The mass of the rig on a sailboard is 20 kg and its centre of gravity is 2 m from the bottom end. The rig is pulled into position using a rope which is connected to the mast, 1.5 m from the bottom end, and is initially at an angle of 25° to the horizontal. There is a frictional torque of 50 N m in the joint that holds the mast to the board. What force is required to lift the rig from the horizontal?

The first step in all mechanics problems is to draw a diagram (Fig. 27) showing all the relevant forces. The next step is to simplify the forces. In this case, the tension, T, can be

Fig. 26 Using your weight

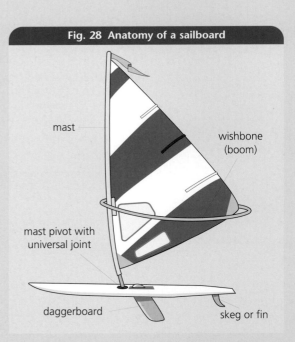
Fig. 28 Anatomy of a sailboard

mast

wishbone (boom)

mast pivot with universal joint

daggerboard

skeg or fin

resolved into horizontal and vertical components. (The horizontal component of the tension, $T \cos 25°$, has no moment since it passes through X.) We calculate the moments of the forces about the joint, X. The sum of the anticlockwise moments is:

$$200\,\text{N} \times 2\,\text{m} + \text{frictional torque} = 450\,\text{N m}$$

The sum of the clockwise moments is:

$$T \sin 25°\,\text{N} \times 1.5\,\text{m} = 0.634\,T\,\text{N m}$$

These moments balance when $0.634\,T = 450$. The rig can be lifted when $T > 710\,\text{N}$.

14 Explain why the tension in the sailboard rope decreases as the sail is lifted to a vertical position.

15 Sailboards use a daggerboard to help them to remain stable (see Fig. 28). Use the idea of moments to explain why the daggerboard is useful.

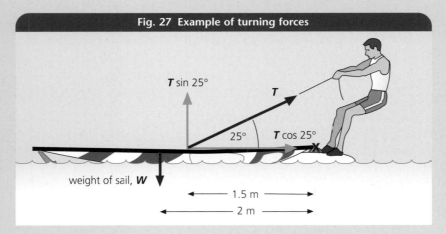
Fig. 27 Example of turning forces

$T \sin 25°$

T

25°

$T \cos 25°$

weight of sail, W

1.5 m

2 m

KEY SKILLS ASSIGNMENTS

The roof over your head

The building you are sitting in at the moment probably has a pitched roof. Try picking up a pile of roof slates and you'll get some idea of the weight of the roof itself. A pitched roof delivers a lot of this force to the walls. Pressing down on an open book gives you some idea of the direction of the forces on a pitched roof – the walls tend to be pushed outwards. This produces problems for architects and civil engineers because these forces must be balanced. The simplest way to do this is to put in a tie beam across the top of the walls, joining the slopes of the pitch. This provides an inward force to balance the outward force trying to push the walls apart. But you still have a problem as the weight of the roof itself will make the roof sag (especially if it is quite a large span.)

But roofs don't have to be pitched, they can be flat, cantilevered or suspended. Flat roofs have their problems as the weight of the materials will make them sag in the middle given enough time. Heating up and cooling down can cause the felt, tar or fibreglass to expand and contract – eventually leading to leaks. Ultra-violet light in the Sun's rays can cause chemical changes in the materials as well.

The cantilever is quite an old structure which we are making use of more nowadays. Many medieval buildings jut out at the second storey to provide an opposite turning moment to balance the turning moment created by the weight of the floor. Without this, the floor would (and did in many cases) sag. The modern equivalent of this is the petrol station canopy covering the petrol pumps. The cantilever sticking out at the sides provides a balancing turning moment to the weight (force) of the roof. Modern hotels and office blocks also take advantage of the cantilever principle by having the structures built on legs with an overhang at each side. The overhang provides the turning moment to balance the weight of the building. It also means that there is a useful space under the building for parking. Sports stadiums are another good example of the cantilever principle.

Suspended roofs use the high strength of woven steel cable to eliminate internal walls and thus create a more open space inside. This is why they are popular for exhibition halls. Usually the cables are slung from pylons or towers outside the building and basically just hold the roof up.

1 a Use the idea of moments to explain why rafters and roof joists are put in place with their longer sides vertical.

b Draw a diagram of a beam being bent and label the forces in the beam at the top surface, in the centre and on the bottom surface.

c Draw a diagram of a pitched roof resting on a wall and label the forces acting at the edges of the wall, where the roof is supported. Show clearly the direction of each component force.

2 Draw a diagram to show how the forces are balanced in a roof joist design to take into account:

a The forces at the wall

b the force due to the weight of the roof.

3 a Draw a diagram of a simple wall bracket which might be used to support a shelf. This is an example of a cantilever. Show the forces acting on the bracket and the screws in the wall when some books are put on the shelf.

b What is the effect of this load on the top and bottom screws holding the bracket on the wall?

4 Prepare a presentation about different types of roofs and how forces are balanced in these structures. You must cover at least three types of roof and prepare some posters or overhead projection transparencies (OHTs) to illustrate your talk. If possible, use a computer to produce your presentation.

1 Three children, A, B and C, sit on a see-saw and balance it, as shown in the diagram.

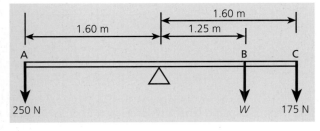

a How heavy is child B? (2)

b Child B is taken off the see-saw. Calculate the magnitude and direction of the resultant torque on the see-saw at the instant child B is taken off the see-saw. (2)

(AQA PH01 Jun 98 Q5)

2 a Explain what is meant by a vector quantity. (1)

b

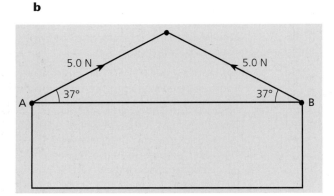

The diagram shows a picture supported by two wires. The left hand wire exerts a force of 5.0 N on the picture at A. The right hand wire exerts a force of 5.0 N on the picture at B.

Resolve the force acting at B to calculate

(i) its vertical component,

(ii) its horizontal component. (3)

c Calculate the weight of the picture assuming it hangs freely. (1)

(AQA PH01 Jun 97 Q5)

3 The diagram shows a child's mobile which is supported from the ceiling by a length of nylon thread of negligible weight. AB is a uniform horizontal rod supported at S.

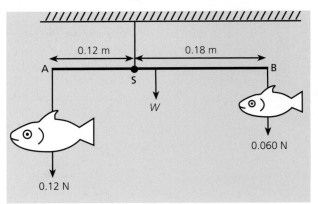

a (i) State the principle of moments.

(ii) By taking moments about point S, show that the weight, W, of the rod is 0.12 N. (5)

b (i) What is the tension in the supporting thread?

(ii) The nylon thread supporting the mobile has a diameter of 0.10 mm and a length of 0.50 m when not supporting the mobile. Calculate the extension of the thread when supporting the mobile, given that the Young modulus of the thread is 3.0×10^{10} Pa. (5)

c A third fish of weight 0.30 N is suspended from the middle of the rod. The thread supporting the mobile is moved along the rod so that the rod remains horizontal. On which side of the centre of the rod is the thread now attached, left or right? Explain how you arrived at your answer. (2)

(AQA PH01 Mar 98 Q6)

In a car crash, your life could be saved by a small, gas-filled balloon. Most modern cars are equipped with an 'air bag', fitted in the centre of the steering wheel, which inflates during a collision to protect the driver's head. The air bag has to be electronically triggered, and then chemically inflated, in less than 50 milliseconds (ms). It takes you 200 ms to blink an eye.

Design features such as the air bag help to explain why UK roads are at their safest level since records began in 1926 (Fig. 1). Despite an enormous increase in traffic, the number of annual road fatalities has actually decreased. This rate has been kept down by developments in two areas of road safety.

Primary safety measures aim to stop accidents happening. Cars are now equipped with better brakes, steering and suspension systems, while driver visibility has been improved through the development of modern headlights, window washers and demisters. Probably the most significant advance in primary safety is the improvement of road design, with better layout, surfaces and street lighting.

Modern cars have safety features intended to reduce the injuries of those involved in an accident. In a crash, it is important that the kinetic energy of the vehicle is absorbed mainly in the bonnet and boot, while the passenger compartment stays rigid. Seat

An air bag is tested using one of Ford's dummies.

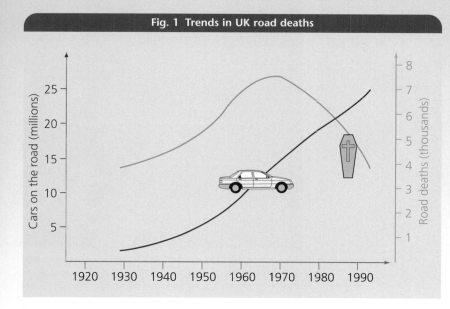

The roll bar (1966), the collapsible steering column (1973) and antilock braking (1984) have all helped improve safety.

belts and air bags are designed to restrain passengers and make their deceleration as controlled as possible, avoiding excessive forces on the head or abdomen.

In an effort to improve safety, accident research teams from manufacturers such as Volvo have analysed thousands of crashes using high-speed video photography and computers. The results of these tests can be interpreted using Newton's laws of motion.

Fig. 1 Trends in UK road deaths

Cars on the road (millions) / Road deaths (thousands)

1920 1930 1940 1950 1960 1970 1980 1990

8.1 Staying alive

Newton's first law

Head-on collisions are the most common cause of severe and fatal injuries in car accidents. A front-end crash into a stationary object at only 30 km h⁻¹ (19 mph) can cause serious injury. Modern cars have a range of 'occupant restraint systems' designed to decelerate passengers in a controlled way. Without them, passengers would carry on at their original velocity, until the steering wheel or the windscreen decelerated them! It would be wrong to say that the passengers are being hurled forward by the force of the crash. Passengers continue at constant velocity until a force changes their motion. The people in the car are obeying Newton's first law:

An object will remain at rest, or continue to move with uniform velocity, unless acted upon by an external, resultant force.

At first sight, many objects do not appear to obey Newton's first law. If you remove the driving force from a car, it will not keep moving at constant velocity; turn off the engine and the car will quickly come to a stop. This is because a combination of air resistance and frictional forces make up the 'external force'. On Earth it is difficult to avoid these forces, but in space, where there is negligible resistance to motion, Newton's first law can be observed more clearly.

1. In a campaign to encourage people to wear rear-seat safety belts, the Department of Transport claimed that, in an accident, 'An adult passenger sitting in the back of a car will be thrown forward with a force of 3½ tonnes. That's the weight of an elephant'.

   Rewrite this safety warning using Newton's first law.

2. Head-restraints are designed to prevent neck injuries. Why are they especially helpful in rear-impact accidents?

Momentum

A quarter of all accidents involve collisions from the side. Many cars now have reinforced bars in the doors to try to maintain a survival space after a collision. The effectiveness of the bars depends on how large the forces are. A greater force is needed to stop a 100 km h⁻¹ juggernaut than a 15 km h⁻¹ bicycle! Clearly, the size of the forces in a crash will depend on the mass and the velocity of the vehicles. The product of mass and velocity is called **momentum**:

momentum = mass × velocity

$$p = mv$$

Momentum is measured in kg m s⁻¹.

Space-walking astronauts experience virtually no restrictive forces to their motion.

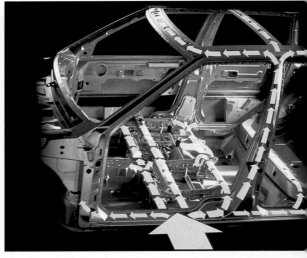

In a side-on crash there is only about 20 cm between the point of impact and the occupant. Volvo's side impact protection system (SIPS) transmits the force of an impact around the roof and floor of the car.

Newton's second law

The more momentum an object has, the harder it is to stop it. If the object has to lose all of its momentum quickly, as in a crash, the force needed will be even greater. Newton's second law puts this formally:

The rate of change of momentum of a body is directly proportional to the external, resultant force acting upon it. The change of momentum takes place in the direction of that force.

A Lamborghini Diablo has a mass of 1449 kg and can accelerate from 0 to 60 mph (26.8 m s⁻¹) in 3.9 s.

In symbols we can write Newton's second law as:

$$F \propto \frac{\Delta p}{\Delta t} \quad or \quad F \propto \frac{\Delta (mv)}{\Delta t}$$

If the mass of the object is constant, Newton's second law can be written as force = mass × acceleration, $F = ma$ (see Fig. 2).

If the mass of the object changes, as in the case of a rocket using up fuel, you need to use the full statement of Newton's second law. The mass of a car does not change significantly as it is driven along, so Newton's second law simplifies to $F = ma$.

We can use $F = ma$ to calculate the average resultant force required by a Lamborghini Diablo to achieve its acceleration. In SI units:

$$a = \frac{v - u}{t}$$
$$= \frac{26.8 \text{ m s}^{-1} - 0 \text{ m s}^{-1}}{3.9 \text{ s}}$$
$$= 6.88 \text{ m s}^{-2}$$

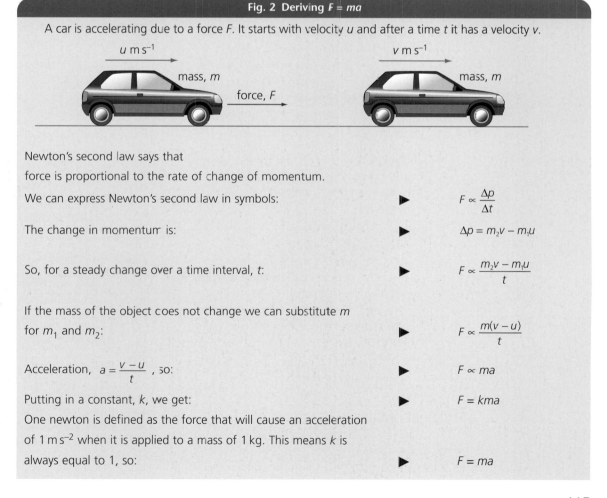

Fig. 2 Deriving $F = ma$

A car is accelerating due to a force F. It starts with velocity u and after a time t it has a velocity v.

u m s⁻¹   mass, m force, F v m s⁻¹   mass, m

Newton's second law says that

force is proportional to the rate of change of momentum.

We can express Newton's second law in symbols: ▶ $F \propto \frac{\Delta p}{\Delta t}$

The change in momentum is: ▶ $\Delta p = m_2 v - m_1 u$

So, for a steady change over a time interval, t: ▶ $F \propto \frac{m_2 v - m_1 u}{t}$

If the mass of the object does not change we can substitute m for m_1 and m_2: ▶ $F \propto \frac{m(v - u)}{t}$

Acceleration, $a = \frac{v - u}{t}$, so: ▶ $F \propto ma$

Putting in a constant, k, we get: ▶ $F = kma$

One newton is defined as the force that will cause an acceleration of 1 m s⁻² when it is applied to a mass of 1 kg. This means k is always equal to 1, so: ▶ $F = ma$

Therefore, the average resultant force on the car has to be:

$F = ma$

$= 1449 \text{ kg} \times 6.88 \text{ m s}^{-2}$

$= 9970 \text{ N}$

The forces that act on a car and its occupants during an accident can be much larger than this. If the Lamborghini is involved in a crash, its speed could drop from 60 mph (26.8 m s^{-1}) to zero in less than one tenth of a second. This is an acceleration of:

$a = \dfrac{v - u}{t}$

$= \dfrac{0 - 26.8 \text{ m s}^{-1}}{0.1 \text{ s}}$

$= -268 \text{ m s}^{-2}$

The average force on the car is given by:

$F = ma$

$= 1449 \text{ kg} \times (-268) \text{ m s}^{-2}$

$= -390\,000 \text{ N}$

The negative sign shows that the force acts in the opposite direction to the velocity; it is a 'retarding' force.

In a head-on collision, even at moderate speed, the deceleration can be as high as 200 m s^{-2}. This is 20 times the acceleration due to the Earth's gravity, g. The force on a passenger will be roughly 20 times their weight.

3 Some people believe that a baby can travel safely in a car if it is held by an adult. Estimate the force needed to restrain a baby (mass = 10 kg) in the event of a crash.

4 The *Highway Code* claims that you need 23 m to come to rest if you make an emergency stop at a speed of 30 mph (48.3 km h^{-1}). Nine metres of this is 'thinking distance', before you apply the brakes. What average braking force is needed if the mass of the car is 1500 kg?

(Hint: you will need to find the average deceleration of the car.)

Resistive forces

In reality, the Lamborghini Diablo must provide a larger driving force than 9970 N because it must also overcome forces holding

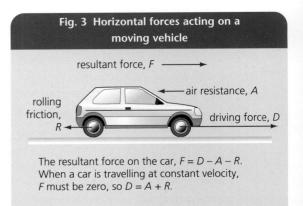

Fig. 3 Horizontal forces acting on a moving vehicle

The resultant force on the car, $F = D - A - R$. When a car is travelling at constant velocity, F must be zero, so $D = A + R$.

the car back. When a vehicle is being driven on a flat, straight road, there are two forces opposing its motion (Fig. 3):

● **Air resistance:** This 'drag' force depends on the size and shape of the vehicle and is roughly proportional to the squared speed of the car;

● **Frictional force:** This 'rolling resistance' is roughly proportional to speed.

Reducing the force

We can use Newton's second law to calculate the force on a passenger in a car crash. During the crash the force will vary, but the average force will be

$F = \dfrac{\text{final momentum} - \text{initial momentum}}{\text{time taken to decelerate}}$

$= \dfrac{\Delta(mv)}{\Delta t}$

The initial momentum depends on the velocity of the car; the final momentum is zero. Therefore all that we can do to reduce the force is to increase the time over which the collision occurs. Design features such as crumple zones, collapsible steering columns

Crumple zones reduce the deceleration of the passenger compartment.

and air bags all increase the time taken for the passenger to come to a stop. Many people believe that modern cars are 'weak' and too easily damaged in a crash. In fact they are designed so that the bonnet and boot deform relatively easily. It is this 'weakness' that saves lives.

5 Motorway crash barriers are designed to deform as a vehicle hits them (as above). Use Newton's second law to explain why this is safer than a rigid safety barrier.

Newton's third law

When a car hits a stationary object, the front of the car stops almost instantly. The passenger compartment takes longer to stop; its deceleration changes as the front of the car crumples. For a car travelling at $60\,\text{km h}^{-1}$ (less than 40 mph) the deceleration may peak at $60\,g$ but it is likely to average about $20\,g$ over the duration of the crash (around 100 ms).

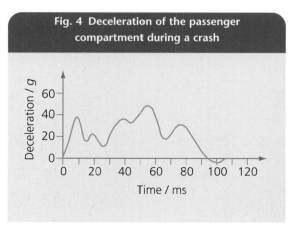

Fig. 4 Deceleration of the passenger compartment during a crash

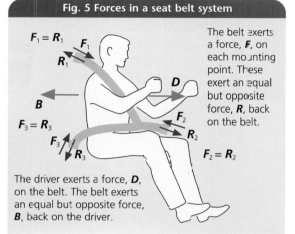

Fig. 5 Forces in a seat belt system

$F_1 = R_1$

$F_3 = R_3$

The belt exerts a force, **F**, on each mounting point. These exert an equal but opposite force, **R**, back on the belt.

The driver exerts a force, **D**, on the belt. The belt exerts an equal but opposite force, **B**, back on the driver.

$F_2 = R_2$

A seat belt can reduce the average deceleration on the driver to between $10\,g$ and $15\,g$. The belt achieves this because of its elasticity. It stretches slightly during the collision. The tension in the belt then restrains the driver. As the driver is exerting a force on the seat belt, the seat belt is exerting an equal but opposite force on the driver (Fig. 5).

The seat belt exerts a force on each of its three mounting points, which in turn pull back on the belt. These pairs of forces are examples of Newton's third law:

When body A exerts a force on body B, body B exerts an equal but opposite force on body A.

This law is often written as 'Every action has an equal and opposite reaction'. This can be misleading. It is important to realise that the two forces, the 'action' and the 'reaction', act on different objects. If the equal and opposite forces acted on the same object there would never be a resultant force and, by Newton's first law, nothing would ever accelerate. The law is not only relevant when two objects are in contact; it also applies when the interaction is at a distance, perhaps due to gravitational attraction.

6 Sketch a parked car and draw in arrows to show the forces acting on:

a the car;

b the Earth.

Carefully explain which pairs of forces are equal according to:

c Newton's first law;

d Newton's third law.

7 What force pushes a car forward as it accelerates?

■ Newton's first law of motion states:
An object will remain at rest, or continue to move with uniform velocity, unless acted upon by an external, resultant force.

■ Newton's second law of motion states:
The rate of change of momentum of a body is directly proportional to the external, resultant force acting upon it. The change of momentum takes place in the direction of that force.

■ For constant mass, $F = ma$.
A force of 1N will accelerate a mass of 1 kg at a rate of $1\,\mathrm{m\,s^{-2}}$.

■ Newton's third law states:
If body A exerts a force on body B, then body B exerts an equal but opposite force back on body A.

8.2 Stopping safely

Work

It is obviously better to stop a car safely, before a crash ever takes place. A reliable braking system is the most important safety mechanism in a car. The frictional forces need to be very large if the car is to stop in a very short distance.

We can calculate how much energy is transferred by using the concept of work. In physics the word 'work' has a particular meaning. Physicists say that work is done when a force moves through a distance. If you push a car along a road you have done some work against resistive forces. If you lift a mass you have done some work against the force of gravity.

work done = force × distance moved in the direction of the force

$$W = Fs$$

Brake pads (seen glowing above) can get extremely hot as the kinetic energy of the car is transferred to them.

F is measured in newtons and s is in metres. The unit of work is the joule ($1\,\mathrm{J} = 1\,\mathrm{Nm}$).

Although the force and the distance moved in a given direction are both vector quantities, work is a **scalar** quantity (see Chapter 6). If the directions of the force and the displacement are at an angle θ, the equation for work becomes:

$W = Fs \cos \theta$ (Fig. 6)

When the road conditions are good, a car travelling at 70 mph ($31\,\mathrm{m\,s^{-1}}$) can usually be brought safely to a halt in 75 m. To calculate the work done we need to find the force required. The acceleration can be found using the equations of linear motion:

$$v^2 = u^2 + 2as$$
$$\text{or, } a = \frac{v^2 - u^2}{2s}$$

Since $v = 0$, $u = 31\,\mathrm{m\,s^{-1}}$ and $s = 75\,\mathrm{m}$:

$$a = -\frac{(31\,\mathrm{m\,s^{-1}})^2}{2 \times 75\,\mathrm{m}}$$
$$= -6.4\,\mathrm{m\,s^{-2}}$$

Fig. 6 Work done at an angle θ

There is no movement in the direction of the vertical component, $F \sin \theta$, so this part of the force does no work.
The tractor moves a horizontal distance, s. The horizontal component of the force is $F \cos \theta$, so the work done = $s \times F \cos \theta$.

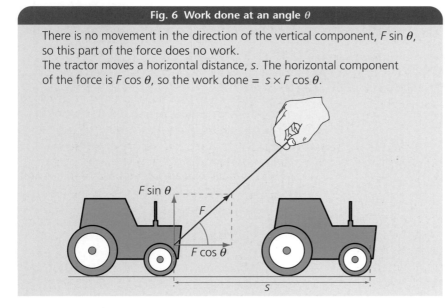

For a car of mass 1000 kg the average braking force is given by:

$F = ma$

$= 1000 \text{ kg} \times 6.4 \text{ m s}^{-2}$

$= 6400 \text{ N}$

The work done is therefore:

$W = Fs$

$= 6400 \text{ N} \times 75 \text{ m}$

$= 480 \text{ kJ}$

Most forces vary with distance. To calculate the total work done by a changing force, we need to divide the total distance moved into short steps, each of length Δx (Fig. 7). If Δx is small enough, the force will not change significantly within each step. The work done in each step is just the force multiplied by Δx. But the force multiplied by Δx is also the area of the rectangle under the curve. To find the total work done we need to add together the work done in each step. This is the sum of the areas of all the rectangular strips. So, for a varying force, the work done is the area beneath the force–distance graph.

Energy

In physics, an object is said to have energy if it can do work. A car may have energy because of its motion (**kinetic energy**), or because of its position (**potential energy**).

Petrol is a very concentrated store of energy, about 50 MJ per litre. This energy can be transferred to kinetic energy of the car by combustion of fuel in the engine.

Whenever work is done, energy is transferred. When a car slows down, work is done by the brakes against friction and the car's kinetic energy is transferred to the brakes. The exchange is exact, so the rise in internal energy of the brakes, air and road is equal to the original kinetic energy of the car. This energy balance applies to all situations:

The principle of conservation of energy says that the total amount of energy in any isolated system is constant.

It is important to stress the word 'isolated' because energy can flow into, or out of, a system. We couldn't apply the principle just to the car alone, because not all of its kinetic energy transfers to the brakes; some will be transferred to the air and the road.

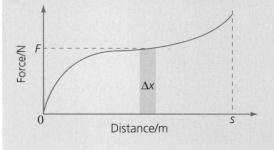

Fig. 7 Work done by a changing force

The work done in moving a distance Δx is $F\Delta x$. This is the area of the shaded rectangular strip. The total work done by the changing force in moving through distance s is the area of all such strips, i.e. the total area below the curve.

The kinetic energy of a moving vehicle depends on its mass, m, and on its velocity, v.

The expression for kinetic energy,

$E_k = \frac{1}{2}mv^2$

shows that the energy depends on the velocity *squared* (see extension box).

8 A recent road safety campaign had the slogan 'Kill your speed, not a child'. Most children hit by a car travelling at 40 mph are killed, while those hit at 20 mph usually escape with only minor injuries. Use the idea of kinetic energy to explain why there is such a major change.

Power

In an emergency stop, kinetic energy has to be transferred from the car as quickly as possible. The rate at which energy is transferred, or work is done, is known as the power of a system:

$$\text{power} = \frac{\text{work done}}{\text{time taken}}$$

$$= \text{energy transferred per second}$$

Power is measured in joules per second, or watts (W). Most cars can manage a safe deceleration of around $1g$ (10 m s^{-2}). For a 1000 kg car travelling at 70 mph (31 m s^{-1}), the braking power is considerable:

$F = ma$

$= 1000 \text{ kg} \times 10 \text{ m s}^{-2}$

$= 10\,000 \text{ N}$

EXTENSION **Finding an expression for kinetic energy**

The amount of energy stored in a moving car depends on its mass and its velocity. Consider the work done against friction as the car slows to a halt:

Suppose a constant frictional force, F, is used to slow the car down over a distance, s. The work done is:

▶ $W = Fs$

In an isolated system, all of this energy must have come from the original kinetic energy of the car, so:

▶ $E_k = W = Fs$

We can replace F using $F = ma$:

▶ $E_k = mas$

and s by using $v^2 = u^2 + 2as$ or $s = \dfrac{v^2 - u^2}{2a}$

▶ $E_k = ma\dfrac{(u^2 - v^2)}{2a}$

$= \tfrac{1}{2}mu^2 - \tfrac{1}{2}mv^2$

The final velocity of the car is zero, so the original kinetic energy of the car was:

▶ $E_k = \tfrac{1}{2}mu^2$

In general, the kinetic energy of an object of mass m and velocity v is given by:

▶ $E_k = \tfrac{1}{2}mv^2$

In this proof we assumed that the force was constant, though the final equation works even if the force varies.

9 The stopping distance for cars travelling at 50 mph is given as 38 m in the *Highway Code.*

a Find the kinetic energy of a van (mass = 2000 kg) moving at 50 mph (22.4 m s^{-1}).

b How much work needs to be done by braking forces to stop the van?

c Calculate the average braking force needed to bring the van to rest.

The stopping distance can be found from:

$$v^2 = u^2 + 2as$$

$$\text{or,} \quad s = \dfrac{v^2 - u^2}{2a}$$

Since $v = 0$, $u = 31$ m s^{-1} and $a = -10$ m s^{-2}:

$$s = \dfrac{0 - (31 \text{ m s}^{-1})^2}{-20}$$

$$= 48 \text{ m}$$

The time taken to stop can be found from:

$$v = u + at$$

$$\text{or,} \quad t = \dfrac{v - u}{a}$$

$$\text{so,} \quad t = \dfrac{0 - 31 \text{ m s}^{-1}}{-10 \text{ m s}^{-2}}$$

$$= 3.1 \text{ s}$$

$$\text{power} = \dfrac{\text{work done}}{\text{time taken}}$$

$$= \dfrac{10\,000 \text{ N} \times 48 \text{ m}}{3.1 \text{ s}}$$

$$= 155 \text{ kW}$$

In reality the situation is more complex. The safest way of stopping a car is not usually to apply the largest possible force to the brakes; the wheels may stop turning but the car can continue in a skid! Modern cars use an antilock braking system, or ABS (Fig. 8).

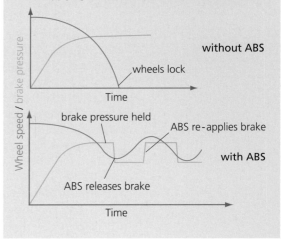

Fig. 8 Braking force and wheel speed

In an ABS system, sensors calculate wheel speed and deceleration. An electronic unit uses this data to detect when the wheels are about to lock and begins releasing and re-applying the brake, up to 10 times per second.

without ABS

wheels lock

Time

brake pressure held

ABS re-applies brake

with ABS

ABS releases brake

Time

Wheel speed / brake pressure

The power of a car engine affects the maximum speed of the car and the maximum force that it can exert on the road.

$$\text{Since power} = \dfrac{\text{work}}{\text{time}}$$

$$\text{and work} = \text{force} \times \text{distance}$$

$$\text{then power} = \dfrac{\text{force} \times \text{distance}}{\text{time}}$$

$$= \text{force} \times \text{velocity}$$

$$P = Fv$$

For a given power, an engine can exert a large force at a low speed, or a smaller force at higher speed. A car's gearbox allows you to control this balance.

10 A car has a mass of 1445 kg and its engine can deliver a maximum power of 112 kW.

a Estimate the maximum force that it can exert at 20 mph (32 km h^{-1}), and at 40 mph (64 km h^{-1}).

b What else would you need to know before you could estimate its maximum acceleration at these speeds?

APPLICATION   Output power of a juggernaut

The forces that resist the motion of a vehicle increase as the vehicle travels faster. Air resistance and rolling resistance combine to resist the motion of a juggernaut.

Resistive forces on a 38-tonne juggernaut	
Road speed (km h^{-1})	Total resistive force (N)
80	4265
88	4740
96	5250
105	5805
113	6395

At steady speed the force driving the lorry forward is equal to the resistive forces on the lorry. So if the lorry is to accelerate, the force supplied by the engine has to increase. The power output of the engine also has to increase at higher road speeds.
  Suppose the vehicle is travelling at a steady 80 km h^{-1} when the driver applies the accelerator pedal.

If the tractive force (i.e. the driving force of the road on the wheels) increases to 5250 N, what would the instantaneous acceleration of the lorry be?

The resultant horizontal force on the lorry is:

5250 N – 4265 N = 985 N

From Newton's second law:

$$a = \frac{F}{m}$$

$$= \frac{985\,\text{N}}{38 \times 10^3\,\text{kg}}$$

$$= 0.026\,\text{m s}^{-2}$$

The table shows how the resistive force increases as the lorry accelerates. As the resultant force gets less, so does the acceleration. Eventually the tractive force and the resistance will be equal again and the lorry will move at a steady speed.

What is the output power of the engine at (a) 80 km h^{-1} (b) 113 km h^{-1}?

The power can be calculated from
power = force × velocity

(a) $v = \dfrac{80\,\text{km h}^{-1} \times 1000\,\text{m}}{3600\,\text{s}} = 22.2\,\text{m s}^{-1}$

power = 4265 N × 22.2 m s^{-1}
       = 94.8 kW

(b) At 113 km h^{-1}, using the same method, power = 201 kW, over twice the output power at 80 km h^{-1}!

The lorry is travelling at 113 km h^{-1} when the engine cuts out suddenly. How much work will the lorry do against the resistive forces as it slows to 80 km h^{-1}?

Since the force varies as the vehicle slows down, it is not possible to use the equation, work = force × distance, directly. An easier approach is to say that the energy to do the work comes from the kinetic energy of the lorry.
  Work done against resistive forces is the kinetic energy transferred from the lorry:

$$E_k = \tfrac{1}{2}m(u^2 - v^2)$$

$$= \tfrac{1}{2} \times 38 \times 10^3\,\text{kg} \times (31.1^2 - 22.2^2)\,\text{m}^2\,\text{s}^{-2}$$

$$= 9 \times 10^6\,\text{J}$$

8.3 Concerning collisions

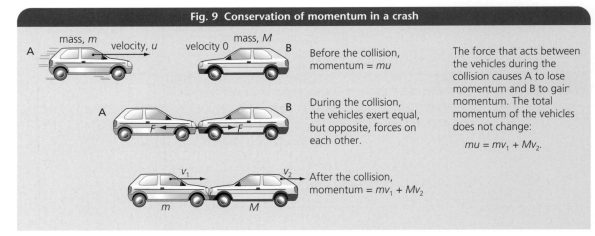

Fig. 9 Conservation of momentum in a crash

Before the collision, momentum = mu

During the collision, the vehicles exert equal, but opposite, forces on each other.

After the collision, momentum = $mv_1 + Mv_2$

The force that acts between the vehicles during the collision causes A to lose momentum and B to gain momentum. The total momentum of the vehicles does not change:

$$mu = mv_1 + Mv_2.$$

Conservation of momentum

When a car travelling at high speed crashes into a stationary car, Newton's second law can be applied to both vehicles:

For Car A
change in momentum = force × time

For Car B
change in momentum = − force × time

Newton's third law says that both vehicles are subject to the same size force. The minus sign shows that they act in opposite directions (momentum is a vector quantity). The time of impact is also the same for both vehicles. Hence, the change in momentum has to be the same size for each car. This means that any momentum lost by the first car will be gained by the second car. Therefore, the total momentum before the crash will be the same as the total momentum after the crash. Of course, external forces such as friction will slow the cars down. If there were no external forces, the total momentum in the system would be the same before and after the collision. This fundamental principle is known as the **conservation of momentum**:

The total momentum of a system does not change, provided that no net external force is acting.

It is not always obvious that this law is being obeyed. When a car's brakes are applied and it comes to rest, where has the momentum of the system gone? The answer depends on what you regard as the system. If you treat the car as the system, then its momentum has not been conserved, but friction between the car and the road is an external force. If you regard the car and the road as the system, there are no significant external forces, since the friction between the two is now an 'internal' force acting between different parts of the same system.

The conservation law suggests that any momentum lost by a car slowing down will be gained by the Earth. Hitting the car brakes must speed up the Earth a little! Of course the reverse is also true; every time a car accelerates away from the traffic lights it pushes the Earth back the other way.

11 During a television advert, a car is driven off a tall building and falls to the ground. How does the conservation of momentum apply here?

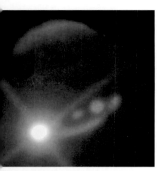

Fragment K of Shoemaker–Levy hits Jupiter

Energy in collisions

The study of collisions is very important in physics, quite apart from its relevance to car crashes. On a microscopic level, collisions between constantly moving gas molecules help us to understand the behaviour of gases. At the other end of the scale, astronomers have learned much by studying the collision of comet Shoemaker–Levy with Jupiter.

Collisions are described as either elastic or inelastic. In an elastic collision, no kinetic energy is lost. Collisions between molecules in a gas can be treated as being perfectly elastic. Some collisions between sub-atomic particles are also elastic, such as those that take place between neutrons and carbon atoms in the moderator of a nuclear reactor.

In an inelastic collision, kinetic energy is transferred to other forms (Fig. 10). Collisions between everyday objects tend to generate sound and heat and are therefore inelastic. Car crashes fall into this category. Safety features, like crumple zones and air bags, are designed to transfer kinetic energy. As the crumple zones progressively collapse, the kinetic energy of the car does work against the inter-atomic forces in the metal and is finally transferred as internal energy in the car body. As the driver hits the air bag, the gas escapes and the energy of the driver is transferred to the kinetic energy of the gas molecules.

The conservation of momentum applies to both types of collision. Suppose that in poor visibility on a motorway a car runs into the back of another larger car, which is stationary. The first car is moving at 50 mph (22.2 m s⁻¹) immediately before the impact and has a mass of 1050 kg. The other car has a mass of 1200 kg. After the collision the two vehicles are locked together. We can use the conservation of momentum to calculate the speed at which the two vehicles move immediately after the collision.

a The first car's momentum before the collision = $1050 \text{ kg} \times 22.2 \text{ m s}^{-1} = 2.33 \times 10^4 \text{ kg m s}^{-1}$.
The other car is stationary before the collision so it has no momentum. Total momentum before the collision = $2.33 \times 10^4 \text{ kg m s}^{-1}$.

Conservation of momentum says that the total momentum after the collision must also be $2.33 \times 10^4 \text{ kg m s}^{-1}$.

b The vehicles are now locked together so that their combined mass is:

$$m = 1050 \text{ kg} + 1200 \text{ kg}$$
$$= 2250 \text{ kg}$$

Since velocity = $\dfrac{\text{momentum}}{\text{mass}}$

the velocity after the collision is:

$$v = \frac{2.33 \times 10^4 \text{ kg m s}^{-1}}{2250 \text{ kg}}$$
$$= 10.4 \text{ m s}^{-1} \text{ (23 mph)}$$

The kinetic energy before the collision is entirely due to the first car:

$$E_k = \tfrac{1}{2} m v^2$$
$$= \tfrac{1}{2} \times 1050 \text{ kg} \times (22.2 \text{ m s}^{-1})^2$$
$$= 2.59 \times 10^5 \text{ J}$$

After the collision:

$$E_k = \tfrac{1}{2} \times 2250 \text{ kg} \times (10.4 \text{ m s}^{-1})^2$$
$$= 1.22 \times 10^5 \text{ J}$$

137 kJ of kinetic energy has been dissipated during this ineleastic collision.

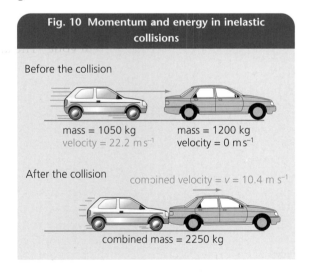

Fig. 10 Momentum and energy in inelastic collisions

Before the collision

mass = 1050 kg
velocity = 22.2 m s⁻¹

mass = 1200 kg
velocity = 0 m s⁻¹

After the collision

combined velocity = v = 10.4 m s⁻¹

combined mass = 2250 kg

Physics and road safety

As you have read in this chapter, there are several basic laws of physics which contribute to our understanding of what happens during road accidents. The initial and final velocities, time taken, momentum, acceleration, deceleration, work done (therefore energy used up or transferred), kinetic energy, potential energy and friction all have a part to play in road safety. Designing safer cars requires a great deal of data and a lot of complex calculations. Much of the data is obtained by crash testing cars in carefully controlled conditions. The crash dummies used today are very sophisticated with between 50 and 60 sensors called accelerometers built into the body.

The principle used in accelerometers is that when a deforming force is applied to a silicon chip, its electrical resistance changes. This change can be used to produce the data as electrical pulses which can be analysed later. The same principle applies when the accelerometer is used as a trigger to set off an airbag.

1 a How much kinetic energy does a driver of mass 90 kg transfer if he decelerated from 13 m s^{-1} to rest in a crash?

b Draw a graph of force against distance to show how the energy from Question a can be reduced to nothing in these two crash scenarios:

(i) when the driver is using a seat belt which will move about 50 cm before stopping;

(ii) when the driver is not using a seat belt and is flung forwards until his head hits the dashboard. The dashboard deforms by 0.5 cm as the kinetic energy is reduced to zero.

c What conclusions can you come to from these calculations?

d Modern cars have 'crumple zones' which are designed to collapse in a crash. Explain how these can help to save the lives of car drivers and passengers.

2 In order to stop a car safely, a driver has to consider two factors:
• the 'thinking distance' needed as the driver reacts to the situation. An average reaction time is about 0.7 seconds. During this time the car can travel quite a distance.
• the 'braking distance' as the car decelerates to a stop. On a dry road with good brakes a car would decelerate at 8.5 m s^{-2}.

Calculate the thinking distance, braking distance and total stopping distance for the following speeds on a dry road:

13 m s^{-1}

22 m s^{-1} (50 mph)

30 m s^{-1} (70 mph).

Put your results in a suitable table. Then construct a graph of total stopping distance (m) against speed (m s^{-1}) and work out the total stopping distance for a speed of 15 m s^{-1}.

3 Prepare an outline report to be given at an assembly in your school or college to make students more aware of the dangers of speeding on motorbikes or in cars. Use the information in this chapter and from other sources such as the Internet.

Your document should contain at least one image to support what you propose to say.

1 A spacecraft, of mass 4500 kg, which is landing on the Moon, uses its engines to keep its speed of descent constant at 5.0 m s^{-1} from the time when the craft is 14 m above the Moon's surface until it is 4.0 m above the surface. The engines are then switched off and the spacecraft falls freely to the Moon's surface.

The acceleration of free fall on the moon is 1.6 m s^{-2}. Calculate, for the spacecraft,

(i) the speed of impact,

(ii) the time taken to travel the last 4.0 m,

(iii) the time taken to fall the full 14 m,

(iv) the power of the engines while the speed is constant,

(v) the work done by the engines while the speed is kept constant. (8)

(AQA PH01 Jun 98 Q2)

2 A stationary ball of mass 6.0 × 10^{-2} kg is hit horizontally with a tennis racquet. The ball is in contact with the racquet for 30 ms and leaves the racquet with a speed of 27 m s^{-1}.

a Calculate

(i) the change in the momentum of the ball,

(ii) the average force which the racquet exerts on the ball. (3)

b Calculate the horizontal distance travelled by the ball before it hits the ground, if it leaves the racquet at a vertical height of 2.5 m. (3)

c (i) Explain what is meant by *inelastic collision*.

(ii) Suggest a reason why the collision between the ball and the racquet is inelastic. (2)

(AQA PH01 Jun 98 Q3)

3 **a** An empty railway truck of mass 10 000 kg is travelling horizontally at a speed of 0.50 m s^{-1}. For this truck calculate the

(i) momentum,

(ii) kinetic energy. (2)

b Sand falls vertically into the truck at a constant rate of 40 kg s^{-1}.

Calculate the additional horizontal force which must be applied to the truck, if it is to maintain a steady speed of 0.50 m s^{-1}. (2)

c Had no additional force been applied to the truck while sand continued to fall, explain without calculation what would happen to the truck's

(i) momentum,

(ii) speed. (3)

(AQA PH01 Jun 97 Q4)

4 A train of mass 1.4 × 10^5 kg accelerates uniformly from rest along a level track. It travels 100 m in the first 26 s.

Calculate

(i) the acceleration of the train,

(ii) the speed reached after 26 s,

(iii) the resultant force required to produce this acceleration,

(iv) the average power required. (6)

(AQA PH01 Feb 97 Q2)

5 A winch is a machine used to raise the sail on a yacht. A winch consists of a cylindrical drum on to which a rope is wound by turning a handle. A simplified sketch of the machine is shown below.

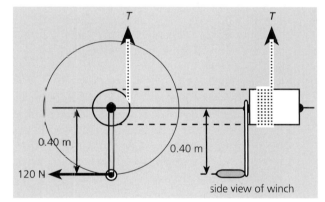

side view of winch

The handle of the winch is attached to the centre of the drum by an arm of length 0.40 m. A steady force of 120 N, applied at right angles to the arm, is needed to rotate the drum of the winch when raising the sail on a yacht. It takes 30 complete turns of the winch handle to raise the sail to the top of the mast, through a vertical height of 8.8 m.

(i) Show that the work done in turning the winch handle through 30 complete turns is 9.0 × 10^3 J.

(ii) Calculate the work done in raising the sail if the winch mechanism is 60% efficient.

(iii) Calculate the tension, *T*, in the rope attached to the sail. (5)

(AQA PH01 Mar 98 Q4)

Earth is constantly being bombarded from space. Fortunately, most of the impacts are from small rocks and dust particles which burn up in our atmosphere. A few of these meteorites are massive enough to make it down to Earth's surface where they can cause local damage. At least three cars have been struck by meteorites in the USA in the last 100 years.

In recent years, scientists have come to realise that an impact by a large asteroid or comet could pose a significant hazard to life. Some scientists link mass extinctions, such as that of the dinosaurs, with impacts from space. Although the probability of Earth being struck by a large asteroid or comet (often called near Earth objects,

Even a small fragment of a comet could cause a major disaster if it collided with Earth.

or NEOs) is extremely small, the consequences of such a collision are so catastrophic that the American congress has commissioned the US space agency, NASA, to assess the threat and prepare to deal with it.

The danger from a cosmic impact increases with the mass of the projectile. If Earth collided with an asteroid or comet with a diameter of between 1 and 2 km, the resulting explosion would transfer an energy equivalent to a million megatons of TNT. This is at least one hundred thousand times more energetic than the largest man-made explosions, the hydrogen bombs detonated during the 1950s and 60s. This sort of collision would radically change Earth's climate by throwing up large quantities of dust into the stratosphere. The dust would reflect and absorb light from the Sun, lowering temperatures around Earth, leading to massive loss of food crops.

The NASA project, known as Space-guard, has been designed to detect the position and velocity of NEOs. At present, no asteroid or comet is known to be on a collision course with Earth. The chances of a collision this century with an object 1 km or more in diameter are small – roughly 1 in 10 000 – but such a collision is possible and could happen at any time. With sufficient warning, the incoming object could be deflected or destroyed.

Meteor showers occur at predictable times of the year, when Earth passes through debris left behind by a comet.

9.1 Conservation of energy

Energy is a crucial factor in determining the effect of a collision. Whether the collision is between an asteroid and Earth, or two cars on the motorway, it is the amount of energy which is transferred that largely determines what will happen. Energy is one of the most

Chemical energy in the rocket fuel is transferred as heat and then as kinetic energy in the exhaust gases. These propel the rocket upwards, lifting a weight.

fundamental concepts in science, but it is an abstract quantity, difficult to define exactly. Energy appears in a number of different forms. A moving car has energy known as kinetic energy, whilst a stationary vehicle parked at the top of a hill has potential energy. A loudspeaker emitting a sound wave and a torch giving out light are both transferring energy. What do all these phenomena have in common? One definition that links all of the forms of energy is:

energy is the ability to do work.

Work is done when a force moves through a distance in the direction of the force (see Chapter 8), so a body has energy when it has the ability to lift a weight (Fig. 1).

Energy exists in many different forms (see Table 1). Energy may be transferred between different objects and from one form to another. However, in any process which transfers energy, the total energy is the same before and after the transfer. This is a fundamental principle in science known as the **conservation of energy**. It is often stated as:

energy cannot be created or destroyed.

Another way to put this is that:

the total energy in an isolated system is constant.

Fig. 1 Energy transfers

Sun

(a) Energy from the Sun in the form of light generates electrical energy in the solar cell which is used to drive a motor and lift a weight.

solar cell

electric motor

weight

(b) Elastic energy in the bowstring is used to fire the arrow into the air, lifting a weight.

James Joule, the son of a brewer from Manchester, did pioneering work on energy transfer. He realised that energy in one form could be transferred to another form. On his honeymoon he measured the temperature of the water at the top of a waterfall and at the bottom. He found a small temperature rise at the bottom of the fall due to the transfer of kinetic energy to internal (random thermal) energy.

Table 1 Different forms of energy		
Form of energy	Example	Approximate amount of energy transferred / joules
Kinetic energy, E_k	a car accelerating to $25\,m\,s^{-1}$	500 000 J
Gravitational potential energy, E_p	a stone dropped off a cliff	1000 J
Elastic potential energy	stored in a stretched guitar string	0.05 J
Internal energy or random thermal energy	bringing a kettle of water to boiling point	500 000 J
Chemical energy	transferred from burning 1 tonne of coal	5×10^{10} J
Radiant energy	received by Earth from the Sun in one day	10^{22} J per day
Sound energy	a symphony orchestra	$10\,J\,s^{-1}$
Electrical energy	an electric current flowing in a kettle element	$2000\,J\,s^{-1}$
Nuclear energy	fusion of hydrogen in the Sun	the Sun transfers about $4 \times 10^{26}\,J\,s^{-1}$

EXTENSION

Mass and energy

The conservation of energy is a well-established principle in physics; there are no known exceptions to this rule. However, the list of energy forms has had to be extended to include mass energy. It seems that objects have energy just by virtue of their existence. Einstein discovered that mass can be transferred to other forms of energy, such as radiant energy. The formula $E = mc^2$ describes how much energy, E, can be transferred if a certain amount of mass, m, is destroyed. The factor which links the two is the speed of light, c, which has a value of $3 \times 10^8\,m\,s^{-1}$.

This discovery, made at the beginning of the twentieth century, is important in understanding nuclear reactions. If an electron and a positron collide they disappear, releasing gamma radiation. The mass of the matter (electron) and antimatter (positron) has been transferred as radiant energy (Chapter 2, p. 25).

Large amounts of energy are transferred when only small amounts of mass are destroyed.

1 If it was possible to completely change 1 kg of mass to other forms of energy, how much energy would be released?

9.2 Gravitational potential energy

The phrase *potential energy* is used to describe energy that is stored by a body due to its position with respect to something else. For example, an electron placed close to another charged object, such as another electron, has electrical potential energy. If the electron was free to move, it would be repelled by the other electron and potential energy would be transferred to kinetic energy.

An object has *gravitational potential energy*, E_p, because of its position relative to another mass, such as a large massive object like Earth. A passing asteroid has gravitational potential energy due to its position in Earth's gravitational field. As it accelerates towards

Charged particles in the thundercloud have electrical potential energy because of their position relative to other charges. Eventually the charges move and the potential energy is transferred as light and sound.

Fig. 2 Calculating gravitational potential energy

We can calculate the change in gravitational potential energy, ΔE_p, of a mass, m, moved through a height, Δh, above Earth's surface by finding the work done in lifting the object through that distance. The work done is equal to the force × distance moved in the direction of the force:

$$\text{work} = \text{weight} \times \text{height} = mg\Delta h$$

Since all this work has now been transferred to gravitational potential energy we can write:

$$\Delta E_p = mg\Delta h$$

Earth its potential energy transfers to kinetic energy. The amount of potential energy transferred depends on the mass of the object, m, the gravitational field strength, g, and the

In 1997, superheavyweight Andrey Chemerkin of Russia set a new world record of 462.5 kg. At a height of 2 m, the weight has a gravitational potential energy of 462.5 kg × 9.81 N kg^{-1} × 2 m = 9074 J.

height that the object moves through, Δh (Fig. 2)

$$\Delta E_p = mg\Delta h$$

Close to Earth, the gravitational field strength can be treated as a constant, $g = 9.81 \text{ N kg}^{-1}$. A mass of 1 kg lifted through a height of 1 m therefore gains 9.81 J of gravitational potential energy.

9.3 Kinetic energy

Kinetic energy is the energy due to the motion of a mass. The amount of kinetic energy, E_k, depends upon the object's mass, m, and its velocity, v. In fact, $E_k = \frac{1}{2}mv^2$ (Chapter 8, p. 120).

We can use this expression to estimate the kinetic energy of a person who is running at maximum speed. A 100 m sprinter can reach a top speed of about 12 m s^{-1}. The typical mass of a male sprinter is in the region of 90 kg. So the kinetic energy is:

$$E_k = \tfrac{1}{2}mv^2 = 0.5 \times 90 \times (12)^2 = 6480 \text{ J}$$

2 An asteroid colliding with Earth is likely to have a speed on impact of around 10 km s^{-1}. Estimate the kinetic energy of an asteroid that has a diameter of around 1 km. (Take the density of the asteroid to be 2000 kg m^{-3}.)

Hydroelectric power

The Glen Canyon dam uses water from the Colorado River to generate electricity

Hydroelectric power stations produce about 15% of the World's electrical power. In countries with mountainous regions and abundant water the proportion is much higher; in Canada, 60% of the electrical power is generated in this way. The electricity is produced by generators driven by water turbines that transfer the potential energy in falling or fast-flowing water to mechanical energy.

At the Dinorwig pumped power station in Wales, water is allowed to fall from the upper reservoir to the lower reservoir at times of high demand for electrical power. At off-peak times, such as the middle of the night, electricity generated in other power stations is used to pump the water back to the upper reservoir.

Dinorwig's reversible pump/turbines are capable of reaching maximum generation from zero output in less than 16 seconds. The maximum flow rate is approximately $400 \, m^3 \, s^{-1}$ and the water falls through a height of around 500 m.

3 How much potential energy per second is transferred when the power station is operating at maximum flow rate? (The density of water is $1000 \, kg \, m^{-3}$.)

4 The working volume of water at Dinorwig is $7 \times 10^6 \, m^3$. How much gravitational energy is transferred when this volume of water falls to the lower reservoir?

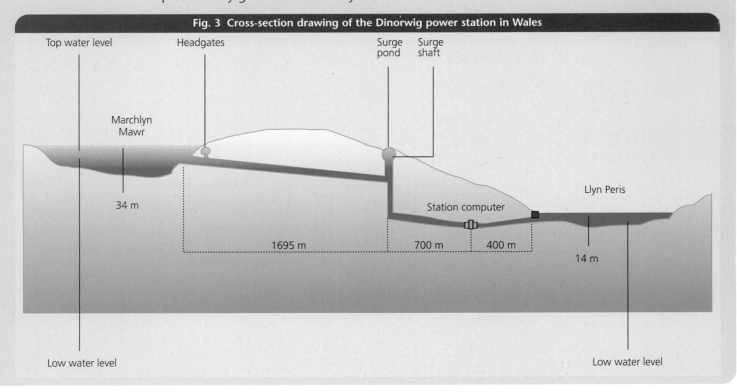

Fig. 3 Cross-section drawing of the Dinorwig power station in Wales

Top water level

Headgates

Surge pond

Surge shaft

Marchlyn Mawr

34 m

1695 m

700 m

400 m

Station computer

Llyn Peris

14 m

Low water level

Low water level

Falling objects transfer gravitational potential energy to kinetic energy. If we ignore air resistance, all the potential energy will be transferred to kinetic energy.

$$\Delta E_p = E_k \quad or$$

$$mg\Delta h = \tfrac{1}{2}mv^2$$

A small, dense object falling from the top of the Empire State Building, 448 m high, in New York would be travelling at very high speed just before its impact with the pavement:

$$mg\Delta h = \tfrac{1}{2}mv^2$$

The mass of the falling object does not affect its speed, since it appears on both sides of the equation.

$$v^2 = 2g\Delta h$$

$$v = \sqrt{2g\Delta h}$$

If the skyscraper is 448 m tall then:

$$v = \sqrt{2 \times 9.81 \times 448}$$
$$= 93.7 \text{ m s}^{-1}$$

5 The transfer of kinetic to potential energy can be used to find out how high an object can be thrown. If you could throw a cricket ball at 20 m s^{-1} vertically upwards, calculate how high it would go.

9.4 Internal energy

The internal energy of the hook is the sum of the kinetic and potential energies of all its particles

The molecules of any object are in constant motion; the molecules in a solid vibrate, those in a gas have high velocities in random directions. In a solid, the total energy of any particular molecule is the sum of its kinetic energy and its potential energy. The potential energy of a molecule in a solid is due to its proximity to other charged molecules. In a gas, the molecules are much further apart and the forces between molecules are so small that they can be safely ignored. The energy of any molecule in a gas is just its kinetic energy.

For any object, the sum of all the energies of its particles is known as its **internal energy**. This is sometimes known as the random thermal energy.

We can increase the random thermal energy of an object by *heating* it. Heat is a flow of energy that occurs as a result of a temperature difference. Heat always transfers

131

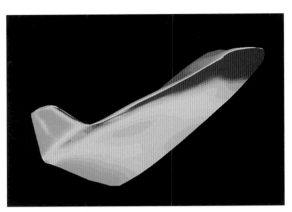

Potential energy is transferred to kinetic energy as the shuttle accelerates towards Earth. When it reaches Earth's atmosphere, kinetic energy is transferred to internal energy and the outside of the shuttle has to withstand high temperatures.

energy from high temperature (hot) objects to low temperature (cold) objects. The energy flow results in a change in internal energy (Fig. 4). For example, if you hold a hot water bottle, energy flows as heat from the hot water bottle into you. The internal energy of the hot water bottle drops and your internal energy increases.

Changes in internal energy are usually linked with a change in temperature. When you put a hot cup of coffee down on a table, energy flows as heat from the cup to the room, the coffee loses internal energy and its temperature drops. The temperature drop depends on the amount of energy transferred, but it also depends on the mass of coffee and on its **specific heat capacity**.

Specific heat capacity

You can investigate the link between energy and temperature quite easily in the laboratory. If you put an electric heater into a beaker of water, the temperature will steadily rise (Fig. 5). The results of experiments like this suggest that the amount of heat energy transferred, ΔQ, is proportional to the temperature change, ΔT. The amount of heat needed for any given temperature change is also proportional to the mass, m, of material. These results can be put together:

$$\Delta Q \propto \Delta T \text{ and } \Delta Q \propto m$$

so, $\Delta Q \propto m\Delta T$

$$\Delta Q = cm\Delta T \text{ or, } c = \frac{\Delta Q}{m\Delta T}$$

The constant of proportionality, c, is called the specific heat capacity. The specific heat capacity of a substance is the energy needed to raise the temperature of one kilogram of the substance by 1 K. Its units are therefore $J\,kg^{-1}\,K^{-1}$ (or $J\,kg^{-1}\,°C^{-1}$).

Fig. 4 Energy transfers using a cricket ball

Heat and work are both ways of transferring energy.

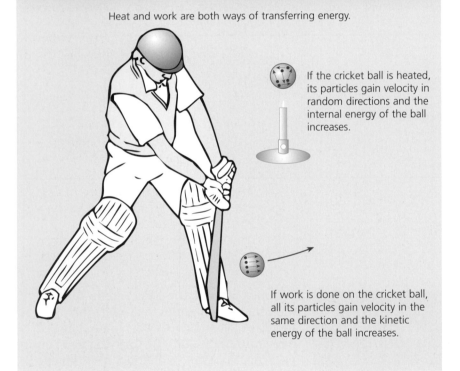

If the cricket ball is heated, its particles gain velocity in random directions and the internal energy of the ball increases.

If work is done on the cricket ball, all its particles gain velocity in the same direction and the kinetic energy of the ball increases.

Fig. 5 Linking energy and temperature

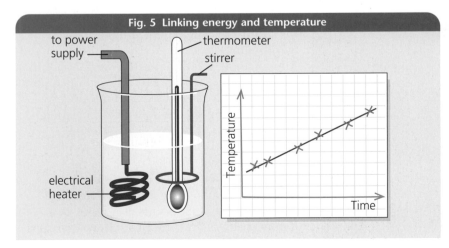

Table 2 Specific heat capacity	
Substance	**c/J kg^{-1} K^{-1}**
hydrogen gas	14 300
water	4200
ethanol	2400
air	993
stainless steel	510
copper	385
mercury	140
Values are quoted at room temperature and standard atmospheric pressure	

The range of specific heat capacities is quite large. Some surprising results – like the high specific heat capacity of hydrogen – are of technological use. For example, hydrogen is used as the coolant in large electrical turbines, despite the problems of handling this compressed, highly explosive gas.

The specific heat capacity of water is relatively high; it takes 4200 J of energy to raise the temperature of 1 kg of water by 1 K. A large amount of energy is required to cause a small temperature increase. This means that water is an ideal substance to use in car radiators for cooling the engine or in central heating radiators for heating the home. It also means that heating the water for a bath or shower is expensive. For example, a typical electrical shower has a flow rate of 9 litres per minute, equal to 0.15 kg s^{-1}. If the incoming water has a temperature of 15 °C and the shower is set at 30 °C, then the energy required each second is:

$$Q = mc\Delta T = 0.15 \text{ kg s}^{-1} \times 4200 \text{ J kg}^{-1} \text{ K}^{-1} \times 15$$

$$= 9450 \text{ joules every second}$$

This electric shower would need a heater rated at about 9.5 kW, and would need a large current supplied to it, around 40 A.

The equation $\Delta Q = cm\Delta T$ assumes that no other chemical or physical changes take place. For example, if you tried to measure the specific heat capacity of water between −2 °C and +2 °C, your results would be wrong. You would have included the heat needed to melt the ice: the **latent heat**.

Adding ice at 0 °C lowers the temperature of a drink much more than adding the same mass of water at 0 °C.

6 Estimate the energy required to heat a room full of air from 0 °C to 20 °C (see Table 2).

7 A kettle holds 2 litres of water at 10 °C. The kettle has a power rating of 2.2 kW. How long will it take the kettle to bring the water to boiling point, 100 °C?

8 The disk brakes on a motorbike are made of high carbon content stainless steel to provide a high level of friction and good heat dissipation. The motorbike has a mass of 800 kg and is travelling at 30 m s^{-1}.

a Calculate the kinetic energy of the motorbike.

b The brakes have a mass of 1 kg each and their specific heat capacity is 500 J kg^{-1} K^{-1}. If 25% of the motorbike's kinetic energy is transferred to the brakes as internal energy, calculate the temperature rise of the brakes.

Specific latent heat

It is possible for substances to change their internal energy without changing their temperature. This happens when ice at 0 °C gains internal energy from its surroundings. The increase in internal energy melts the ice, but does not change its temperature.

The change from one phase (solid, liquid or gas) to another is a change in the distance between molecules and the way in which molecules are arranged. During a change of phase, heat flows into, or out of, the substance, but its temperature stays constant.

As temperature is not changing, heat which flows into the substance is only being used to change the internal structure. When a substance melts or boils, its molecules are pulled further apart and allowed to move more freely. There is an increase in the potential and kinetic energies of the molecules: the internal energy of the material is greater. Energy has therefore flowed into the material, changing the internal energy, but leaving the temperature unaltered. In a sense, this energy is 'hidden' or latent.

The amount of energy needed to change the phase of a kilogram of material is called the specific latent heat, l.

$$l = \frac{\Delta Q}{m} \text{ or, } \Delta Q = ml$$

133

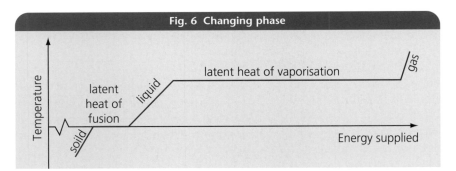

Fig. 6 Changing phase

Table 3 Specific latent heat

	Vaporisation/kJ kg^{-1}	Fusion/kJ kg^{-1}
water	2260	334
oxygen	243	14
helium	25	5
mercury	290	11
iron	6339	276
lead	854	25

The specific latent heat of vaporisation for water is more than five times the energy needed to warm water from 0 °C to boiling point (Fig. 6 and Table 3).

When an ice cube at 0 °C is dropped into a glass of water at 15 °C, energy is transferred to the ice from the warmer water. This transfer of energy first changes the state of the ice from solid to liquid, then raises the temperature of the melted ice to the final temperature of the drink. If the mass of the ice cube is 30 g and the mass of the water is 250 g, we can calculate the final temperature, T, of the mixture.

If we neglect the energy transferred from the glass itself and any energy transferred from the surroundings:

The internal energy lost by the water = internal energy gained by the ice: or

The internal energy lost by the water = energy required to melt the ice + energy required to raise the melted ice to the final temperature of drink:

$$m_{\text{water}} \times c_{\text{water}} \times (15 - T) = (m_{\text{ice}} \times l_{\text{ice}}) + (m_{\text{ice}} \times c_{\text{water}} \times T)$$

$$0.250 \times 4200 \times (15 - T) = 0.030 \times 334 \times 10^3 + 0.030 \times 4200 \times T$$

$$1050 \times (15 - T) = 10020 + 126\,T$$

$$1050 \times 15 - 10020 = 1176\,T$$

$$T = \frac{5730}{1176} = 4.9\,°C$$

So the final temperature of the drink is just below 5 °C.

9 Explain why a scald from steam at 100 °C is likely to be more damaging than coming into contact with the same mass of water at 100 °C.

10 A kettle of power 2 kW holds 2 litres of water, initially at 20 °C. If the kettle is left on for 5 minutes, will it boil dry?

Specific latent heat

The specific latent heat of a material is the energy required for 1 kg of a substance to change state, without changing its temperature. Some of this energy is used to do work against inter-molecular forces as the molecules in a material move further apart. However, some of the energy is needed to do work against external forces as the material expands.

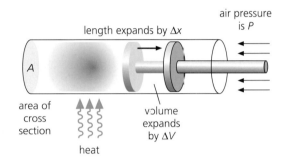

length expands by Δx

air pressure is P

A

area of cross section

heat

volume expands by ΔV

If the material expands by distance Δx, the volume has changed by an amount:

$\Delta V = A \Delta x$

The force exerted by the material is:

$F = PA$

where P is the external pressure. The work done by the system is therefore:

$W = F \Delta x$

$\quad = PA \times \Delta x$

$\quad = P \times A \Delta x$

$W = P \Delta V$

Take the case of water at 1 atmosphere pressure ($= 10^5$ Pa). The density of water changes from 958 kg m^{-3} to 0.598 kg m^{-3} as it vaporises at 100 °C. A kilogram of water undergoes a volume change:

$$\Delta V = \frac{1}{0.598} - \frac{1}{958} = 1.7 \, \text{m}^3$$

against pressure 10^5 Pa. The work done per kilogram is therefore $W = P \Delta V = 1.7 \times 10^5$ J. The specific latent heat is 2260 kJ kg^{-1}, so over 7% of the energy supplied is used in doing work against atmospheric pressure.

11 0.2 kg of liquid benzene has a volume of 0.25×10^{-3} m^3 at 353 K. The same mass of benzene vapour has a volume of 74×10^{-3} m^3 at 353 K.

a If 0.2 kg of benzene evaporates at 353 K and at an atmospheric pressure of 100 kPa, calculate the work done. ($W = P\Delta V$)

b Calculate the energy needed to evaporate 0.2 kg of benzene at 353 K. (The specific latent heat of vaporisation of benzene at 353 K is 3.94×10^5 J kg^{-1})

c Explain the difference between your answers to (a) and (b).

Identifying bias in a scientific article

When articles are written, they are usually for a particular audience. This can affect the author's style and content in an article – in other words, they can be biased. Scientists often pride themselves on the fact that their writing is 'objective' – but you need to be aware that a science based article can also be biased. Think about these questions when reading an article:

● What is the background of the author – do they work for a particular organisation which might have a vested interest in putting a particular view forward?

● If 'evidence' for a point of view is presented – does the author quote where it comes from?

● Do phrases like … 'Everyone knows that' or … 'It's a well-known fact that …' keep appearing without any idea of where these 'facts' come from?

● Are there attempts in the writing to name drop in order to impress the reader (so-called 'appeals to authority' which you may never have heard of before)?

● Following on from this tactic, some authors will put in words like 'obviously', 'clearly' or 'it can easily be shown that' in order to appeal to the readers' vanity (implying that you are as clever as the author is trying to be).

● Is there an over reliance on technical jargon which the reader cannot question and has to accept?

● Does the author try to belittle any opponents by resorting to sarcasm or innuendo? It is fairly easy to imply a low opinion of another person by making an amusing description of their case.

● Does the author make assumptions in arguments? Even worse, are these assumptions then used to build a case?

● Are the fears or prejudices of the reader being played on to win an argument? This is most typically found by looking at the type of publication the article appears in, where the readership may want to believe certain ideas. Having your own prejudices confirmed is a technique used by polititians who are trying to win your vote.

● Does the author use rhetorical questions? This tactic encourages the reader to subconsciously provide the answer and therefore be more receptive to any arguments which may follow.

Environmental issues like power stations and electricity generation can often bring out the worst in journalists! The temptation to be sensationalist and to campaign rather than to report facts can be impossible to resist.

1 Your task is to locate physics based articles about power generation which illustrates five of the tactics outlined above. You may use articles from magazines, newspapers, advertising literature or from the Internet.

It may be possible to find an article which illustrates all five examples in the same article or you may have to use several examples.

You must provide the evidence for the tactics by highlighting the parts of the article and producing a written explanation of why you think this tactic is being used.

Remember to quote:

Where the article is from

Who wrote it

Who published it and the date of publication.

1 Use values from the data booklet in this question.

150 cm^3 of water at 30 °C is mixed thoroughly with 250 cm^3 of ethanol at 10 °C.

a Calculate

(i) the mass of the water,

(ii) the mass of the ethanol. (2)

b The final temperature of the mixture is 21.2 °C.

Show that the thermal energy lost by the water is approximately equal to the thermal energy gained by the ethanol when the liquids mix. (3)

2 In an 'expresso' coffee maker, steam is passed through cold coffee to heat it.

The cold coffee has a mass of 200 g and is originally at 15 °C.

a Explain why adding steam at 100 °C has a greater heating effect than adding water at 100 °C.

b What mass of steam at 100 °C needs to be added to raise the final temperature of the coffee to 80 °C?

(Assume coffee has the same specific heat capacity as water. Use your data booklet to find other values.)

3 Data for use in this question should be taken from the AQA data booklet.

1.00 kg of water is brought to the boil inside an electric kettle. Throughout the heating process the heating element supplies energy at a constant rate.

Assume that the energy supplied to the kettle itself is negligible.

a Calculate the rate at which energy is supplied to convert water to steam if 0.50 g of steam is produced each second after the water has reached boiling point.

b Estimate the rate at which the temperature increases just before the water reaches boiling point.

c State and explain the main reason why the rate of increase in temperature is not constant during the heating process.

(AQA PH03 March 1998 Q5)

4 The Saturn V rockets which launched the Apollo space missions had the following specifications

mass at lift-off = 3.0×10^6 kg

velocity of exhaust gases = 1.1×10^4 m s^{-1}

initial rate of fuel consumption at lift-off = 3.0×10^3 kg s^{-1}

a Calculate

( ) the force (thrust) produced at lift-off,

(i) the resultant force acting on the rocket at lift-off. (4)

b If the thrust of the engines were constant, give **one** reason why the acceleration increased as the flight progressed. (1)

(AQA PH01 Feb 97 Q3)

5 A toy locomotive of mass 0.50 kg is initially at rest on a horizontal track. The locomotive is powered by a twisted rubber band which, as it unwinds, exerts a force which varies with time as shown in the table.

time /s								
0.0	1.0	2.0	3.0	4.0	5.0	6.0	7.0	8.0
force /N								
0.20	0.18	0.15	0.12	0.10	0.08	0.05	0.02	0.00

a (i) On graph paper plot a graph of force against time for the rubber band power source.

(ii) State what is given by the area between the graph and the time axis. (4)

b The rubber band is wound up and released to power the locomotive. Use your graph to show that the speed of the locomotive 8.0 s after the twisted rubber band is released is 1.6 m s^{-1}. Ignore the effects of air resistance and energy losses due to friction. (2)

c 8.0 s after release the locomotive collides with and couples to a toy truck, initially at rest, which has a mass of 1.50 kg.

(i) Calculate the speed of the coupled locomotive and truck after collision.

(ii) Calculate the combined kinetic energy of the locomotive and truck immediately after collision,

(iii) Show, with the aid of a calculation, whether or not the collision is elastic. (5)

(AQA PH01 Mar 99 Q1)

Humans can survive in a limited temperature range. Life is tough at −50 °C.

Our planet is normally a comfortable place. The atmosphere shields us from the harsh extremes of space. It acts as a blanket, keeping us warm. A severe winter frost in arctic Greenland might dip down to temperatures of only −50 °C.

In space, the temperature can be lower. Measurements of the cosmic background radiation give the temperature of deep space as around −270 °C. This is still not the coldest place in the universe: as far as we know, that title belongs to a few selected places on planet Earth.

We now know that there is a lowest possible temperature called absolute zero. At this temperature, which is about −273 °C, everything would stop: gas molecules would be stationary; no heat radiation would be emitted; nothing would move or vibrate. We also know that absolute zero is unreachable. Many universities have facilities for getting to temperatures approaching absolute zero.

A cylindrical magnet floats freely above a nitrogen-cooled, superconducting ceramic specimen. Liquid nitrogen is needed to keep the ceramic within its superconducting temperature range.

As superfluid helium at 1.2 K is heated from above, the increase in its pressure causes the helium to undergo a fountain effect.

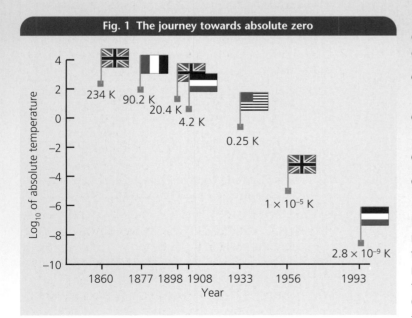

Fig. 1 The journey towards absolute zero

234 K
90.2 K
20.4 K
4.2 K
0.25 K
1 × 10⁻⁵ K
2.8 × 10⁻⁹ K

Log₁₀ of absolute temperature

1860 1877 1898 1908 1933 1956 1993

Year

When we reach these low temperatures, we open up a mysterious world. The unexpected is commonplace:

● some electrical conductors lose all their resistance;

● fluids lose their viscosity, flowing freely through tiny gaps;

● oxygen becomes magnetic;

● liquid helium creeps over the walls of containers.

Researchers in this field – cryogenics – strive to reach and sustain low temperatures to investigate the unusual properties of materials. There are many practical problems including inventing new thermometers and avoiding heat transfer.
Of course, there is always the temptation to break the current record.

10.1 Temperature

'Our low-temperature research needs accurate ways of measuring temperature. We have real problems here: mercury thermometers are no good because the mercury freezes. Many of our measurements rely on electrical measurements – of resistance, for example. We often need to define our own practical temperature scales when we get really close to absolute zero.'

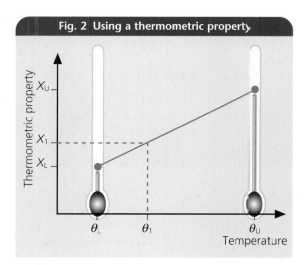

Fig. 2 Using a thermometric property

We all have an intuitive idea of temperature based on the messages our brains receive from certain nerve endings in our skin. But our intuitions often let us down.

If two things are at the same temperature then there will be no net flow of energy between them. Both objects will stay in the same state. We say that they are in **thermal equilibrium**. All objects at the same temperature are in thermal equilibrium. This might seem obvious but we are really making an assumption, sometimes called the zeroth law of thermodynamics: 'If two objects are in thermal equilibrium with a third object, they will be in thermal equilibrium with each other'.

Defining a temperature scale

Temperature is a fundamental quantity, like mass or time. The size of the unit and the way we measure it are entirely arbitrary. This has led to a puzzling variety of different scales: Fahrenheit, Centigrade and Celsius are among the more familiar. But all practical temperature scales are based on a change in the property of some substance – a **thermometric property**.

A chosen thermometric property is measured at two definite temperatures – the **fixed points**. Normally the entire scale is worked out by assuming a linear variation between these points (Fig. 2). For example, school science experiments often use mercury-in-glass thermometers which are calibrated on the Celsius scale at fixed points of the melting point of pure ice (0 °C), and the boiling point of pure water (100 °C) at 1 atmosphere pressure. Cryogenics researchers, on the other hand, might choose to use a resistance thermometer calibrated at the boiling points of liquid hydrogen (= –253 °C) and liquid helium (= –269 °C).

The Kelvin temperature scale

Alcohol and mercury do not expand at exactly the same rate as they warm up. Alcohol thermometers and mercury thermometers often disagree with each other. There are a variety of contradictory practical temperature scales, so a single theoretical scale has been devised: the Kelvin scale. This is based on the behaviour of an 'ideal' gas – a gas where the molecules do not attract one another. Dry gases at low **pressure** show such ideal behaviour. If an ideal gas is kept in a container of fixed volume, the gas pressure drops as the temperature drops.

This graph can be extrapolated back to low temperatures: eventually, the line cuts the *x* axis (Fig. 3). At this point, the ideal gas is

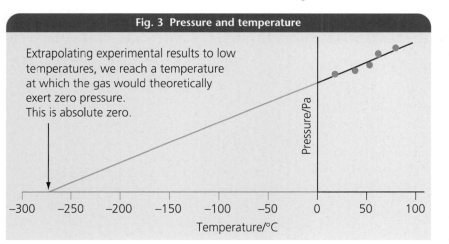

Fig. 3 Pressure and temperature

Extrapolating experimental results to low temperatures, we reach a temperature at which the gas would theoretically exert zero pressure. This is absolute zero.

Heat and work

'We make liquid gases and compressed gases for industry and research. Liquid nitrogen is used to shrink metal components to make tightly fitting joints. Liquid argon can be isolated from the air so cheaply that it is used for welding. Liquid oxygen used in hospitals saves thousands of lives every year. Liquefaction processes often work by making gases expand. Why does this work?'

Heat is energy which flows from one place, or object, to another as a result of a temperature difference. The energy flow results in a change in the **internal energy** of objects. The internal energy of an object is the sum of the kinetic and potential energies of all its particles. When heat flows into an object, its internal energy rises. Changes of internal energy are usually linked with a change in temperature.

Removing internal energy from something is easy if you have a colder object – heat flows between objects at different temperatures. We could never make liquid nitrogen on Earth this way: the Earth's temperature never drops below nitrogen's boiling point. Instead we can exploit the link between internal energy, heat and work.

The first law of thermodynamics

It was the English brewer James Prescott Joule who first demonstrated convincingly that heat and work were both aspects of the same thing: energy. In a series of experiments in the 1840s, Joule measured mechanical work and temperature rise in all sorts of devices – expanding gases, paddle wheels in drums of water, even in a waterfall while he was on his honeymoon. Joule was able to show that no matter what device did the mechanical work, one unit of work always produced the same heating effect. His work led to one of the fundamental laws of physics: *the principle of conservation of energy*.

When **thermodynamics** was in its early development, the equivalence of work and heat was expressed in a different way: as the **first law of thermodynamics**. If you supply heat to a system, it will increase the internal energy of the system and the system can do mechanical work. Take the case of a cylinder full of air. Heating the cylinder warms up the air, so its internal energy rises. The hot gas expands and lifts the weight, doing mechanical work (Fig. 4).

Joule's apparatus. On turning a paddle wheel in water or mercury, Joule noticed that the temperature of the water increased.

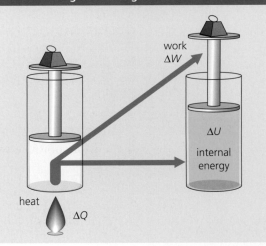

Fig. 4 Working with hot air

work ΔW

ΔU internal energy

heat ΔQ

Conservation of energy states that:

Heat transferred to a system (ΔQ) is equal to the sum of the increase of internal energy of the system (ΔU) and the work done by the system (ΔW):

$$\Delta Q = \Delta U + \Delta W$$

Sudden expansion of gases can produce dramatic cooling because there is no time for heat to flow into or out of the material ($\Delta Q = 0$). The material does work as it expands and pushes against atmospheric pressure. This work is done at the expense of the internal energy of the gas.

Sudden compression produces high temperatures in the same way. Diesel engines work by compressing the fuel–air mixture so quickly that work done on the gas is nearly all changed into internal energy. The temperature rise is enough to ignite the mixture.

When a fire extinguisher is activated, the sudden decompression causes dramatic cooling of the carbon dioxide which freezes temporarily into a fog of dry ice.

1 Why is there a difference between specific heat capacities (see Chapter 9, p. 132) measured at constant volume and at constant pressure?

2 Eighty joules of heat energy is supplied to 0.02 kg of air in a cylinder. The specific heat capacity (see Section 9.4) of air measured at constant volume is 700 J kg^{-1} K^{-1}. The temperature rises by 5 °C. How much work is done by the air as it expands?

exerting no pressure. Its molecules have stopped moving; they have no kinetic energy left. This is the lowest conceivable temperature: we call it **absolute zero**.

The pressure of the ideal gas is used as the thermometric property. This *constant-volume ideal gas thermometer* is calibrated with two fixed points:

● absolute zero – a theoretical fixed point. This is zero on the Kelvin scale.

● the triple point of water: the unique condition of pressure and temperature at which all three phases of water (ice, liquid and vapour) can exist in thermal equilibrium. You may not believe it is possible, but it *does* happen when pressure is only 0.6% of normal atmospheric pressure.

The triple point is chosen to be 273.16 on the Kelvin scale. This is done to make 1 kelvin the same size as 1 degree Celsius. On this scale, the ice point works out to be 273.15 K, so converting between Celsius temperatures

and Kelvin temperatures means adding or subtracting 273.15. To avoid confusion, it is usual to use θ for Celsius temperatures and T for temperatures on the Kelvin scale:

$$\theta \,(°C) = T \,(K) - 273.15$$

All temperatures on the Kelvin scale are then defined by the ratio of pressures in the constant-volume ideal gas thermometer:

$$\frac{P}{P_{triple}} = \frac{T}{T_{triple}}$$

so,

$$T = 273.16 \times \frac{P}{P_{triple}}$$

From this standard scale based on a standard instrument, real thermometers can be calibrated. This gives confidence that temperature measurements – while still arbitrary – are at least consistent.

3 What is the Celsius temperature of the triple point of water?

10.2 Kinetic theory for a theoretical gas

The early drive in cryogenic research was to test ideas about the nature of matter. One important question was: 'What does the concept of temperature mean on an atomic or molecular scale?'. The kinetic theory of gases has an answer to this. Kinetic theory is based on the idea that all matter is made up of atoms or molecules which are in constant movement.

The temperature of a substance is a measure of the average kinetic energy of its particles; the faster the particles move, the higher the temperature.

In fact, absolute temperature, T, is proportional to the average kinetic energy of

the molecules for an ideal gas. Absolute zero is therefore when all molecular motion has ceased, though in practice this can't happen.

The kinetic energy of the molecules in a gas is shared randomly between the molecules. At any time the actual distribution of molecular speeds is shown by the Maxwell distribution (Fig. 5). This is a theoretical result, based on statistical considerations, but it agrees well with experimental evidence.

Since the temperature is proportional to the average kinetic energy of the molecules, for a gas with molecules of mass m,

$$T \propto \langle \tfrac{1}{2}mc^2 \rangle$$

where the brackets < > denote the **mean** of the expression inside the brackets.

Since $\frac{1}{2}m$ is constant, $T \propto \frac{1}{2}m <c^2>$ or $T \propto \frac{1}{2}m\overline{c^2}$.

$\overline{c^2}$, read as c-squared-bar, is the mean-squared speed of the molecules. This is **not** the same as $(\overline{c})^2$, c-bar-squared, which is the mean speed squared – read the following example to see why.

Worked example

Suppose five people were moving at speeds of 1, 2, 3, 4 and 5 m s^{-1}, respectively. Calculate (a) their mean-squared speed and (b) their mean speed squared.

(a) mean-squared speed =
$1^2 + 2^2 + 3^2 + 4^2 + 5^2 / 5 = 11$ m^{2}s^{-2}.

(b) mean speed squared =
$((1 + 2 + 3 + 4 + 5)/5)^2 = 9$ m^{2}s^{-2}.
The square root of the mean-squared speed is called the root-mean-squared speed, r.m.s. speed. In this example the r.m.s. speed is $\sqrt{11} = 3.32$ m s^{-1}, compared to the mean speed of 3 m s^{-1}.

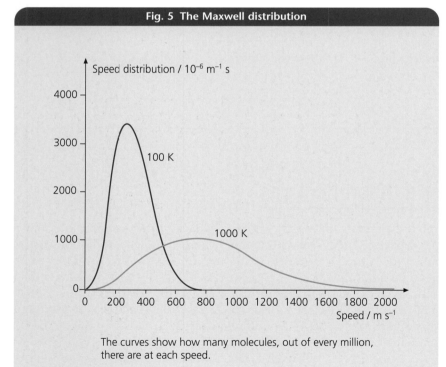

Fig. 5 The Maxwell distribution

Speed distribution / 10^{-6} m^{-1} s

100 K

1000 K

Speed / m s^{-1}

The curves show how many molecules, out of every million, there are at each speed.

Gases are the easiest system to analyse because the space between molecules is so large. The molecules spend most of their time flying around freely. The simplest possible gas would be made up of particles that:

- are very small so that most of their container is empty space;
- collide quickly and without energy loss, like perfect snooker balls;
- don't exert any inter-molecular forces except when they collide;
- are present in large numbers, so that statistics can be used;
- are moving in random directions.

You can calculate the expected behaviour of this theoretical gas by using basic Newtonian mechanics. The process is long (see Fig. 6), but the results are surprisingly simple:

pressure $= \frac{1}{3} \times$ density of gas $\times$ average of squared speeds of particles

$$p = \frac{1}{3}\rho\overline{c^2}$$

and

pressure $\times$ volume $= \frac{1}{3} \times$ number of particles $\times$ particle mass $\times$ average of squared speeds of particles

$$pV = \frac{1}{3}Nm\overline{c^2}$$

We know that at any particular temperature, the total kinetic energy of the particles is constant, and so the mean-squared speed will be constant. This theoretical gas therefore has the predicted property that:

$pV = $ constant

at any particular temperature. This fits well with experimental work with real gases. The inverse proportionality between pressure and volume is one of the earliest observed properties of real gases, a result published by Robert Boyle in 1662. We call it Boyle's law, but the French call it Mariotte's law. (Mariotte discovered the effect fifteen years later, but to be fair he did make the important qualification that temperature needed to be kept constant.)

Fig. 6 Applying the kinetic theory

1 Start with a single particle in a box

As the particle bounces inside the box, it hits the sides. On every collision, its momentum changes. The walls of the box exert a force on the particle. The walls of the box experience an equal but opposite force. If you calculate this pressure for one particle, you can estimate the pressure of all the particles in the gas.

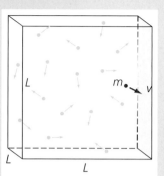

2 Find the force from a single collision

In the x direction, the momentum before the collision was mv_x. After the perfectly elastic collision, the particle is moving backwards at the same speed, so its momentum is $-mv_x$. The change of momentum is therefore $mv_x - (-mv_x) = 2mv_x$.

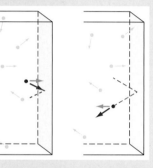

The particle strikes this face again after it has travelled to the other side of the box and back at speed v_x. This takes time $2L/v_x$.

Force is equal to the rate of change of momentum (Newton's second law), so the average force on the particle is:

$$F_1 = \frac{\text{change in momentum}}{\text{time}}$$

$$= \frac{2mv_x}{2L/v_x} = \frac{mv_x^2}{L}$$

3 Find the pressure for one particle

The wall of the container experiences a force of the same magnitude, so the pressure on it is:

$$\text{pressure} = \frac{\text{force}}{\text{area}}$$

$$p_1 = \frac{mv_x^2/L}{L^2} = \frac{mv_x^2}{L^3} = \frac{mv_x^2}{V}$$

where V is the volume of the box.

4 Add in all the other particles

$$p = p_1 + p_2 + p_3 + \ldots p_N$$

$$= \frac{mv_{x1}^2}{V} + \frac{mv_{x2}^2}{V} + \frac{mv_{x3}^2}{V} + \ldots + \frac{mv_{xN}^2}{V}$$

$$= \frac{m}{V}(v_{x1}^2 + v_{x2}^2 + v_{x3}^2 + \ldots + v_{xN}^2)$$

The quantity in brackets is the total speed squared in the x direction. We can rewrite this in terms of the average value:

$$\text{total} = N \times \text{average}$$

$$p = \frac{Nm\overline{v_x^2}}{V}$$

5 Take into account the other directions

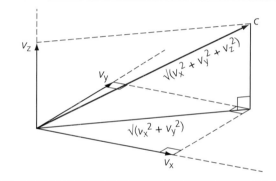

The particles move in random directions. Some will hit the walls head-on but others will only glance off. The speed c of the particle can be found by Pythagoras' theorem:

$$c^2 = v_x^2 + v_y^2 + v_z^2$$

The particles are equally likely to be travelling in any direction, so the average values of v_x^2, v_y^2 and v_z^2 will be the same. Then:

$$\overline{c^2} = 3\overline{v_x^2}$$

$$\text{so, } p = \frac{Nm}{V} \times \frac{\overline{c^2}}{3}$$

$$pV = \tfrac{1}{3}Nm\overline{c^2}$$

Nm is the total mass of the gas, so $\dfrac{Nm}{V} = \dfrac{\text{mass}}{\text{volume}} = \text{density}$

Then: $p = \tfrac{1}{3}\rho\overline{c^2}$

We can use the equations for a theoretical gas to calculate how fast air particles travel. Air at room temperature has a density of 1.20 kg m⁻³ at 1 atmosphere pressure (101 000 Pa).

From $p = \frac{1}{3}\rho\overline{c^2}$

$$\overline{c^2} = 3\frac{p}{\rho}$$

$$\sqrt{\overline{c^2}} = \sqrt{\frac{3 \times 101\,000 \text{ Pa}}{1.20 \text{ kg m}^{-3}}}$$

$$= 503 \text{ ms}^{-1}$$

Air molecules are therefore striking you at an average (r.m.s., or **root mean square**) speed of over 1800 km h⁻¹!

4 A cylinder contains dry air at a temperature of 120 K. The volume is reduced to half its initial value and the temperature allowed to return to 120 K. What has happened to:

a the pressure exerted by the gas;

b the density of the gas;

c the r.m.s. speed of the molecules?

5 Follow through the derivations in Fig. 6. Write down where the main assumptions of the kinetic theory are used.

10.3) The gas laws

Boyle's law apparatus shows the relationship between pressure and volume.

volume = 19.5 cm³
pressure = 280 kPa

volume = 45 cm³
pressure = 120 kPa

Researchers in the eighteenth century found that most gases behave in similar ways. The similarities become even greater when the gases are hot and at low pressure – when the molecules are a long way apart. In these conditions, you get an 'ideal' behaviour, and the gases were found to obey three simple laws.

1. Boyle's law

Boyle's law – that pressure was inversely proportional to volume – came from experimental observations on real gases. Most gases give a close approximation to the rule that $p \times V$ is constant at any fixed temperature (Fig. 7).

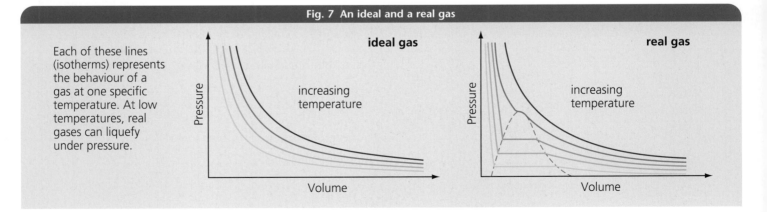

Fig. 7 An ideal and a real gas

Each of these lines (isotherms) represents the behaviour of a gas at one specific temperature. At low temperatures, real gases can liquefy under pressure.

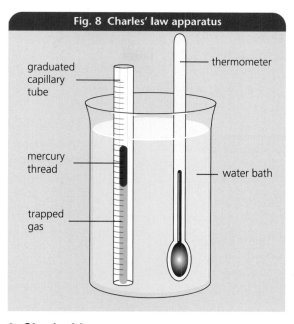

Fig. 8 Charles' law apparatus

- graduated capillary tube
- thermometer
- mercury thread
- water bath
- trapped gas

2. Charles' law

In about 1787, the French physicist Jacques Charles discovered that different gases, kept at constant pressure, all expand by the same amount. For every degree they get warmer, they expand by about 1/273 of their volume at 0 °C. Research at low temperatures has confirmed that this rule holds at temperatures close to absolute zero for gases at low pressure. If you measure temperature on the Kelvin scale, Charles' law becomes simply: *volume is proportional to temperature.*

3. The pressure–temperature law

If a gas is trapped in a container of fixed size, its pressure will go up when temperature rises. This observation forms the basis of the constant-volume gas thermometer, which is used to define the Kelvin temperature scale. If we measure temperature on the Kelvin scale, pressure is by definition proportional to temperature (for a fixed volume of gas).

The ideal gas equation

An ideal gas is one which obeys these three laws exactly. For a fixed mass of dry gas:

$$p \propto \frac{1}{V} \quad \text{constant } T$$
$$p \propto T \quad \text{constant } V$$
$$V \propto T \quad \text{constant } p$$

These can all be combined into one equation $pV = RT$ where R is a constant. If any one of the variables is held constant, the appropriate gas law follows.

For a given pressure and temperature, the volume is proportional to the amount of gas present. Early in the investigation into gases, it was discovered that all gases have approximately the same volume for one mole of gas. One mole of material has a mass of M grams, where M is the molecular mass in unified mass units. So, one mole of helium-4 has a mass of 4 g. The constant R for one mole of gas is therefore independent of the type of gas. We call it the **universal molar gas constant**. It has the value 8.314 J mol^{-1} K^{-1}. For n moles of gas:

$$pV = nRT$$

This equation is called the **equation of state** for an ideal gas. Although it works well for real gases at low pressures and high temperatures, the accuracy becomes poor if the gas is close to liquefying (Fig. 9).

The ideal gas equation is often used in problems where an amount of gas moves from one state (p_1, V_1, T_1) to another (p_2, V_2, T_2). In these problems it is often easier to use the equation as:

$$\frac{p_1 V_1}{T_1} = \frac{p_2 V_2}{T_2}$$

With the equation in this ratio form, non-SI units can be used. For example, pressures could be in atmospheres and volumes in litres. Care is needed with temperature, however: proportionality only applies if temperature is measured from absolute zero.

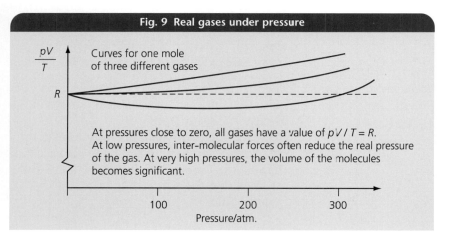

Fig. 9 Real gases under pressure

$\frac{pV}{T}$

Curves for one mole of three different gases

R

At pressures close to zero, all gases have a value of $pV / T = R$. At low pressures, inter-molecular forces often reduce the real pressure of the gas. At very high pressures, the volume of the molecules becomes significant.

100   200   300
Pressure/atm.

For example, suppose air in a cylinder at 27 °C and 2 atmospheres pressure is cooled to –173 °C and reduced to half its volume (Fig. 10). What would the new pressure be?

$p_1 = 2$ atm. $V_1 = 2$ units $T_1 = 27\,°C = 300\,K$

$p_2 = ?$ $V_2 = 1$ unit $T_2 = -173\,°C = 100\,K$

Using $\dfrac{p_1 V_1}{T_1} = \dfrac{p_2 V_2}{T_2}$

$$\frac{2\text{ atm.} \times 2\text{ units}}{300\text{ K}} = \frac{p_2 \times 1\text{ unit}}{100\text{ K}}$$

$$p_2 = 1.33\text{ atm.}$$

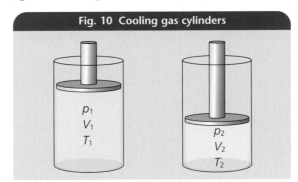

Fig. 10 Cooling gas cylinders

p_1
V_1
T_1

p_2
V_2
T_2

6 Use the equation of state to calculate the volume of one mole of ideal gas at standard temperature and pressure (s.t.p. = 273.15 K and 1.013×10^5 Pa). Convert your answer to litres. (1 m³ = 1000 l)

7 Calculate to see if air is an ideal gas. (One mole of dry air has a mass of 28.97 grams and its density at s.t.p. is 1.293 kg m⁻³.)

10.4 Molecular energies

When substances get cold, most of their properties change. They become stiffer, denser, more brittle, better electrical conductors, and so on. One property which changes surprisingly little is the heat capacity of gases. Can we explain this with the simple theories we have built up so far?

Kinetic theory gives us a formula which links pressure, volume and the speed of molecules. The equation of state links pressure, volume and temperature. The similarity of the two equations leads us to the tempting conclusion that the kinetic theory is the right answer – it successfully describes the behaviour of gases. The equations allow us to make testable predictions about energies of the molecules of gases. Consider one mole of gas.

equation of state predicts: $pV_m = RT$

kinetic theory predicts: $pV_m = \frac{1}{3} N_A m \overline{c^2}$

If we assume that the kinetic theory is the correct description of an ideal gas, these two equations should be equivalent. This allows us to find the mean kinetic energy of a gas molecule:

$$RT = \tfrac{1}{3} N_A m \overline{c^2} = \tfrac{2}{3} N_A \tfrac{1}{2} m \overline{c^2}$$

So,

$$\tfrac{1}{2} m \overline{c^2} = \frac{3RT}{2N_A} = \tfrac{3}{2} kT \quad \text{where} \quad k = \frac{R}{N_A}$$

(The ratio R/N_A is called the **Boltzmann constant**, k.) This last equation leads to predictions about the heat capacities of different gases. The molar heat capacity is the amount of energy needed to raise the temperature of 1 mole by 1 K:

$$\text{molar heat capacity} = \frac{\text{energy change}}{\text{temperature rise}}$$

$$= \frac{N_A \times \dfrac{3R\Delta T}{2N_A}}{\Delta T} = \tfrac{3}{2} R$$

This gives two surprising predictions:

- that **molar heat capacity** does not depend on temperature;
- that all gases will have the same molar heat capacity.

The first prediction matches observations quite well, at least where gases are behaving ideally. The second observation does not. However, the theory can be made to match observations accurately by taking into account the shapes of molecules – the kinetic theory assumed that the particles concerned were perfect spheres.

The simple particle of an ideal gas has an average energy $\frac{3}{2}kT$. It can only use this energy as kinetic energy along the x, y and z axes – each axis receives $\frac{1}{2}kT$ of energy. Larger molecules are also able to rotate and vibrate. These extra 'degrees of freedom' also take up $\frac{1}{2}kT$ of energy. When the degrees of freedom are considered, the theoretical predictions are impressively accurate (Table 1).

Table 1 Heat capacity of gases

Gas	Degrees of freedom	Molar heat capacity / J mol^{-1} K^{-1}	
		Predicted	Actual
He	3	20.8	20.96
Ar	3	20.8	20.93
H_2	5	29.1	28.6
O_2	5	29.1	29.2
N_2	5	29.1	29.1

Values measured at s.t.p.

KEY FACTS

■ The kinetic theory model of a gas assumes a large number of perfectly elastic point masses in rapid random motion. Newtonian mechanics and statistics can be used on a particle in a box to predict that:

$$p = \frac{1}{3}\rho\overline{c^2} \quad \text{and} \quad pV = \frac{1}{3}Nm\overline{c^2}$$

■ Ideal gases obey the equation of state $pV = nRT$. Real gases at low pressure and high temperature (well away from liquefying) obey the equation well. The equation is often used in the form:

$$\frac{p_1 V_1}{T_1} = \frac{p_2 V_2}{T_2}$$

■ The mean kinetic energy of an ideal gas molecule is:

$$\frac{3}{2}kT \quad \text{where} \quad k = \frac{R}{N_A}$$

(k is called Boltzmann's constant). Real gas molecules have more energy because of rotation and vibration.

Superconductivity

In this chapter, you have read about the mysterious world of cryogenics (low-temperature physics), where strange things happen to materials near absolute zero. The most significant effect is probably the development of superconductivity. This is not just of scientific interest; we are now finding applications for materials which have no electrical resistance. Power cables at normal temperatures lose about 10% of the power that passes along them due to resistance. A superconducting cable with zero resistance could save valuable energy and so reduce the need for power stations which often release polluting gases as a waste product of the generation process.

The challenge in recent years has been to develop materials which are superconducting at temperatures nearer to room temperature, as the cost of liquid helium to cool a cable is quite high (about £3 per litre in 2000). Liquid nitrogen (77 K) is a few pence per litre by comparison. Recently a mercury based cuprate oxide which is superconducting at temperatures as high as 135 K (165 K under pressure) has been developed. The problem is that many of these new superconducting materials are ceramics and therefore brittle; they are only superconducting where their grains touch. The amount of oxygen and its distribution in the copper oxide also affect the conductivity of the material dramatically. Below a critical value, superconductivity decreases and very small magnetic fields can affect the critical temperature at which the material becomes superconducting.

In spite of these problems, research into superconductivity continues apace – the value of a material that is superconducting at even slightly higher temperatures is so great a prize! Already we have produced very powerful magnets using superconducting materials. These superconducting magnets have the advantage that they use up hardly any power, because there is virtually no electrical resistance, and they do not get as hot as a conventional electromagnet. This property has found application in medical body scanners, e.g. the nuclear magnetic resonance (NMR) scanner. New materials using liquid nitrogen instead of liquid helium could save £17 000 of the annual running costs of a body scanner.

Other applications of superconductivity include:
- removing the magnetic contaminants from china clay which would otherwise dull its colour;
- the Maglev train in Japan which uses the Meissner effect to reduce the friction between conventional wheels and track by levitating it above the track;
- more powerful particle accelerators to give a better insight into the structure of matter and very fast switches for smaller, faster computers (Josephson junctions).

1 Prepare and write an extended essay about the story of superconductivity. You will need to research the following scientists who have made a contribution to the field of superconductivity: H. K. Onnes; Georg Bednorz & Alex Müller; Ching-Wu (Paul) Chu and colleagues. You will need to say what they did and how this has helped our understanding of superconductivity.

Your essay must be between 750 and 1000 words and include at least one diagram. You should also include a bibliography of all the sources that you consulted, including web sites, while you were researching your essay.

1 a

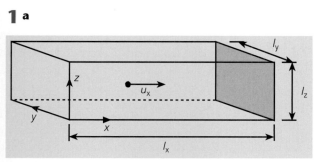

A single gas molecule of mass m is moving in a rectangular box with a velocity of u_x in the positive x-direction as shown in the diagram. The molecule moves backwards and forwards in the box, striking the end faces normally and making elastic collisions.

(i) Show that the time, t, between collisions with the shaded face is

$$t = \frac{2l_x}{u_x}$$

(ii) If it is assumed that the box contains N identical molecules, each of mass m, all moving parallel to the x-direction with speed u_x and making elastic collisions at the ends, show that the average force, F, on the shaded face is given by

$$F = \frac{Nmu_x^2}{l_x}$$

(iii) In a better model of molecular motion in gases, molecules of mean-squared speed $\overline{c^2}$ are assumed to move randomly in the box. By considering this random motion, show that a better expression for F is

$$F = \frac{Nm\overline{c^2}}{3\,lx}$$

and hence derive the equation

$$pV = \frac{1}{3}Nm\overline{c^2} \tag{9}$$

b Use data from the data booklet in this part of the question.

For 1.0 mol of helium at a temperature of 27 °C, calculate

(i) the total kinetic energy of the molecules,

(ii) the root mean square speed of the molecules. (4)

c 1.0 mol of the gas neon is mixed with the 1.0 mol of helium in part (b). Calculate the total kinetic energy of the molecules at 27 °C. (2)

2 a With reference to the appropriate physical principles, explain the following in terms of the motion of the gas molecules.

(i) A gas in the container exerts a pressure on the container walls.

(ii) The pressure increases if the temperature of a gas is increased, keeping the mass and volume constant. (7)

b (i) State what is meant by the root mean square speed of the molecules of a gas.

(iii) Calculate the r.m.s. speed of four molecules travelling at speeds of 400, 450, 500 and 550 m s^{-1}, respectively. (2)

c For a constant mass of gas, explain how the r.m.s. speed of the molecules changes, if at all, when

(i) the gas expands at constant temperature,

(ii) the gas expands by pushing back a piston so that work is done without heat entering or leaving the system. (3)

d The broadening of a line in the visible spectrum is proportional to the r.m.s. speed of the atoms emitting the light. Determine which source would have the greater broadening: a mercury source at 300 K or a krypton source at 77 K.

Support your answer with a calculation.

molar mass of mercury = 0.200 kg mol^{-1}

molar mass of krypton = 0.083 kg mol^{-1} (3)

3 a The equation of state of an ideal gas is

$$pV = nRT.$$

For each of these symbols, state the physical quantity and the SI unit. (4)

b An ideal gas of volume 1.0×10^{-4} m^3 is trapped by a piston in a cylinder. There is negligible friction between the piston and the cylinder. Initially, the temperature of the gas is 20 °C and the external atmospheric pressure acting on the piston is 100 kPa.

The gas expands slowly when heat is supplied by an electric heater inside the cylinder.

(i) Calculate the work done by the gas when its volume slowly increases by 5.0×10^{-5} m^3, at constant pressure, while being heated.

(ii) What is the temperature of the gas, in °C, following its expansion?

(iii) Describe **two** changes that occur in the motion of a typical molecule of the gas during the expansion. (8)

In the UK 1500 people die of asthma every year. Air filtration masks are increasingly popular in smog-ridden cities such as Los Angeles.

Exhaust emissions from cars account for much of the airborne pollution of cities. About 90% of atmospheric carbon monoxide comes from car exhausts. The poisonous gas can kill red blood cells. Nitrogen oxides at levels of only two parts per million are enough to trigger an asthma attack. About half of the nitrogen oxides in the UK come from car exhausts. Unburnt hydrocarbons from vehicle exhausts are responsible for corrosive and irritant 'petrochemical smog' in cities throughout the world.

In an effort to reduce vehicle-related pollution, the state of California has laid down strict requirements for car exhaust emissions. By the year 2003, 10% of cars sold in California must be 'zero-emission'. Electrically powered vehicles seem to offer the best chance of meeting these requirements. However, electrically powered vehicles have disadvantages compared to conventional petrol driven vehicles. They tend to have a limited range, and they need to carry heavy, bulky batteries. Even so, the major car manufacturers of the world are taking the challenge seriously. In late 1999 General Motors released their new EV1, an electric car which sells for around $34 000.

The EV1 boasts a maximum power output of 102 kilowatts and a range of approximately 100 miles between charges. It is designed to be recharged overnight, using off-peak electricity. Cars like this may well become a common sight over the next few years.

The EV1 from General Motors has a top speed of 80 mph and no exhaust pipe!

11.1 Power and energy

In 1899 an electrically powered car, *La Jamais Contente*, set the land speed record at 105 kilometres per hour.

Electric cars have been around for a hundred years, but they have always had a major disadvantage compared to petrol engines. Chemical fuels offer a more compact energy store than batteries; a litre of petrol has roughly the same energy content as 100 kg of lead–acid batteries. The main problem with electric cars lies in storing enough energy to transfer rapidly into kinetic energy.

Scientists use the word **power** to describe the rate of transfer of energy:

$$\text{Power} = \frac{\text{energy transferred}}{\text{time}} \quad or \quad \frac{\text{work done}}{\text{time taken}}$$

$$P = \frac{\Delta W}{\Delta t}$$

Energy transferred, or work done, is measured in joules (J); power is measured in watts (W). One watt is a power output of 1 joule per second.

Table 1 Power – orders of magnitude	
light emitting diode dashboard warning light	~ milliwatts (mW)
car radio	~ watts
car headlamps	~ 100 W
sports car petrol engine	~ 100 kW

Table 2 Typical vehicle specifications		
	Electric car	Petrol car
top speed	80 km h^{-1}	140 km h^{-1}
acceleration to 50 km h^{-1}	10 s	5 s
carrying capacity	250 kg	400 kg
vehicle mass	1000 kg	900 kg

An alternative unit of energy is the kilowatt hour. This is equivalent to a power of 1 kW transferring energy for 1 hour. (1 kWh = 1000 W × 3600 s = 3.6 MJ.)

1. A typical family uses about 1000 kWh of energy every 3 months. How many joules of energy is this?

2. An electric light bulb has a power of 100 W. If it is left on all day (24 hours) how much energy does it transfer? Give your answer in joules and in kilowatt hours.

3. The electric car EV1 has a nickel–metal hydride battery pack which has a capacity of 26.4 kW hours. How many joules of energy is this?

Most motorists want cars with a reasonable top speed and adequate acceleration. These factors depend on the car's power and its mass.

Electric cars tend to be heavier because of the mass of the batteries (Table 2). An idea of the power needed by a vehicle to accelerate can be found by calculating the change in kinetic energy. For example, what power is needed to accelerate a 1000 kg car to 50 km h^{-1} in 10 seconds?

Kinetic energy at 50 km h^{-1} = $\frac{1}{2} mv^2$

$$v = 50 \text{ km h}^{-1} = \frac{50\,000 \text{ m}}{3600 \text{ s}}$$
$$= 13.9 \text{ m s}^{-1}$$

$$E_k = \frac{1}{2} mv^2$$
$$= \frac{1}{2} \times 1000 \text{ kg} \times (13.9 \text{ m s}^{-1})^2$$
$$= 96\,600 \text{ J}$$

$$P = \frac{\Delta W}{\Delta t}$$
$$= \frac{96\,600 \text{ J}}{10 \text{ s}}$$
$$= 9660 \text{ W, or } 9.7 \text{ kW}$$

This is actually an underestimate because the calculation ignores energy transferred because of friction and air resistance.

4 Work out the electric vehicle's kinetic energy at its top speed. How long would it take to reach top speed at a constant power of 9.7 kW? (Ignore work done against friction, etc.)

5 A sports car has the same mass as the electric vehicle but a more powerful engine. How will this affect:

a its acceleration?

b its kinetic energy at 50 km h^{-1}?

c its top speed?

EXTENSION **The efficiency of a car**

The EV1 is the most aerodynamic production vehicle on the road today. It has a drag coefficient which is 25% lower than any other production vehicle. It is shaped like a tear drop when viewed from above. In fact, the rear wheels are 9 inches closer together than the front wheels, which gives the tear drop shape. The EV1 is the world's most energy-efficient vehicle.

Efficiency measures how much of the energy supplied is transferred into a useful form. For example, an electric light bulb transfers electrical energy into light and heat. However, a 100 W light bulb only transfers about 5 W as useful light energy, the rest is transferred to the surroundings as heat. We say that the light bulb is 5% efficient.

$$\text{Efficiency} = \frac{\text{useful power output}}{\text{total power input}} \times 100\%$$

Or

$$\text{Efficiency} = \frac{\text{useful energy output}}{\text{total energy input}} \times 100\%$$

A perfectly efficient machine, efficiency = 100%, would transfer all the input energy (or power) into useful output energy (or power).

The useful output energy of a car may be kinetic, or potential, when the vehicle is climbing a hill. Suppose an electric car of mass 800 kg climbs a 10% gradient at 10 m s^{-1}. The input electrical power to the motors is 12 kW.

In 1 second, the increase in potential energy is:

$$mg\Delta h = 800 \text{ kg} \times 10 \text{ m s}^{-2} \times 1 \text{ m} = 8000 \text{ J}$$

$$P = \frac{\Delta W}{\Delta t} = \frac{mg\Delta h}{\Delta t}$$
$$= \frac{800 \text{ kg} \times 10 \text{ ms}^{-2} \times 1 \text{ m}}{1 \text{ s}}$$
$$= 8 \text{ kW}$$

$$\text{efficiency} = \frac{\text{power output}}{\text{power input}}$$
$$= \frac{8 \text{ kW}}{12 \text{ kW}}$$
$$= 0.67, \text{ or } 67\%$$

Petrol engines are only about 30–40% efficient. Electric motors can increase their overall efficiency by acting in reverse, as generators. During braking, the electric motor generates electricity which is then used to partially recharge the battery pack.

6 A petrol-powered car holds about 50 litres of petrol in its tank. Each litre of petrol represents 50 MJ of chemical energy. The car is 30% efficient and has a mass of 1000 kg. It can accelerate to 25 m s^{-1} in 10 s.

a Calculate the average useful power output of the car during acceleration (neglect any work done against drag forces).

b Calculate the necessary power input and use this to find the rate at which petrol is used during this 10-second period. How many times could the car repeat this acceleration on one full tank of petrol?

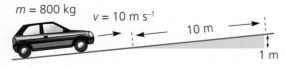

$m = 800$ kg $v = 10$ m s^{-1} 10 m   1 m

11.2 Electric current and potential difference

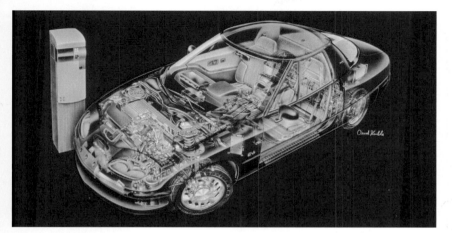

The EV1 has a modern nickel–metal hydride battery pack which has a mass of 521 kg and a capacity of 26.4 kW hours (about 100 MJ).

A petrol driven car can deliver around 600 MJ of energy from a tank of fuel. This compares to about 25 MJ of useful energy from about half a tonne of lead–acid batteries. The electric car of the future needs a lightweight battery with a high energy capacity.

Batteries are chemical reactors which transfer energy as electricity. But what does that mean?

Charge

Electricity concerns the flow of charge in a circuit. Objects which feel electrical forces possess electrical charge. Charge is a fundamental property of matter, like mass. We know that particles can have different amounts of mass and that masses are affected by gravitational forces. In a similar way, particles can have different amounts of charge and can be affected by electric forces. Particles can have either positive or negative charge. Particles with the same sort of charge will repel each other and particles with opposite charges attract.

Atoms have negatively charged electrons which are held close to the positively charged nucleus of the atom. Atoms as a whole are electrically neutral; there is no net charge.

If an electron is added to an atom, a negative ion is formed. A positive ion is created by taking an electron away from a neutral atom (Fig. 1). Batteries transfer charge between ions in chemical reactions. We measure charge in coulombs (C). The charge of one electron is only 1.6×10^{-19} C.

7 How many electrons make up a charge of 1 coulomb?

Charging conductors and insulators

A material which does not readily conduct electricity, such as glass or plastic, is known as an **insulator**. Insulators do not allow charges to flow through them.

In metals, some electrons are free to move around between the atoms. This enables metals to conduct electricity. If a conductor is placed near an electric charge, charges can be induced on the conductor (Fig. 3).

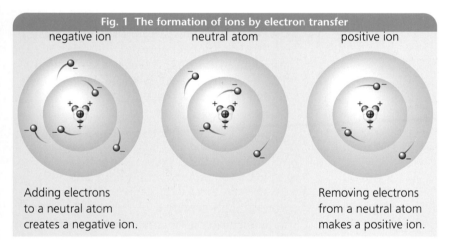

Fig. 1 The formation of ions by electron transfer

negative ion   neutral atom   positive ion

Adding electrons to a neutral atom creates a negative ion.

Removing electrons from a neutral atom makes a positive ion.

Fig. 2 Charging an insulator using friction

Some non-conductors or insulators can be electrically charged by friction. When a balloon is rubbed with a dry cloth, some of the electrons on the surface of the balloon move to the cloth, leaving the balloon with a net positive charge. If the cloth was insulated, it would now be negatively charged. However, you are quite a good conductor, so this negative charge passes through your body to Earth.

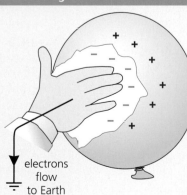

electrons flow to Earth

Fig. 3 Induced charge

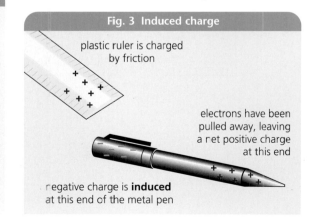

plastic ruler is charged by friction

electrons have been pulled away, leaving a net positive charge at this end

negative charge is **induced** at this end of the metal pen

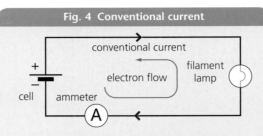

Fig. 4 Conventional current

We traditionally show current moving in the direction that positive charges would move. This is known as conventional current. In a metal wire it is actually the negative charges (the electrons) that move the other way, but this has the same effect.

Current

Current is a flow of charged particles of any sort. For example, positive and negative ions moving through a battery produce a current. Current is measured in amperes (A).

A current of 1 ampere means that 1 coulomb of charge passes a given point in a circuit every second.

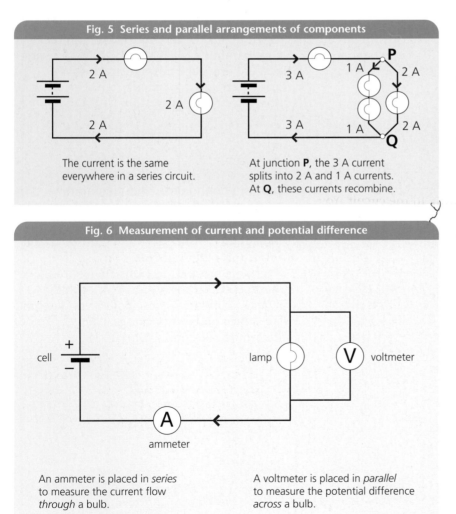

Fig. 5 Series and parallel arrangements of components

The current is the same everywhere in a series circuit.

At junction **P**, the 3 A current splits into 2 A and 1 A currents. At **Q**, these currents recombine.

Fig. 6 Measurement of current and potential difference

An ammeter is placed in *series* to measure the current flow *through* a bulb.

A voltmeter is placed in *parallel* to measure the potential difference *across* a bulb.

Current is the rate of flow of charge.

In symbols this is written: $I = \dfrac{\Delta Q}{\Delta t}$

Any charge which flows into a component must also flow back out. Therefore, in a series circuit the current is the same all around the circuit. Where it splits into several branches, the total current must stay the same.

8 In 2 seconds, 5 coulombs of positive particles flow to the right and 5 coulombs of negative particles flow to the left (Fig. 5). Is there any current? If so, how much and in which direction is the conventional current flowing?

9 If 32 coulombs of charge flow into a motor in 0.2 seconds, what is the current?

Capacity

One of the most useful things to know about a battery is its capacity. Capacity is measured in ampere-hours (A h). One ampere-hour means a current of 1 A can flow for 1 hour, or 0.5 A for 2 hours, etc. The capacity is a measure of the total amount of charge which the battery can push around a circuit.

The battery pack for the prototype Vauxhall 'Astra Impuls II' has a capacity of 42.5 A h. This battery therefore delivers the equivalent of 42.5 A of current for 1 hour. Using charge = current × time:

charge = 42.5 A × 3600 s = 153 000 C

When this battery is discharged, 153 000 coulombs could flow around the circuit.

Potential difference

In an electric car, energy from the battery is transferred into kinetic energy. The amount of energy that is transferred when unit charge moves between two points in a circuit is represented by the **potential difference**, or **p.d.** (sometimes called the voltage).

Electrical p.d. is similar to gravitational p.d. If you drop something, its gravitational potential energy changes to kinetic energy as it falls. The higher you lift the object, the greater its final velocity and the higher the energy with which it hits the ground. In the same way, a higher electrical p.d. tends to make charge move faster.

The unit of potential difference is the volt (V). When a charge of 1 coulomb passes

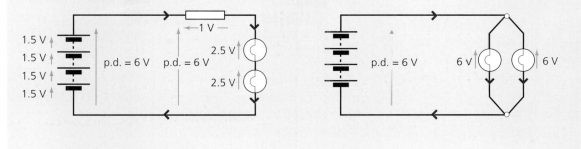

Fig. 7 Potential difference

Potential differences across series circuits simply add up.

1.5 V
1.5 V   p.d. = 6 V   p.d. = 6 V
1.5 V
1.5 V

1 V

2.5 V

2.5 V

Potential differences across parallel components are equal.

p.d. = 6 V   6 V   6 V

through a potential difference of 1 volt, it does 1 joule of work. This is how physicists define the volt.

$$\text{potential difference (V)} = \frac{\text{work done (J)}}{\text{charge (C)}}$$

$$V = \frac{W}{Q}$$

Potential difference is measured using a voltmeter connected in parallel with the component. Since p.d. is a measure of the difference across a component, the probes are placed on either side of the component (Fig. 6).

Power

The power delivered by a battery depends on the p.d. between the terminals and the amount of current flowing in the circuit. You can combine the definitions of current and p.d. to derive the equation for electrical power.

Suppose a current of I amperes flows through a p.d. of V volts for t seconds.

We can deduce an equation for power output:

$$\text{From } P = \frac{W}{t}, \ V = \frac{W}{Q} \text{ and } I = \frac{Q}{t},$$

$$P = \frac{QV}{t}$$

$$= \frac{ItV}{t}$$

$$= IV$$

So, power = current × voltage

This formula will help you to calculate the current passing through any device. This is important when selecting the right thickness of cable or the correct fuse. For example, the

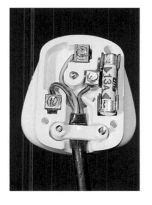

The standard ratings for cartridge fuses in a three-pin plug are 3A, 5A and 13A.

electrical power supplied to a light bulb is typically about 100 W. The domestic mains voltage in this country is 240 V, so the current passing through the light bulb is:

$I = P/V = 100\,\text{W}/240\,\text{V} = 0.42\,\text{A}.$

Since it is sensible to select the smallest possible fuse that will carry the required current, a 2 A fuse could be used for this bulb if it were to be used in a table lamp.

10 Find the current drawn by a 1400 W vacuum cleaner. What fuse would you use for the vacuum cleaner?

11 Electric showers are high power appliances, typically 7 kW. Find the current supplied to an electric shower. Why are electric showers not connected via a standard three-pin plug?

Energy in electric car batteries

Under the bonnet of Fiat's 'Downtown'.

Energy storage

Fiat intend to use a sodium–sulphur battery in the 'Downtown' electric car. The battery has a rating of 108 V and a capacity of 160 A h. How much energy is stored in this battery? First we need to calculate how much charge the battery delivers. A capacity of 160 A h means 160 A for 1 hour. Since charge = current × time, this gives

$$Q = 160\,A \times 3600\,s = 576\,000\,C$$

108 V means that each coulomb of charge transfers 108 J from the battery to the circuit. From $V = W/Q$:

Energy = potential difference × charge = $V \times Q$

Available energy: $W = 108\,V \times 576\,000\,C$
$$= 62.2\,MJ$$

12 A charge of 2 C was moved through a p.d. of 160 V in an electric motor. How much energy was transferred?

13 In a battery charger, a current of 3 A flowed through a p.d. of 12 V for 5 seconds.

a What charge passed?

b How much energy was converted?

c Calculate the power (using energy/time).

Recharging the battery

The Fiat Panda Elettra has a 72 V, 13.6 kWh battery and an electric motor rated at 9.2 kW. How long would it take to recharge the battery with a charger rated at 220 V, 8 A?

First we need to find the current that passes through the battery. For the motor $P = IV$:

$$9.2\,kW = I \times 72\,V$$

$$I = \frac{9200\,W}{72\,W} = 128\,A$$

Then find the power of the charger:

$$P = IV = 8\,A \times 220\,V = 1760\,W$$

Now find out how long it takes to deliver the energy needed:

Power = W/t; $1760\,W = 13.6\,kWh/t$

so $t = \dfrac{13.6 \times 1000 \times 36\,000\,J}{1760\,W}$

$$= 27\,800\,s,\ or\ 7.7\ hours\ to\ recharge.$$

With this powerful battery charger, an overnight charge would be just enough.

14 The General Motors EV1 has a nickel–metal hydride battery with a capacity of 77 A h at 343 V. The battery charger operates at 220 V, 30 A.

a Calculate the energy stored by the battery.

b Calculate the time taken to recharge the battery.

11.3 Resistance

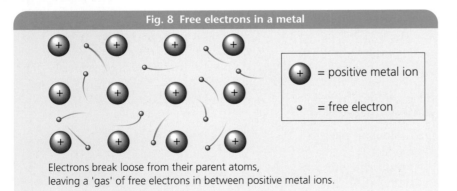

Fig. 8 Free electrons in a metal

● = positive metal ion

∘ = free electron

Electrons break loose from their parent atoms, leaving a 'gas' of free electrons in between positive metal ions.

Resistance of metals

Metals are the most common conductors used in electrical circuits. They are good conductors of electricity because of the presence of free electrons which can move between the positively charged metal ions (Fig. 8).

A potential difference applied across the metal sets up an **electric field**. This makes the electrons accelerate until they collide with positive ions in the metal. The electrons then

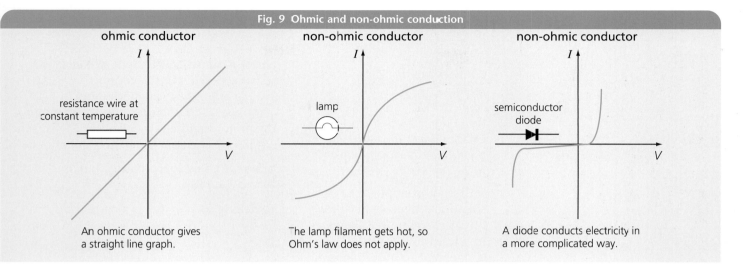

Fig. 9 Ohmic and non-ohmic conduction

ohmic conductor	non-ohmic conductor	non-ohmic conductor
resistance wire at constant temperature	lamp	semiconductor diode
An ohmic conductor gives a straight line graph.	The lamp filament gets hot, so Ohm's law does not apply.	A diode conducts electricity in a more complicated way.

accelerate and collide again with other positive ions. All these collisions mean that the wire resists the flow of electrons. Therefore, a potential difference is needed across the conductor to keep the current flowing – i.e. to replace the energy lost by the electrons in collisions.

The energy lost by the electrons is transferred to the positive ions as vibrational energy so the wire gets hotter. More current would mean more collisions and so more heating.

A resistor transfers electricity to heat energy. This can be exploited in vehicle design: e.g. in heating elements for a windscreen demister. However, resistive heating of wires is one of the main causes of inefficiency in electric motors.

Ohm's law

In 1827, Georg Simon Ohm showed that the current flowing through a metal conductor was proportional to the p.d. across the conductor (Fig. 9). This simple rule holds for metals and a few other substances, but only under limited conditions. The rule breaks down if temperature changes. Other physical conditions, such as light intensity, pressure, strain and magnetic fields, can affect the resistance of some materials. There are some things (water, electrolytes, semiconductor diodes, light bulbs) for which the rule does

not work at all. These are called non-ohmic conductors.

Ohm's law must be stated very cautiously: 'Provided that temperature and other physical conditions remain constant, the current through a conductor is proportional to the potential difference across the conductor.'

If a component is a good resistor, it needs a high p.d. to make a current flow. A good conductor only needs a small p.d. to make the same current flow. The ratio of p.d. to current is the resistance of a conductor:

$$resistance = \frac{potential\ difference}{current}$$

$$R = \frac{V}{I}, I = \frac{V}{R} \text{ or } V = IR$$

Resistance is measured in ohms (Ω). A resistance of $1\,\Omega$ would need a p.d. of $1\,V$ to make a current of $1\,A$ flow through it.

15 A vehicle designer wants resistance to be low for connecting wires for the main drive motor. Why? Use the information in Table 3 to estimate the p.d. across 1 metre of both sorts of copper connecting wire when the current is $100\,A$.

16 The p.d. across a heating element is $4\,V$ when $6\,A$ flows. What will the p.d. be when $9\,A$ flows? What have you assumed?

Table 3 Orders of magnitude of resistance relating to electric vehicles	
1 m copper connecting wire from battery to motor	$\sim 0.002\,\Omega$
1 m copper connecting wire from battery to headlights	$\sim 0.1\,\Omega$
PVC insulation between adjacent wires	$\sim 1\,M\Omega$

11.4 Power and resistance

'I need to connect lots of batteries together for use in a prototype electric car. Should I connect them all in series and risk a dangerously high voltage? Or would it be better to put them in parallel, and have very high currents?'

This is an example of a situation where we need to calculate the power dissipated in a resistor. It is often convenient to use equations which relate power and resistance directly.

We know: $P = IV$ and $V = IR$

Eliminating V gives: $P = I \times IR$
$$P = I^2R$$
Eliminating I gives: $P = \dfrac{V}{R} V$
$$P = V^2/R$$

The battery modules in an electric vehicle could all be connected in series or in parallel. The total energy storage in either case would be the same, but the p.d. across the cells would be different. The series (high p.d. or 'voltage') arrangement would be more dangerous for service engineers: high voltages cause electric shocks. To deliver the same power to the motor, we can see from the equation $P = IV$ that the parallel (low voltage) arrangement would need to provide a much bigger current. This current would cause resistive heating of the connecting wires. Would this be a severe limitation?

Suppose wires connecting the battery to the motor in an electric van have a resistance of $0.005\,\Omega$ and that the battery supplies 6 kW.

In the series case, the battery p.d. is $28 \times 6\,\text{V} = 168\,\text{V}$.

To deliver 6 kW requires a current of:

$$I = \frac{P}{V}$$
$$= \frac{6000\ \text{W}}{168\ \text{V}} = 35.7\ \text{A}$$

Then the power lost in the wires is:

$$P = I^2R$$
$$= (35.7\ \text{A})^2 \times 0.005\ \Omega = 6.4\ \text{W}$$

The efficiency of energy transfer is:

$$\text{efficiency} = \frac{6000\ \text{W} - 6.4\ \text{W}}{6000\ \text{W}}$$
$$= 0.999 \text{ or } 99.9\%$$

In the parallel case, the battery p.d. is 6 V. To deliver 6 kW requires a current of:

$$I = \frac{P}{V}$$
$$= \frac{6000\ \text{W}}{6\ \text{V}} = 1000\ \text{A}$$

Then the power lost in the wires is:

$$P = I^2R$$
$$= (1000\ \text{A})^2 \times 0.005\ \Omega = 5000\ \text{W}$$

The efficiency of energy transfer is:

$$\text{efficiency} = \frac{6000\ \text{W} - 5000\ \text{W}}{6000\ \text{W}}$$
$$= 0.167 \text{ or } 16.7\%$$

It is clear that the series arrangement is preferable in electric cars despite the risk of electric shock. The dramatic difference of efficiency (16.7% compared with 99.9%) could be overcome by making the connecting wires thicker, but this would add weight and cost more.

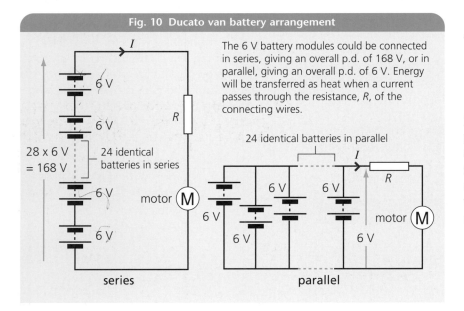

Fig. 10 Ducato van battery arrangement

The 6 V battery modules could be connected in series, giving an overall p.d. of 168 V, or in parallel, giving an overall p.d. of 6 V. Energy will be transferred as heat when a current passes through the resistance, R, of the connecting wires.

series

parallel

17 An engineer suggests a compromise arrangement of batteries in series and parallel as shown.

Calculate the efficiency of energy transfer for the same system using this arrangement of batteries. Comment on the safety and suitability of the proposal.

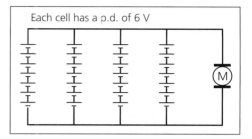
Each cell has a p.d. of 6 V

■ Conventional current flows from + to –.

■ Current, I, is the rate of flow of charge,

$$I = \frac{Q}{t}$$

■ Potential difference, V, is the energy per unit charge,

$$V = \frac{W}{Q}$$

■ Resistance, R, is a measure of a component's opposition to current,

$$R = \frac{V}{I}$$

■ Power, P, is the rate of transfer of energy,

$$P = \frac{E}{t} = IV = I^2R = \frac{V^2}{R}$$

11.5 Internal resistance and e.m.f.

You may have noticed that the lights go dim and the car stereo dies when the starter motor of a petrol-engined car is switched on. The battery has an **internal resistance** which is only significant when large currents are needed. The starter motor draws a very large current, over 100 A, and the internal resistance of the battery resists this flow. Energy is wasted as heat in the battery, leaving less energy available to the rest of the circuit. This dims the lights until the starter motor has finished starting the engine.

When a current flows in a circuit, work must be done by the battery to move the charge. We say that the battery produces an **electromotive force**, or e.m.f., which gives

each coulomb of charge the energy required to keep the current flowing.

$$\epsilon = \frac{E}{Q}$$

where ϵ = electromotive force
E = energy generated
Q = charge

However, a potential difference is needed to push current through the internal resistance of the battery. Energy is wasted by heating this resistance. When a current passes through the battery, the p.d. across its terminals (the **terminal p.d.**) is less than the e.m.f.

$$\text{p.d.}_{terminal} = \epsilon - \text{p.d.}_{internal\ resistance}$$

Fig. 11 Internal resistance and e.m.f.

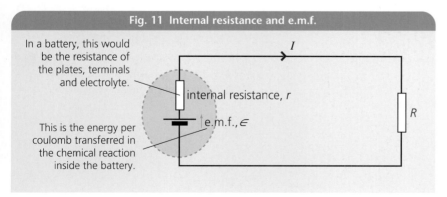

In a battery, this would be the resistance of the plates, terminals and electrolyte.

This is the energy per coulomb transferred in the chemical reaction inside the battery.

Table 4 The difference between e.m.f. and terminal p.d.		
	Energy	**Voltmeter**
e.m.f.	energy per coulomb produced by battery	reading across terminals when no current is flowing
terminal p.d.	energy per coulomb delivered to circuit	reading across terminals when current is flowing

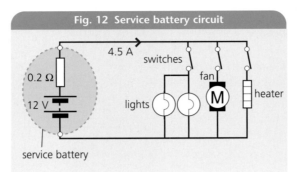

Fig. 12 Service battery circuit

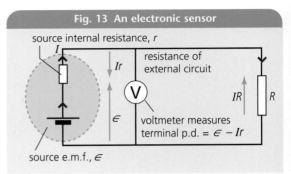

Fig. 13 An electronic sensor

The terminal p.d. depends on the current flowing. The efficiency of energy transfer to a circuit therefore depends on current. The larger the current flowing, the larger the energy lost in the internal resistance.

The service battery in an electric vehicle is used to operate the lights, fans, radio, etc. (see Fig. 12). The current through the service battery varies, depending on which devices are switched on. Suppose 4.5 A flows through a battery with internal resistance 0.2 Ω and e.m.f. of 12 V. How efficient is the battery at transferring energy to this circuit?

$$\text{p.d.}_{\text{internal resistance}} = IR$$
$$= 4.5\,\text{A} \times 0.2\,\Omega$$
$$= 0.9\,\text{V}$$

$$\text{p.d.}_{\text{terminal}} = \epsilon - \text{p.d.}_{\text{internal resistance}}$$
$$= 12\,\text{V} - 0.9\,\text{V}$$
$$= 11.1\,\text{V}$$

For every coulomb of charge which flows through it, the battery produces 12 J but only delivers 11.1 J. The efficiency is therefore:

$$\text{efficiency} = \frac{11.1\,\text{J}}{12\,\text{J}}$$
$$= 0.925 \text{ or } 92.5\%$$

18 What is the efficiency when 30 A flows through the battery?

In an electric car the motor current is large, so the power wasted in the internal resistance of the car battery will also be large. It is therefore important that the internal resistance is kept as low as possible in the main storage batteries. Even so, the batteries may need a cooling system.

E.m.f. and terminal p.d. calculations can often be solved using formulae.

$$\epsilon = \text{p.d.}_{\text{terminal}} + \text{p.d.}_{\text{internal resistance}}$$
$$= V + Ir$$
$$= IR + Ir$$
$$\epsilon = I(R + r)$$

This is the statement of Ohm's law for the whole circuit.

Example: An electronic sensor (Fig. 13) acts as a source of e.m.f. The p.d. across the sensor is 5.0 V when 1.2 mA flows but drops to 1.8 V when 3.0 mA flows. What is the internal resistance of the sensor?

From $\epsilon = V + Ir$

$$\epsilon = 5.0\,\text{V} + 0.0012\,\text{A} \times r$$
$$\epsilon = 1.8\,\text{V} + 0.0030\,\text{A} \times r$$

Eliminating ϵ,

$$5.0\,\text{V} + 0.0012\,\text{A} \times r = 1.8\,\text{V} + 0.0012\,\text{A} \times r$$

$$5.0\,\text{V} - 1.8\,\text{V} = 0.0030\,\text{A} \times r$$
$$- 0.0012\,\text{A} \times r$$

$$3.2\,\text{V} = 0.0018\,\text{A} \times r$$

$$r = \frac{3.2\,\text{V}}{0.0018\,\text{A}}$$

$$= 1777\,\Omega \text{ or } 1.8\,\text{k}\Omega$$

19 The current through an electric vehicle's main storage battery is 120 A, the terminal p.d. is 168 V and the internal resistance is 0.1 Ω. What is the e.m.f.?

20 A car battery delivers 112 W of power to a 7 Ω resistor. The e.m.f. of the battery is 30 V. What is the internal resistance?

11.6 Wiring it up

If you look at any car wiring diagram, you are confronted by a huge mass of circuitry and wire. Electronic circuits in an electric car are even more complicated. They would be impossible to follow if they couldn't be simplified to a few basic arrangements.

Resistors in series

The same current passes through all resistors in a series circuit. The p.d. across the whole series is the sum of the p.d.s across each resistor (Fig. 14).

Fig. 14 P.d. across resistors in series

The p.d. across the chain of resistors is the sum of the p.d.s across each of the resistors.

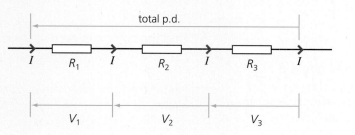

This arrangement could be replaced by a single resistor R_T which would pass the same current for the same total p.d.

$$R_T = \frac{\text{p.d.}_{total}}{\text{current}}$$
$$= \frac{V_1 + V_2 + V_3 + \cdots}{I}$$
$$= \frac{V_1}{I} + \frac{V_2}{I} + \frac{V_3}{I} + \cdots$$
$$R_T = R_1 + R_2 + R_3 + \cdots$$

Resistors in parallel

We can assume the connecting wires in circuit diagrams have no resistance. Therefore the p.d. across each parallel resistor is the same. The total current is the sum of the currents through each resistor (Fig. 15).

$$\text{total resistance } (R_T) = \frac{\text{p.d. } (V)}{\text{current } (I)}$$
$$I = \frac{V}{R_T}$$
$$\text{and } I = I_1 + I_2 + I_3 + \cdots$$
$$= \frac{V}{R_1} + \frac{V}{R_2} + \frac{V}{R_3} + \cdots$$
$$\text{so, } \frac{V}{R_T} = \frac{V}{R_1} + \frac{V}{R_2} + \frac{V}{R_3} + \cdots$$
$$\text{Divide by } V, \quad \frac{1}{R_T} = \frac{1}{R_1} + \frac{1}{R_2} + \frac{1}{R_3} + \cdots$$

For just two resistors, the formula
$$R_T = \frac{R_1 \times R_2}{R_1 + R_2}$$
is often easier to use, but it does not extend simply for more resistors.

Fig. 15 P.d. across parallel resistors

Parallel resistors have the same p.d. across them. The total current I is the sum of currents through each of the resistors.

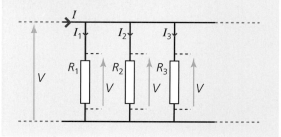

161

Fig. 16 Power and resistor arrangements

A demister is to be made up of $3\,\Omega$ and $6\,\Omega$ heating elements operated from a 12 V service battery of negligible internal resistance. Different powers could be obtained by using just one element or by combining the two in series or parallel. What would be the power in each case?

	total resistance	power = V^2/R
1 single A	$3\,\Omega$	$144/3 = 48\,W$
2 single B	$6\,\Omega$	$144/6 = 24\,W$
3 in series	$6 + 3 = 9\,\Omega$	$144/9 = 16\,W$
4 in parallel	$\frac{1}{R_T} = \frac{1}{6} + \frac{1}{3} = \frac{1}{2}$	
	$R_T = 2\,\Omega$	$144/2 = 72\,W$

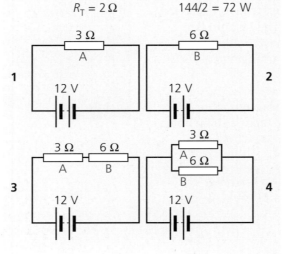

Combining series and parallel circuits

Real circuits can consist of a mixture of series and parallel elements. Suppose that the series arrangement of demister elements (Fig. 17) is connected in parallel with the rear-screen heating element which has a resistance of $1\,\Omega$. How could you calculate what current flows?

Fig. 17 Combined series and parallel circuits

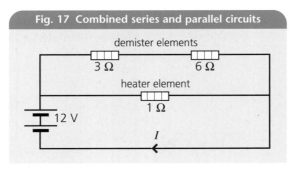

First, tackle series elements: the resistance of the top branch is $9\,\Omega$. Then add the parallel parts together: the total resistance is given by:

$$\frac{1}{R_T} = \frac{1}{R_1} + \frac{1}{R_2} = \frac{1}{9\,\Omega} + \frac{1}{1\,\Omega}$$

$$R_T = \frac{9\,\Omega}{10} = 0.90\,\Omega$$

So, $I = \frac{V}{R}$

$$= \frac{12\,V}{0.90\,\Omega} = 13.3\,A$$

Fig. 18 Current problems

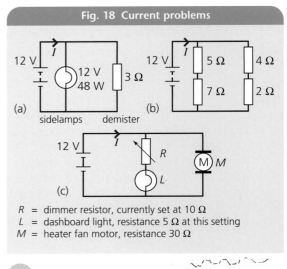

R = dimmer resistor, currently set at $10\,\Omega$
L = dashboard light, resistance $5\,\Omega$ at this setting
M = heater fan motor, resistance $30\,\Omega$

21 Find the current in each of the circuits in Fig. 18.

22 Find the p.d. marked V in each of the circuits in Fig.19.

Fig. 19 P.d. problems

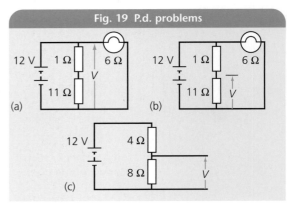

11.7 Complex circuits

It can take a long time to reduce complex circuits to simple series and parallel arrangements. **Kirchhoff's laws** offer a formal set of rules for simplifying circuits (Fig. 20).

Kirchhoff's first law: *the algebraic sum of currents at a junction is zero.*

$$\sum I = 0$$

Charge is conserved: the charge entering a junction is equal to the charge leaving.

Kirchhoff's second law: *around a closed circuit loop, the algebraic sum of the e.m.f.s is equal to the algebraic sum of the p.d.s.*

$$\sum \epsilon = \sum IR \qquad \text{(for a resistive circuit)}$$

Energy is conserved.

A 'closed circuit loop' means exactly that; the rule works for any closed path around a circuit, whether it contains a battery or not (Fig. 21).

The term 'algebraic' is very important: it means that direction must be taken into consideration. Quantities are positive in the direction of conventional current and negative if opposing this current. For example, in a battery charger circuit, the e.m.f. of the charger 'opposes' the e.m.f. of the battery which you are charging.

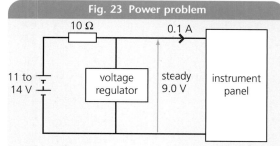

Fig. 23 Power problem

23 A voltage regulator for an instrument panel keeps a steady 9.0 V across the instruments. The service battery is nominally 12 V but can fluctuate between 11 and 14 V. The instrument panel needs a fairly constant 0.1 A. Find the maximum power dissipation in the 10 Ω resistor (Fig. 23).

24 Calculate the current I in each of the circuits in Fig. 24.

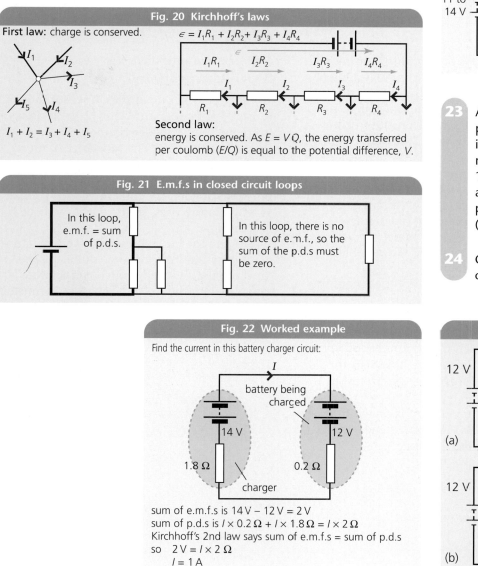

Fig. 20 Kirchhoff's laws

First law: charge is conserved.

$$I_1 + I_2 = I_3 + I_4 + I_5$$

$$\epsilon = I_1R_1 + I_2R_2 + I_3R_3 + I_4R_4$$

Second law:
energy is conserved. As $E = VQ$, the energy transferred per coulomb (E/Q) is equal to the potential difference, V.

Fig. 21 E.m.f.s in closed circuit loops

In this loop, e.m.f. = sum of p.d.s

In this loop, there is no source of e.m.f., so the sum of the p.d.s must be zero.

Fig. 22 Worked example

Find the current in this battery charger circuit:

battery being charged

14 V   12 V

1.8 Ω   0.2 Ω

charger

sum of e.m.f.s is 14 V – 12 V = 2 V
sum of p.d.s is $I \times 0.2\,\Omega + I \times 1.8\,\Omega = I \times 2\,\Omega$
Kirchhoff's 2nd law says sum of e.m.f.s = sum of p.d.s
so $2\,V = I \times 2\,\Omega$
     $I = 1\,A$

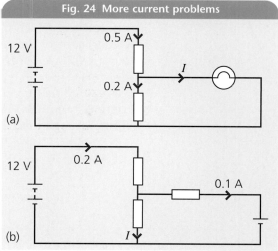

Fig. 24 More current problems

12 V   0.5 A   0.2 A I

(a)

12 V   0.2 A   0.1 A I

(b)

- Resistors in series: $R_T = R_1 + R_2 + R_3 + \cdots$
- Resistors in parallel: $\dfrac{1}{R_T} = \dfrac{1}{R_1} + \dfrac{1}{R_2} + \dfrac{1}{R_3} + \cdots$

- Kirchhoff's laws are:
  (1) sum of currents at a junction is zero;
  (2) sum of e.m.f.s = sum of p.d.s around any closed loop.

11.8 Potential dividers

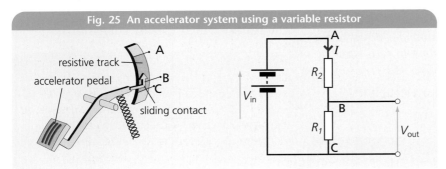

Fig. 25 An accelerator system using a variable resistor

resistive track
accelerator pedal
sliding contact

Electrical methods of measuring are very popular in science and technology. One of the main advantages is that the measuring instrument can be 'remote', so you do not need to be able to see the engine to know whether it is too hot or if the oil has fallen to a dangerously low level.

Many sensors rely on a change of resistance to make their measurement. These sensors are often used in an arrangement of resistors called a potential divider. The accelerator in an electric vehicle could be a potential divider which uses a variable resistor (Fig. 25).

As the pedal is depressed, it changes the point of contact on the resistive track, so changing the relative values of the two resistors. This alters the output voltage, information which the computer control unit uses to control the motor. How does the output voltage depend on the size of the resistors?

Assume that no current is drawn from the 'output' terminals. Then the same current, I, flows through both resistors:

$$I = \frac{V}{R} = \frac{V_{in}}{R_1 + R_2}$$

V_{out} is the p.d. across resistor R_1.

Substituting I into the expression

$$V_{out} = IR$$
$$= \frac{V_{in}}{R_1 + R_2} \times R_1$$
$$V_{out} = V_{in} \times \frac{R_1}{R_1 + R_2}$$

The voltage is divided in the same ratio as the resistors, i.e.

$$\frac{V_{out}}{V_{in}} = \frac{\text{output resistance}}{\text{total resistance}}$$

To measure other quantities, a sensor resistor is used. For temperature, one of the resistors in the potential divider can be replaced by a thermistor (Fig. 26). The resistance of most thermistors goes down as temperature rises. By putting the thermistor at the top of the potential divider, the total resistance will fall as temperature rises, so the output voltage gets bigger.

Despite the curved resistance–temperature graph, the thermistor can be quite a useful 'linear' sensor. Over a limited temperature range – when the resistance of the thermistor is around the same size as the resistor – the potential divider's output rises roughly linearly with increasing temperature.

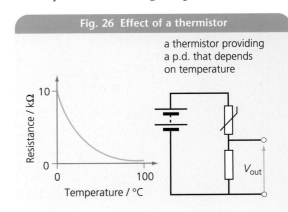

Fig. 26 Effect of a thermistor

a thermistor providing a p.d. that depends on temperature

Fig. 27 Potential dividers

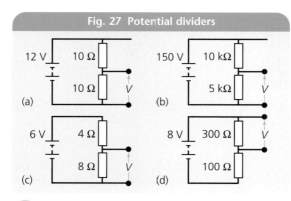

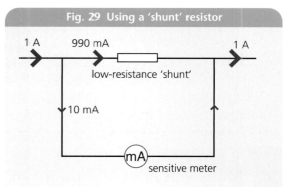

25 Write down the output voltage of these potential dividers in Fig. 27.

Meter displays

Displaying results of electrical measurements is done in two ways: moving coil meters (analogue) or digital meters.

Digital meters have replaced moving coil meters in most scientific instruments because they are easier to read accurately and often give a more precise reading. However, car drivers are not as concerned with accuracy; they need to be able to take in the reading at a glance. The analogue display can give a better picture of the information, including red zones for danger!

Changing scales

Ammeters measure the current which flows through a circuit so the circuit needs to be broken to put an ammeter in. The meter should not stop the flow at all, so an ideal ammeter has zero resistance.

Voltmeters, on the other hand, measure the potential difference across a component. Voltmeters should not allow current to bypass the component: ideally, a voltmeter has infinite resistance. Putting a voltmeter in series with the circuit effectively switches the

Analogue and digital displays.

circuit off. Putting an ammeter across a battery is effectively a short circuit.

Digital meters are very high resistance voltmeters, typically reading up to 0.2 V with a resistance of well over 1 MΩ. P.d.s in electric cars may be up to 300 V. The range of the basic meter is extended using a potential divider. A voltmeter module cannot measure current directly: hardly any current could flow through its high resistance. Instead, current is allowed to pass through a low resistance, and the digital meter measures the voltage across the resistor (Fig. 28).

In moving coil meters, it is the current through the coil which makes the coil turn around. The current needed for full scale deflection (f.s.d.) varies between types of meter, but is usually between 100 mA and 10 A. To allow a sensitive meter to measure a bigger current, you have to make some of the current bypass the meter. This is done with a **'shunt'** resistor (Fig. 29).

To convert a moving coil meter into a voltmeter, you put a resistor in series with it. This resistor is called a **'multiplier'** because it multiplies the range of the meter (Fig. 30). It cuts down the current entering the voltmeter at the higher voltage.

Fig. 29 Using a 'shunt' resistor

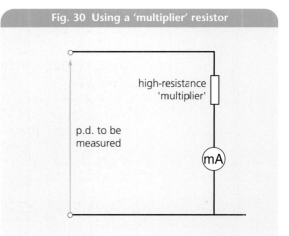

Fig. 28 Digital meters

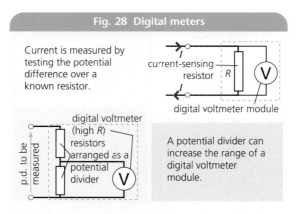

Current is measured by testing the potential difference over a known resistor.

digital voltmeter module

A potential divider can increase the range of a digital voltmeter module.

Fig. 30 Using a 'multiplier' resistor

26 The main motor current in an electric car is to be monitored by using the motor supply leads as the 'shunt' of an ammeter. Each supply lead has resistance 0.003 Ω. Draw the required circuit and suggest a suitable moving coil meter to allow 300 A to be measured. Why would a moving coil meter be better than a digital meter in this application?

11.9 Resistance of materials

If electric cars are to be successful, they need to be as light and efficient as possible. Car developers need to avoid energy losses by choosing the right materials. Weight and cost are both important. How can they be sure that copper wire is the right material to use?

Resistivity

Copper is a good conductor but has a high density and is increasingly expensive. Development of electric vehicles is likely to put pressure on dwindling world reserves of copper. Aluminium is more abundant, less dense but not as good a conductor. How can we compare different materials and shapes of conductor to make this evaluation?

The length and cross-sectional area of a material affect its resistance (Fig. 31).

Using the model of resistance arising from collisions between electrons and lattice ions, we can deduce that:

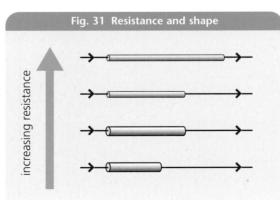

Fig. 31 Resistance and shape

increasing resistance

● Resistance is proportional to length, because doubling the length would double the chance of collision:

$$R \propto l$$

● Resistance is inversely proportional to cross-sectional area, because doubling the area would double the number of moving electrons, thereby doubling the current and halving the resistance:

$$R \propto \frac{1}{A}$$

Combining these relationships gives:

$$R \propto \frac{l}{A}$$

We write:

$$R \propto \frac{l}{A} \text{ or } R = \frac{\rho l}{A} \text{ or } \rho = \frac{RA}{l}$$

where r is a constant called resistivity.

Resistivity has the unit $\Omega\,m$.

If you set $l = 1\,m$ and $A = 1\,m^2$, then the resistivity, ρ, is the resistance of a standard size sample of material of unit length and unit area of cross section.

Good resistors are bad conductors and vice versa. We often talk about conduction rather than resistance:

$$\text{conductivity} = \frac{1}{\text{resistivity}}$$

Table 5 Typical resistivity values	
Class	Resistivity/Ω m
metals	~ 10^{-7}
semiconductors	~ 10^{2}
insulators	~ 10^{10}

Table 6 Resistivity data		
Material	Resistivity/Ω m	Density/kg m^{-3}
copper	1.7×10^{-8}	8930
aluminium	2.7×10^{-8}	2710

Conductivity is measured in siemens per metre (S m^{-1}).

Nichrome wire can be used in a heating element for a windscreen demister. A 100 cm length of wire of diameter 1.22 mm has a resistance of 0.50 Ω. What is the resistivity of Nichrome?

$$\text{Area} = \pi r^2$$
$$= \pi \times (0.61 \times 10^{-3} \text{ m})^2$$
$$= 1.17 \times 10^{-6} \text{ m}^2$$

So, $\rho = \dfrac{RA}{l}$

$$= \frac{0.50 \ \Omega \times 1.17 \times 10^{-6} \text{ m}^2}{1.00 \text{ m}}$$
$$= 5.8 \times 10^{-7} \ \Omega \text{ m}$$

We can use resistivity to evaluate alternative materials for connecting leads. Suppose the connecting lead from the storage battery to the motor in an electric van is 3.5 metres long and must have a resistance of less than 0.001 Ω. How would the diameters and masses of copper and aluminium wires (Table 6) compare?

For copper,

$$\rho = \frac{RA}{l}$$
$$A = \frac{\rho l}{R}$$
$$= \frac{1.7 \times 10^{-8} \ \Omega \text{ m} \times 3.5 \text{ m}}{0.001 \ \Omega}$$
$$= 6.0 \times 10^{-5} \text{ m}^2$$

and $A = \pi r^2$

$$r^2 = \frac{6.0 \times 10^{-5} \text{ m}^2}{\pi}$$
$$r = 0.0044 \text{ m}$$

diameter = 8.8 mm

$$\text{mass} = \text{density} \times \text{volume}$$
$$= 8930 \text{ kg m}^{-3} \times 6.0 \times 10^{-5} \text{ m}^2 \times 3.5 \text{ m}$$
$$= 1.9 \text{ kg}$$

Similarly, for aluminium,

$$A = \frac{\rho l}{R}$$
$$= \frac{2.7 \times 10^{-8} \ \Omega \text{ m} \times 3.5 \text{ m}}{0.001 \ \Omega}$$
$$= 9.5 \times 10^{-5} \text{ m}^2$$

So radius = 0.0055 m, diameter = 11 mm and mass = 0.90 kg.

The poorer conduction of aluminium can be compensated for by making the aluminium cable about 25% thicker than copper cable. The aluminium cable would still be lighter. Though this results in a weight saving of more than 50%, the manufacturer would need to take into account the cost of manufacture and other properties (ease of connecting, flexibility, corrosion resistance, etc.) of the materials before making a decision.

27 To save money, the designer suggests that the return current travels along the steel body panels. The distance travelled by the current would average 4.5 metres. What width of panel would be required to give 0.001 Ω resistance, given that the panels are 1 mm thick and the resistivity of the steel is $1.5 \times 10^{-7} \ \Omega$ m?

Resistance and temperature

Cars need to operate in temperatures as low as –40 °C, while temperatures of electrical equipment in the engine compartment could reach as high as 150 °C. It is clearly important to know about the electrical properties of materials at these extremes of temperature.

Temperature always affects conduction. The effect depends on the type of material.

Metals: there are free electrons in metals even at absolute zero. Increasing the temperature makes the random motion of the electrons faster and the positive ions vibrate more. This leads to more collisions between the drifting electrons and the ions, so that current is reduced. Resistance increases when temperature goes up.

The effect can be significant: both aluminium and copper show about an 80% increase in resistance over the range –40 to +150 °C.

Table 6 Effect of increasing temperature on resistivity		
Material	**Change in resistivity**	**Reason**
metal	increases	more vibration of ions
semiconductor	decreases (usually)	more ion vibration makes resistivity rise more charge carriers makes resistivity fall
insulator	decreases	thermal energy releases more charge carriers

Insulators: at absolute zero, all the electrons are tied to the atoms. There is no conduction at all. At room temperature this is still roughly true. At much higher temperatures, thermal energy may be enough to free some electrons, thereby allowing conduction. Resistance decreases with increased temperature.

At high temperatures, you would need to be careful about choosing insulators for use in the motors, near brakes or inside high-temperature sodium–sulphur batteries.

Semiconductors: the energy needed to release charge carriers in semiconductors is much less than it is in insulators. Thermal energy is enough to release some electrons for conduction.

Pure semiconductors conduct a little at room temperature. Increasing the temperature increases ion vibrations, which tends to reduce current, as in metals. The increasing number of charge carriers at higher temperatures is dominant, however, so for most semiconductors the resistance decreases as temperature goes up.

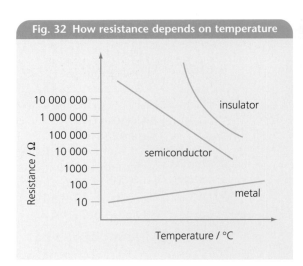

Fig. 32 How resistance depends on temperature

28 When you first switch on a light bulb the current is high, but quickly drops to a steady value. Why does this happen?

Fuel cells – the environmentally friendly power source?

Fuel cells have been used in spacecraft since the 1960s, but they have come a long way since then and an even longer way since their invention by Sir William Robert Grove in 1839. In recent years, research has been spurred by the depletion of fossil fuels: new materials have meant higher outputs of electrical energy and in some cases quite a useful source of heat as well.

Table 1 Types of fuel cells currently available
alkaline fuel cell
direct methanol fuel cell
phosphoric acid fuel cell
molten carbonate fuel cell
solid oxide fuel cell

So what are fuel cells? As the name suggests, they use a fuel – in this case hydrogen – to produce a flow of electrical energy. The anode of the cell is supplied with hydrogen and the cathode with an oxidant (oxygen or air). The hydrogen is oxidised, releasing electrons which flow through the circuit that the cell is connected to. These electrons are moving, so an electric current flows as they pass from the negative electrode to the positive electrode. At the positive electrode, the electrons are absorbed, reducing the oxidant. The product of this reaction is water (and in some types of fuel cell there is heat energy as well).

An environmental benefit is that the hydrogen can be obtained from renewable sources such as landfill sites. When rubbish breaks down, it produces methane gas which contains hydrogen. The heat produced by fuel cells in a stationary power plant can be used in combined heat and power (CHP) systems, where buildings such as housing estates and offices are heated. The size of this stationary power supply is preferable to more weighty types of cell.

Another benefit is that fuel cells only use up fuel at a rate proportional to the electrical load, so fuel consumption is low when load demands are low.

Fuel cells are also now quite efficient, as high as 50% at full power and 60% at partial power. In contrast, a typical internal combustion engine is around 15–20% efficient.

There are several projects being built at the moment around the world. One of these which uses the phosphoric acid fuel cell began operation in Germany in January 2000, built by the Canadian firm Ballard Power (in partnership with Alsthom, Europe). This is a 250 kW CHP station.

On the down side, the most efficient fuel cells are quite heavy and expensive to make which has restricted their development as a power source for cars, buses and lorries. However, progress is being made with lightweight fuel cells, e.g. the 'proton-exchange membrane' (PEM) type. This uses an ion-conducting polymer bonded to the electrodes. The electrodes are carbon mats coated with finely divided platinum. This means that there is good contact between the electrodes and the electrolyte and between the gas and the catalyst.

1 Explain why there is renewed interest in developing fuel cells.

2 List the environmental benefits in using fuel cells as:

a a power supply for something that does not move, e.g. an electricity generator;

b a power supply for something that moves, e.g. a car or train.

3 Draw a diagram to illustrate how a fuel cell works.

4 Use the answers to the above questions to prepare a presentation about fuel cells as a replacement for conventional power supplies like power stations.

Your presentation will need to consider

a the environmental advantages and disadvantages of fuel cells in this context;

b the current state of the technology in terms of cost of production and operation and reliability;

c the range of fuel cell types listed in Table 1;

d likely developments over the next ten years.

Your presentation should last for approximately ten minutes and must use at least one diagram or chart and provide a handout for people to take away with the important information.

Since developments in fuel cells are happening at such a rapid rate you will probably need to use the Internet to research your topic. When you are searching the Internet make sure you record:
● the search engines you use;
● the words and terms you search on;
● all the sites you visit.

Keep a note of the most useful sites and be prepared to explain why these sites were more useful than the ones you discarded.

1 a Some electrical components may be described as *non-ohmic*.

(i) Name an example, other than a diode, of a non-ohmic electrical component.

(ii) State how the current–voltage characteristic of your chosen component shows that it is non-ohmic. (2)

b A semiconducting diode has special electrical properties that make it useful as an electrical component.

(i) On a graph sketch the current–voltage characteristic of a diode.

(ii) State, with reference to the current–voltage characteristic you have drawn, how the resistance of the diode varies with the potential difference across its terminals. (5)

(AQA PH01 Jun 98 Q7)

2 The diagram shows the way in which eight heating elements of the rear window heater in a car are connected.

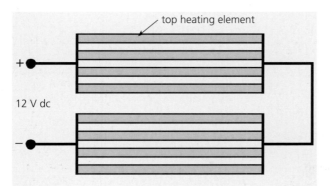

top heating element

12 V dc

Each of the elements of the heater has a resistance of 8.0 Ω and the heater is connected to a 12 V d.c. supply.

a Calculate

(i) the resistance of the heater,

(ii) the potential difference across each of the elements,

(iii) the current through each of the elements. (4)

b The top heating element, marked with the arrow in the diagram, is damaged in use and stops conducting.

Calculate

(i) the new resistance of the heater,

(ii) the current flowing in each of the top three conducting elements. (3)

(AQA PH01 Jun 98 Q8)

3

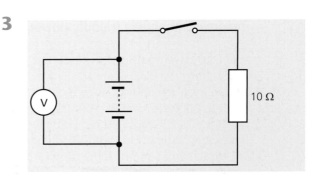

10 Ω

A battery is connected to a 10 Ω resistor as shown. The e.m.f. (electromotive force) of the battery is 12 V.

(i) Explain what is meant by the e.m.f. of a battery.

(ii) When the switch is open the voltmeter reads 12.0 V and when it is closed it reads 11.5 V. Explain why the readings are different.

(iii) Calculate the internal resistance of the battery. (6)

(AQA PH01 Feb 97 Q5)

4 Thin films of carbon are sometimes used as resistors in electronic circuits. The diagram shows a thin film of carbon, of resistivity, ρ, which is being used as a resistor with current flowing perpendicular to the shaded face.

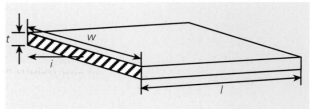

a (i) Show that the resistance, R, of the film to a current flowing perpendicular to the shaded area is given by

$$R = \frac{\rho l}{wt}$$

(i) The film has a length, l, of 12 mm, a width, w, of 6.0 mm and a thickness, t, of 0.0010 mm. If the resistivity of the carbon is $4.0 \times 10^{-5}\ \Omega\,m$, calculate the resistance of the film. (3)

b (i) If $l = w$ show that the resistance is independent of the length of the side of the square.

(ii) Explain what limits the minimum size of a square in a given application. (2)

(AQA PH01 Feb 97 Q8)

12 The cathode-ray tube

LCD (liquid crystal display) projectors are already widely used to project images from computer monitors on to large screens. The brightness is a problem as the image cannot match the brightness of a conventional CRT tube.

Cathode-ray tubes are also used in oscilloscopes to display voltage signals and are used widely in industry and medicine. CRTs are reliable, robust and relatively cheap, so it seems that the technology may survive a while longer yet.

The demand for home cinema is increasing. Around three million large-screen TVs were sold in the UK in 1999. Home movies can be live on digital TV or recorded on videotape or DVD disks. Soon it will be possible to buy movies on-line on the Internet. But however the films reach them, home viewers want cinema-style performance and that means large screens and realistic, loud sounds.

Until recently all televisions have been based on the cathode-ray tube (CRT) but these are heavy and bulky. The largest CRT televisions have 37" screens, but they weigh over 80 kg. Two new technologies are beginning to challenge the CRT television: plasma screen TVs and LCD projectors.

Plasma screen TVs are already larger and lighter: a 42" screen is only 7" thick and weighs about 40 kg. The manufacturers claim that it can be hung on the wall. Plasma sets use thousands of small gas envelopes. The gas inside these elements is superheated by electrical charges, creating a luminescent plasma. Unfortunately, the picture quality does not yet rival conventional CRT televisions.

Cathode-ray tubes in a different guise illuminate our cities.

12.1 Rays from the cathode

Towards the end of the nineteenth century, one of the most interesting areas of scientific study was the discharge of electricity through gases at low pressures. At very low pressures the gas in the glass discharge tube started to glow in the region opposite the negative electrode (cathode). The glow seemed to be due to rays coming from the cathode. It was found that the 'cathode rays' could be moved around (deflected) by electric and magnetic fields. Deflection experiments in the 1890s showed that these rays from the cathode were negatively charged particles of very small mass. The properties did not depend on the type of gas in the tube. We now call these particles 'electrons'.

Some of the most expensive hi-fi amplifiers still use valves rather than transistors.

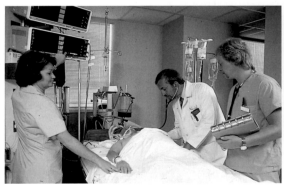

Fig. 1 A thermionic valve

Electrons are emitted in larger quantities by heating the cathode. This gives the electrons enough energy to escape from the metal surface in a process called thermionic emission (Fig. 1). When the metal has lost electrons, it develops a net positive charge which pulls the electrons back. If another positive electrode (the anode) is fitted to the tube, electrons can be pulled away from the cathode. A high-voltage supply connected between cathode and anode will therefore set up a stream of electrons (a current) through the tube.

The energy required to remove an electron from a material is known as the work function. In modern CRTs the cathode is normally coated with a compound with a low work function. Even so, the operating temperature is usually above 1200 K.

1 Explain why a higher cathode temperature is needed if the material of the cathode has a high work function.

2 The heater circuit needs a high-current supply at low voltage. The anode–cathode circuit needs a high voltage but little current. Why?

The cathode-ray display tube

In the second half of the twentieth century, the cathode-ray display tube in its guise as the television set has changed the nature of leisure time. The ability to display a moving picture has also been a great advantage to scientists and technologists. Physicists use cathode-ray tubes in oscilloscopes and most computers still use cathode-ray tubes as monitors. The underlying mechanism is the same in all these applications (Fig. 2).

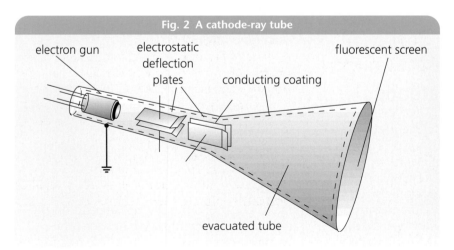

Fig. 2 A cathode-ray tube

A patient's heartbeat can be displayed using a cathode-ray oscilloscope.

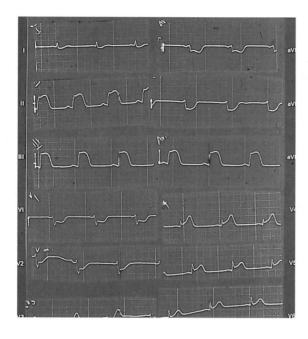

An electrocardiogram (ECG) pattern of a person suffering from a heart attack

The electron gun

Electrons are fired at the screen from the electron 'gun' (Fig. 3). Colour televisions or monitors have three guns, one for each of the primary colours on the display screen. The main components of an electron gun are:

- **An indirectly heated cathode** Electrons are released from the cathode by thermionic emission. In a small cathode-ray tube, these electrons are accelerated away from the cathode by a cathode–anode potential difference of about 800 V. Large televisions could use up to 25 000 V.

- **A 'grid' electrode** for brightness control. Brightness can also be controlled by changing the cathode temperature or altering the accelerating voltage, but these two methods affect focusing. The grid is more negative than the cathode, so it repels electrons, thereby reducing the number emitted. Fewer electrons means a dimmer display. The grid is typically between 0 and 50 V more negative than the cathode.

- **Anodes** for focusing and accelerating the electrons. The beam of electrons tends to spread apart because electrons repel each other. The shape of the electric field between the anodes acts as a sort of electron 'lens'. The final accelerating anode is often earthed – at 0 volts – to avoid a further electric field being set up between itself and the screen.

The display screen

Some chemical compounds (e.g. zinc sulphide) accept energy from the high-speed electrons and emit the energy in the form of visible light. Chemicals which undergo this 'fluorescence' are usually called phosphors. Some screens have a glow which persists after the electron beam has passed – an effect called phosphorescence.

Electrons are continually hitting the screen. Eventually, the screen will build up a negative charge and start to repel electrons. To prevent this happening, electrons on the screen must be allowed to reach the anode. The inside of the tube is coated with a conductor (e.g. graphite) to allow this current to flow.

The deflection system

A cathode-ray tube would only produce a bright dot in the middle of the screen if it did not steer the electron beam. The trace on an ECG screen is produced by the electron beam scanning across the face of the tube. To do this, a deflection system is needed.

The deflection system can be of two types: electrostatic or magnetic. Electrostatic deflection is more commonly used in small or portable equipment like defibrillators.

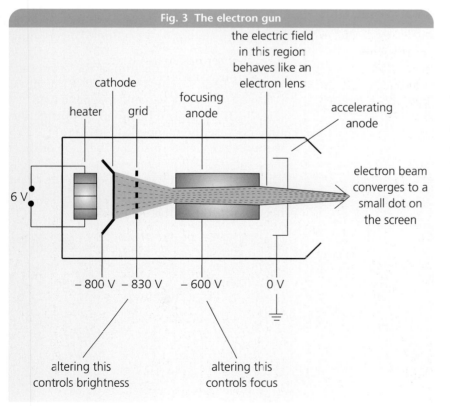

Fig. 3 The electron gun

heater
cathode
grid
focusing anode
the electric field in this region behaves like an electron lens
accelerating anode
electron beam converges to a small dot on the screen
6 V
– 800 V – 830 V – 600 V 0 V
altering this controls brightness
altering this controls focus

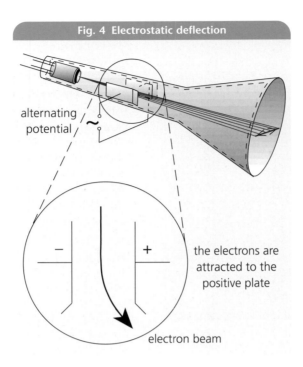

Fig. 4 Electrostatic deflection

alternating
potential

−   +

the electrons are
attracted to the
positive plate

electron beam

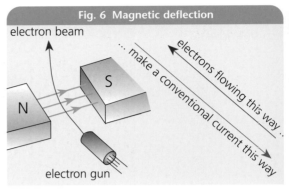

Fig. 6 Magnetic deflection

electron beam

S

N

electron gun

... make a conventional current this way

electrons flowing this way ...

Electrostatic deflection

Charged particles are attracted and repelled
by the electric fields produced by other
charged particles. We can exploit this by
using electric fields to deflect an electron
beam. The simplest way to produce a uniform
electric field is to use a pair of parallel plates
with a p.d. across them. Electrons have a
negative charge, so they are attracted to the
positive plate (Fig. 4). The pair of plates is
able to move the beam horizontally. A second
pair of plates at right angles would give
vertical deflection.

Magnetic deflection

Magnetic deflection is commonly used in
televisions, as they can accommodate heavy
deflecting coils. Moving charged particles are
deflected by magnetic fields. A wire carrying a
current experiences a force if you put it in a
magnetic field. The wire is deflected at right
angles to the current and to the magnetic field.

Fleming's left-hand rule is a convenient
way of remembering the relative directions of
conventional current, magnetic field and
resulting force (Fig. 5). Conventional current
moves in the direction of the positive charges.
You can use Fleming's left-hand rule to find
the direction of the force on individual
positively charged particles.

Electrons are negatively charged. An
electron moving to the right gives a
conventional current to the left (Fig. 6).
Fleming's left-hand rule works with
conventional current, i.e. middle finger points
from + to −.

The size of the deflection of the beam can
be controlled. Varying the current through
coils will provide a variable magnetic field
(Fig. 7). The coils can be mounted outside the
tube because the magnetic field passes
through glass. Coils placed either side of the
glass tube will allow the beam to be deflected.
The pair of coils shown is deflecting the beam
vertically – a second pair of coils would be
needed for horizontal deflections.

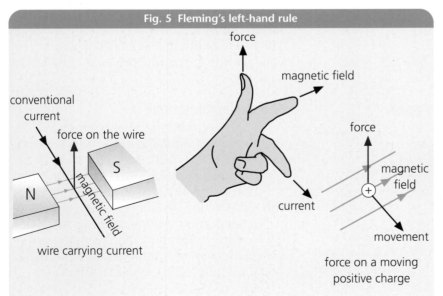

Fig. 5 Fleming's left-hand rule

force

magnetic field

conventional
current

force on the wire

S

N

magnetic field

wire carrying current

current

force

magnetic
field

+

movement

force on a moving
positive charge

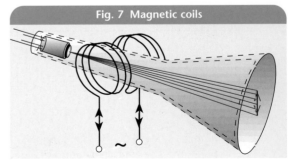

Fig. 7 Magnetic coils

Making the picture

I research the way that nerve cells work together in heart tissue. A lot of my work involves using oscilloscopes to show electrical signals from the nerves. I need to be able to measure voltages and times from the screen.

Oscilloscopes need to measure quantities in relation to time. Therefore, we need a deflection system that allows the bright spot to be steered in a regular, repeating pattern across the screen. If the voltages being measured are represented by a vertical deflection, the result is a voltage–time graph on the screen.

Horizontal deflection: the time base

To achieve a linear time scale, in which the dot moves from the left to the right of the screen, a steadily increasing p.d. must be applied across the horizontal X-plates. When the dot reaches the right-hand side of the screen, it clearly needs to go back to the left-hand side and start again. Using electrostatic deflection, a voltage 'ramp' waveform is required (Fig. 8).

In moving the dot back from right to left, it is impossible to get an instantaneous 'flyback'. Instead, the beam is temporarily switched off while the ramp resets. This is done by making the grid much more negative than the cathode for a short time.

The frequency of the ramp waveform will control the time which the dot takes to sweep across the front of the tube. It is often called the 'time base' or 'sweep' waveform. For oscilloscopes and heart rate monitors, the front of the display tube often has a 1 cm grid drawn across it. The time base is then calibrated in terms of the time taken for the dot to cross 1 cm of the display. Oscilloscopes often have settings between $0.5\,\mathrm{s\,cm^{-1}}$ and $0.5\,\mathrm{\mu s\,cm^{-1}}$. The horizontal time calibration allows measurement of the period (time between repeating events) and frequency of waves.

Measuring the period

In heart rate monitors, the time base is a standard $0.40\,\mathrm{s\,cm^{-1}}$. The distance between adjacent peaks on the display in Fig. 9 is:

$$\frac{5\text{ cm}}{4\text{ heartbeats}} = 1.25 \text{ cm per heartbeat}$$

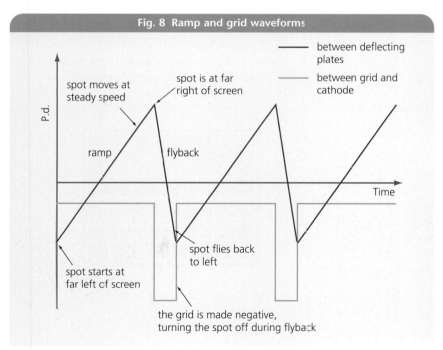

Fig. 8 Ramp and grid waveforms

— between deflecting plates

— between grid and cathode

P.d.

spot moves at steady speed

spot is at far right of screen

ramp

flyback

Time

spot flies back to left

spot starts at far left of screen

the grid is made negative, turning the spot off during flyback

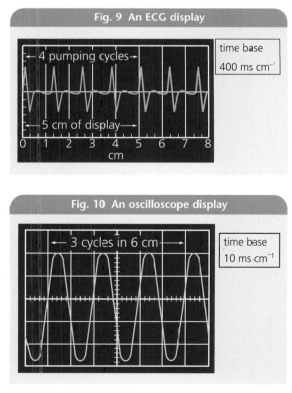

Fig. 9 An ECG display

← 4 pumping cycles →

time base 400 ms cm⁻¹

← 5 cm of display →

0 1 2 3 4 5 6 7 8
cm

Fig. 10 An oscilloscope display

← 3 cycles in 6 cm →

time base 10 ms cm⁻¹

Fig. 11 Signals in phase and antiphase

plotting both signals against time:

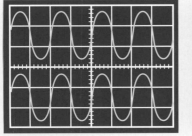

in phase

in antiphase (180° phase)

plotting A on the *x*-axis and B on the *y*-axis

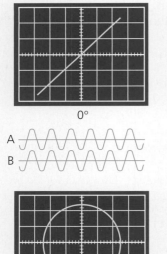

0°

45°

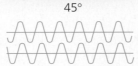

A

B

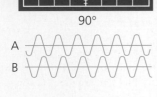

90°

180°

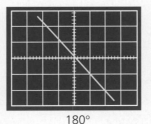

A

B

cycles of the wave are 6.0 cm wide, so each full cycle of the wave is 2.0 cm wide.

The period of the wave is therefore:

$$T = 2.0\,\text{cm} \times 10\,\text{ms cm}^{-1} = 20\,\text{ms}$$

Frequency = number of cycles per second

$$f = \frac{1}{T} = \frac{1}{20 \times 10^{-3}\,\text{s}} = 50\,\text{Hz}$$

Comparing phase

Oscilloscopes can also be used to compare the phase of two signals. Two signals are 'in **phase**' if they peak at the same time. They are 'in antiphase' if the peak of one coincides with the trough of another.

Phase can be compared directly by using a dual-beam oscilloscope. This has two signal input channels. The display alternates between the two signals, giving two lines on the screen (Fig. 11).

Accurate measurements of phase relationships can also be made by using both horizontal (X) and vertical (Y) inputs of a single-beam oscilloscope. If two waves are in phase, then the Y input would always be proportional to the X input: this gives a straight line graph. Other phase relationships give different patterns (Fig. 11).

Vertical deflection: the signal

The vertical height of a trace on the screen can be used to measure p.d. values. Display screens are calibrated so that each centimetre on the *y*-axis of the display screen stands for a known voltage. For example, suppose the Y-amplifier is set to the 2 mV cm⁻¹ range (Fig. 12).

Complications arise where an alternating current (a.c.) signal is added to a steady d.c. voltage. This is common in sensitive

The time taken for 1 heartbeat is therefore:

$$1.25\,\text{cm} \times 0.40\,\text{s cm}^{-1} = 500\,\text{ms} = 0.5\,\text{s}.$$

This heart is beating at a frequency of 2 Hz, or 120 beats per minute.

Measuring frequency

An engineer is using an oscilloscope to test the capacitor-charging circuit in a defibrillator. She needs to measure the frequency of a sine wave signal. The timebase is set at 10 ms cm⁻¹.

To measure the frequency of the wave, the engineer must first find the period by measuring the width of one cycle. Three

Fig. 12 Measuring p.d.

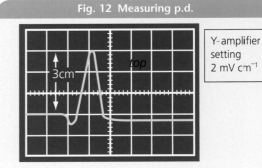

Height of pulse = 3 cm, range = 2 mV cm⁻¹
so p.d. = 3 cm × 2 mV cm⁻¹ = 6 mV

electronic amplifier circuits like those which amplify the tiny electrical signals from nerve cells. The amplitude of the alternating signal may be only a few millivolts, while the d.c. level could be several volts. In this situation, a capacitor can be used to separate the a.c. and d.c. components. The capacitor blocks off the steady d.c. voltage, letting only the fluctuating signal through. Without a d.c. blocking capacitor, the a.c. trace would be indiscernible from the d.c. line (Fig. 13).

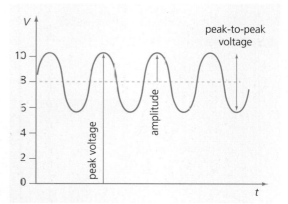

Fig. 13 Blocking capacitors

d.c. mode
In c.c. mode, a useful millivolt signal can be swamped by a large d.c. level

a.c. mode
Switching to a.c. mode masks out the d.c. so we can then amplify the small a.c. signal and examine the waveform

d.c.
a.c.
Y-amplifier
to Y-plates

EXTENSION

Using a capacitor to block d.c.

A capacitor is a device that stores charge. In its simplest form it is made of two metal plates separated by an insulator, like air or plastic. A capacitor blocks d.c. but allows a.c. to flow.

Suppose we apply only a d.c. voltage to the circuit shown. Initially, current will flow through the resistor to allow negative charge to build up on the bottom plate of the capacitor. When the capacitor is 'full', the current stops, resulting in

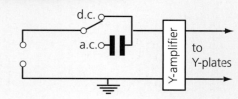

peak-to-peak voltage

peak voltage

amplitude

there being no d.c. voltage across the resistor.

Effectively, this has eliminated the d.c. voltage level, so the sensitivity of the amplifier can be increased. A small a.c. signal will cause fluctuations in the amount of charge on the upper plate. A current will flow through the resistor to allow matching fluctuations of the charge on the lower plate. This leads to an a.c. voltage across the resistor which matches the initial a.c. signal. This can be amplified to give a useful display.

Where both a.c. and d.c. are present, you need to be quite clear about which voltage is being measured.

The a.c. signal (shown in the diagram above) fluctuates by ± 2 V about a d.c. level of 8 V. The amplitude of this a.c. signal is 2 V.

The peak voltage is the highest voltage reached (10 V).

The peak-to-peak voltage is measured from peak to trough of the a.c. signal (4 V).

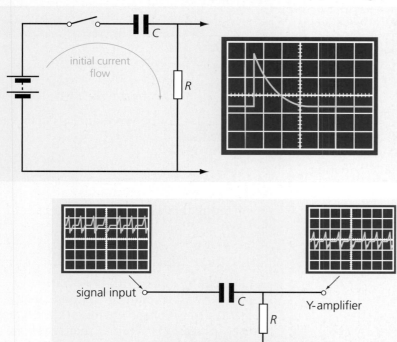

initial current flow

C

R

signal input

C

R

Y-amplifier

12.3 Alternating current, direct current and power

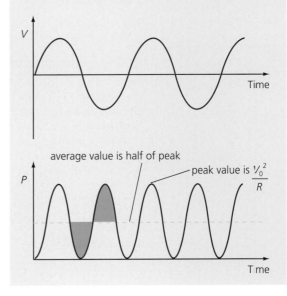

Fig. 14 Variation of alternating p.d. and power with time

The power delivered to a load of resistance R is $P = V^2/R$, so the power fluctuates continuously for an a.c. generator.

average value is half of peak

peak value is $\frac{V_0^2}{R}$

We need to buy a new 'amp' for our band. It is really confusing: there are lots of different power ratings on the amplifiers. In the end we were left with a choice of two amplifiers, both similar in cost and performance. One was rated 100 watts peak power, the other 70 watts r.m.s. power. Which should we choose?

If a resistor is connected to an alternating potential difference, the power fluctuates between zero, when the voltage is zero, and a maximum when the voltage reaches its highest value. The 'peak power' rating of amplifiers and loudspeakers is equal to this maximum value. However, it is rather a misleading value, because the average power is much lower (Fig. 14).

If the peak p.d. output is V_0, the maximum power will be V_0^2/R. By symmetry, you can see that the average power will be only half of this:

$$P = \tfrac{1}{2}\frac{V_0^2}{R}$$

This equation for power in an a.c. circuit can be written as:

$$P = \frac{\left(V_0/\sqrt{2}\right)^2}{R}$$

Comparing this with the d.c. formula:

$$P = \frac{V^2}{R}$$

you can see that a d.c. voltage of $(V_0/\sqrt{2})$ is equivalent to an a.c. with peak voltage V_0.

To derive this result, we have in effect taken the mean of the squares of the voltage values (because $P \propto V^2$) and then taken the square root. This is therefore called the root mean square (r.m.s.) voltage.

$$V_{\text{r.m.s.}} = \frac{V_0}{\sqrt{2}}$$

You could do the same for current using the d.c. formula $P = I^2R$ giving $I_{\text{r.m.s.}} = I_0 / \sqrt{2}$.

R.m.s. current and voltage can be used in exactly the same way as d.c. current and voltage in equations such as $R = V/I$ and $P = IV$. Most a.c. electrical meters will give r.m.s. readings. For example, a voltmeter connected to the mains supply in the UK will give a reading of about 240 V. This is the r.m.s. level, so the mains supply reaches a peak voltage of about 340 V. On an oscilloscope, this would show as a wave with peak-to-peak voltage of 680 V.

3 Calculate the peak current through an 8 Ω loudspeaker connected to an amplifier which is generating 72 W r.m.s. from a sine wave a.c.

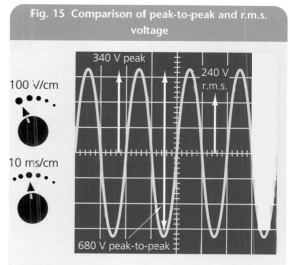

Fig. 15 Comparison of peak-to-peak and r.m.s. voltage

The mains in the UK is around 240 V r.m.s., but an oscilloscope reveals the much larger p.d. reached.

KEY FACTS

■ The root mean square values of voltage and current can be substituted into the equations $P = IV = I^2R = V^2/R$. In a pure resistor, a r.m.s. current of I A would cause the same heating effect as a d.c. current I A.

■ Peak and r.m.s. values of sine waves are given by:

$$V_{\text{r.m.s.}} = \frac{V_0}{\sqrt{2}} \quad \text{and} \quad I_{\text{r.m.s.}} = \frac{I_0}{\sqrt{2}}$$

■ The r.m.s. power is half of the peak power value of the a.c. sine wave.

Developing new technology

'2000 – the year the Internet went mobile.' This advertising claim relates to the announcement that mobile phones that can access the Internet directly and display modified websites on their screens would be available at reasonable cost to the public. 'Add some colour to your life' is another glossy magazine advertisement – this time for the first colour palm top computer to achieve widespread acceptance. Both of these technologies depend on screens that are easy to read, cheap to produce and use very little electrical power.

The gap between the development of a new technology and its incorporation into devices you can buy over the counter gets shorter and shorter with every passing year. Whereas telephones took over five decades before they were accepted everywhere and televisions took many years, the video recorder went from an expensive device used mainly in schools and colleges to an everyday household item over roughly five years. CD players took less time and DVD players are moving even faster towards acceptance.

This acceleration of change means it can be difficult to track the latest hot technology before it becomes yesterday's news. High-tech companies need to ride an ever-accelerating wave of innovation or sink with the has-beens.

Imagine that you work for a small electronics company which is trying to develop the next generation of mobile phones. Your task as the company materials scientist is to search for information about the latest types of screen for use on small portable devices. Given the speed of development of these technologies almost anything you read in a printed text is already out of date. Where do you search for information?

You have to look at the benefits and limitations of two types of screen: liquid crystal displays (LCDs) and light emitting plastics (LEPs). LEPs are a very recent development (a working display was only unveiled in 1998) so finding information will be quite difficult. You have to report to your Managing Director within a week with information about the two types of screens, where they can be purchased and the relative advantages and disadvantages of each type. This is necessary so that the company can make plans for its bid to supply the new mobile phones to a large telecommunications consortium.

1 Where will you get your information from? Books? The Internet? CD-ROMs? Computer files on the college intranet? List the possible sources of information and rank them according to expected usefulness.

2 Starting with the most useful source of information conduct a search. Remember to keep a detailed 'search trail' as evidence of your work. The trail can include:

Information source	Search trail items
Printed text searches	title, author, publication date, page reference
Internet searches	search engines used, key words searched on, website addresses of all sites accessed
Database searches	database searched, publication date, author/source of individual articles or items as appropriate, key words searched on
Telephone conversations and interviews	date and time of conversation, contributors to conversation, status of contributors

3 Assemble the information you have collected into a suitable report. The report must include:

● An executive report of less than one side of A4

● The main body of the report (less than four sides of A4 including at least two diagrams)

● An appendix containing all of your research data.

EXAMINATION QUESTIONS

1 An oscilloscope is connected across a signal generator as shown below.

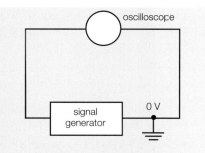

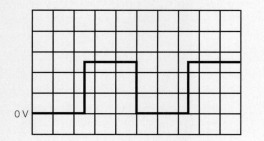

a The oscilloscope display has a Y-sensitivity of 2 V div⁻¹ and the time base is set to 50 ms div⁻¹. Calculate

(i) the maximum voltage of the signal,

(ii) the time period of the signal,

(iii) the frequency of the signal. (3)

b A 2.0 V cell is now included in the circuit as shown below. On the grid provided draw the display you would expect to see. (2)

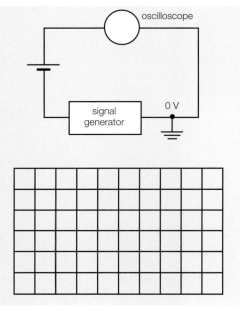

(AQA PH01 Jun 97 Q7)

2 The diagram shows a trace on the screen of an oscilloscope. The Y-sensitivity of the oscilloscope is set at 5.0 V per division and the time base is set at 0.50 ms per division.

a

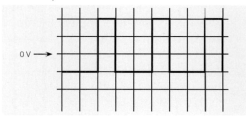

For the trace, determine

(i) the maximum positive value of the p.d.,

(ii) the maximum negative value of the p.d.,

(ii) the frequency of the signal. (4)

b The trace shows the variation in the potential difference across a 100 Ω resistor. Calculate the energy dissipated in the resistor.

(i) for the first 1.00 ms,

(ii) between 1.00 ms and 1.50 ms,

(iii) in one cycle,

(iv) in one second. (5)

(AQA PH01 Mar 99 Q4)

3 In each of the circuits below, the potential difference across the Y-input terminals of an oscilloscope is displayed on the oscilloscope screen. The signal is applied across the d.c. terminals of the oscilloscope. The Y-input voltage sensitivity is set at 1.0 V per division and the time base at 5.0 ms per division.

The oscilloscope is adjusted so that an input of 0 V corresponds to a straight line trace along the horizontal axis of the grid. Draw grids like the one below and sketch the trace you would expect for each circuit. (8)

(AQA PH01 Mar 98 Q1)

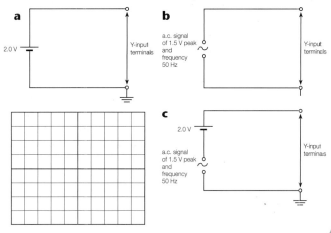

13 Strength of materials

Some of the latest recruits to the US army have eight legs. Golden Orb spiders have been enlisted for their ability to manufacture silk with remarkable mechanical properties. Researchers 'silk' the spiders by taping them, on their backs, to a table. The silk is slowly withdrawn from their spinnerets by winding it around the spindle of a low-speed electric motor. In a day, each spider can produce a thread over 300 m long.

The spider's silk is at least twice as strong as ordinary steel, yet it can absorb enormous amounts of energy and stretch by more than 30% of its original length before breaking. Furthermore, it only becomes brittle at temperatures below –60 °C. For these reasons, the US army are investigating the feasibility of making light, bullet-proof vests from the silk.

Research teams all over the world are currently attempting to unravel the silk's structure, so far without success. Molecular biologists are trying to isolate the genes that are responsible for the silk's production. The silk has an enormous range of potential uses, from the manufacture of parachutes to the soles of running shoes.

Spider silk can cope with sudden loads, which makes it an ideal material to make stronger, lighter parachutes.

The Golden Orb spider produces seven different kinds of silk. The longest strands in the web are the strongest and can trap small birds.

13.1 Hanging by a thread

A spider can suspend itself on a thread that is only a few thousandths of a millimetre thick. A human abseiling down a cliff face needs something more substantial. The most important physical property of a climber's rope is its strength, the maximum load that it can support without breaking. Ropes for rock-climbing are usually designed to withstand a load 25 times the climber's weight. However, the rope mustn't be too heavy, or it would be difficult to carry.

Mountain climbers need ropes that are strong and light. This requires a material of low density and high strength.

An important property of a rope is its **density**, ρ. The density of a substance is defined as the amount of mass in a given volume.

$$\text{density} = \frac{\text{mass}}{\text{volume}}$$

$$\rho = \frac{M}{V}$$

In SI units, density is measured in kilograms per cubic metre, kg m^{-3}, though g cm^{-3} are sometimes used. At standard temperature and pressure, air has a density of $1.29\ \text{kg m}^{-3}$. Water has a density of approximately $1000\ \text{kg m}^{-3}$. A typical nylon climbing rope has a density of $1130\ \text{kg m}^{-3}$. If the rope is 50 m long and has a diameter of 10 mm, we can calculate its mass:

$$\text{volume of a cylinder} = \pi r^2 h$$
$$= \pi \times (5 \times 10^{-3})^2 \times 50$$
$$= 3.93 \times 10^{-3}\ \text{m}^3$$

Since

$$\text{mass} = \text{density} \times \text{volume}$$
$$\text{mass of the rope} = 1130 \times 3.93 \times 10^{-3}$$
$$= 4.44\ \text{kg}$$

1 Show that $1000\ \text{kg m}^{-3}$ is equivalent to $1\ \text{g cm}^{-3}$.

2 The kilogram is defined as the mass of a standard cylinder, which is kept in Sèvres, France. The cylinder is actually made of a platinum–iridium alloy. If it was made of pure platinum, what would its volume be? (Density of platinum = $21\,450\ \text{kg m}^{-3}$.)

3 Calculate the mass of water held in a household hot-water tank. These are usually 0.5 m diameter cylinders, about 1 m high.

Under stress

We can assess the strength of a material using the idea of tensile stress. The **tensile stress**, σ, applied to a material is the force per unit cross-sectional area (Fig. 1).

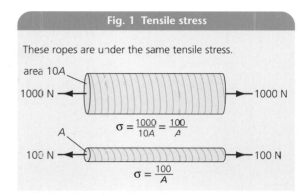

Fig. 1 Tensile stress

These ropes are under the same tensile stress.

$$\sigma = \frac{1000}{10A} = \frac{100}{A}$$

$$\sigma = \frac{100}{A}$$

$$\text{tensile stress} = \frac{\text{force}}{\text{area}}$$

$$\sigma = \frac{F}{A}$$

Tensile stress has units of N m^{-2}, or pascals (Pa). The largest tensile stress that can be applied to a material before it breaks is known as its **ultimate tensile stress** (UTS). This value is sometimes referred to as the material's breaking stress (Table 1).

Kevlar is a strong synthetic polymer. Cables made from Kevlar are so strong that they are used to tether oil rigs. We can use the equation for tensile stress to calculate how thick a Kevlar climbing rope would have to be to support a load of 15 000 N.

From Table 1, the ultimate tensile stress of Kevlar is 3100 MPa. The cross-sectional area of the rope is:

$$A = \frac{F}{\sigma}$$
$$= \frac{15\,000\ \text{N}}{3100 \times 10^6\ \text{Pa}}$$
$$= 4.84 \times 10^{-6}\ \text{m}^2$$

As the cross-sectional area of the rope is πr^2, $r = 1.24 \times 10^{-3}\ \text{m}$. The rope would need to have a diameter of only 2.5 mm. A 50 m length of this rope would have a mass of only 0.35 kg.

Table 1 Materials with high tensile strength		
Material	**Density (kg m^{-3})**	**UTS (MPa)**
Nylon	1130	85
Stainless steel	7930	600
Carbon fibre	1750	1900
Kevlar 49	1440	3100

4a What is the heaviest fish that could be lifted out of the water using a 2 mm diameter line made from nylon (UTS = 85 MPa)?

b If the fish struggles, the force on the line may increase to five times its weight. How thick will the nylon line need to be now?

Spider's silk can deform without breaking, making it a useful material for the manufacture of bullet-proof vests.

Taking the strain

The most remarkable property of the Golden Orb spider's silk is the distance that it can stretch before it breaks. The increase in length of a material caused by a tensile force is called the extension. A rope's extension under a given load depends upon the original length of the rope. A long rope will stretch further than a short one if they are subjected to the same force, so the extension is usually given as a fraction of the original length. This ratio is known as the **tensile strain**.

$$\text{tensile strain} = \frac{\text{extension}}{\text{original length}}$$

Strain has no units, because the extension and original length are both measured in metres.

Steel wire can undergo a strain of 0.01 before it breaks and Kevlar can manage 0.04. The silk from a spider has a breaking strain of between 0.15 and 0.30. This enables it to absorb the kinetic energy of an insect, transferring it to internal energy in the web.

Spider silk is highly **elastic**. After being stretched it will return to its original length. Many materials do not return to their original length after being subjected to a strain. When the tensile force is removed, the material remains deformed. This is called **plastic** behaviour. Putty behaves in this way.

We tend to classify materials as either elastic or plastic, but many materials show both types of behaviour depending on the stress applied. For small values of stress, polythene behaves elastically, returning to its original dimensions when the stress is removed. Above a critical value of stress, known as the yield stress, the polythene begins to be plastically deformed. We say that it has passed its elastic limit. Materials which have large plastic deformations are known as **ductile**. Glass fibres can be extremely strong but they show hardly any plastic deformation before they break. Materials like this are said to be **brittle** (Fig. 2).

5 A 50 m nylon rope will stretch about 7.5 cm when supporting an 80 kg man. What is the size of the tensile strain?

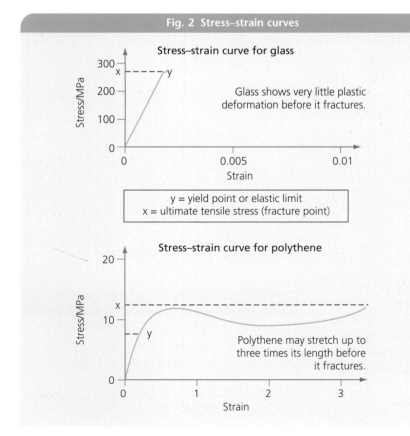

Fig. 2 Stress–strain curves

Stress–strain curve for glass

Glass shows very little plastic deformation before it fractures.

y = yield point or elastic limit
x = ultimate tensile stress (fracture point)

Stress–strain curve for polythene

Polythene may stretch up to three times its length before it fractures.

- Tensile stress is the force per unit area acting on a material.

- Tensile strain is the extension of a material per unit length.

- Elastic materials regain their original shape when an applied stress is removed.

- Plastic materials are permanently deformed following the application of stress.

- Plastic deformation begins to occur at the elastic limit.

- Ductile materials show large plastic deformations.

- Brittle materials do not deform plastically.

13.2 Stiffness

Strength is not the only important property of climbing rope. It is important that the rope does not stretch too much when the mountaineer is suspended from it. The amount of strain caused by a given stress depends on the stiffness of a material.

In a school laboratory the stiffness of small samples of material can be measured using a tensile tester, or Searle's apparatus (Fig. 3).

A tensile tester can measure the stiffness of metal samples. A small bar is gripped between two jaws. A large tensile force is gradually applied and the extension at each load is automatically measured.

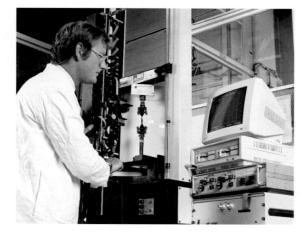

For some materials, plotting a graph of tensile force against extension produces a straight line at low values of stress (Fig. 4). In this linear region, the material obeys Hooke's law. The load (F) is proportional to extension (e), or:

$$F = ke$$

The constant, k, is measured in $N\,m^{-1}$ and is equal to the force needed to stretch the wire by 1 metre. A large value of k means that the material is difficult to stretch, and it is said to be stiff. For a wire which obeys Hooke's law:

$$F \propto e$$

Since A and l are both constants for a particular wire:

Fig. 3 Searle's apparatus

Searle's apparatus

1 Two identical wires are suspended from the same support.

2 Both wires are initially loaded with a small mass to remove any kinks.

3 One wire is loaded and its new length is compared to the control wire to find the extension.

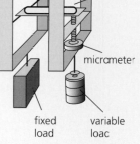

Changes in temperature do not affect the results. If temperature increases, both wires will expand by the same amount, since they are made of the same material.

Fig. 4 Hooke's law graph

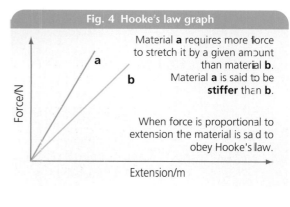

Material **a** requires more force to stretch it by a given amount than material **b**. Material **a** is said to be **stiffer** than **b**.

When force is proportional to extension the material is said to obey Hooke's law.

$$\frac{F}{A} \propto \frac{e}{l}$$

tensile stress $\propto$ tensile strain

tensile stress = constant $\times$ tensile strain

This constant is known as the Young modulus and is given the symbol E.

$$E = \frac{\text{tensile stress}}{\text{tensile strain}}$$
$$= \frac{Fl}{eA}$$

Because stress is measured in pascals and strain has no units, the Young modulus has units of pascals, Pa.

The Young modulus is the gradient of the stress–strain graph and therefore measures the stiffness of a material. A high Young modulus means that a large stress is needed to produce even a small strain. The Young modulus takes into account the cross-sectional area and original length of the sample. This means it can be used to compare the stiffness of different materials, even if they have different dimensions (Table 2).

A rigid structure, such as a bridge, needs a material with a high Young modulus, like steel. Something that is designed to deform easily, such as a squash ball, relies on a material with a low Young modulus, like rubber.

Table 2 Stiffness of materials	
Material	**Young modulus (GPa)**
Carbon fibre	270
Steel	210
Kevlar 49	124
Copper	117
Bone	28
Polystyrene	3.8
Nylon	3
Rubber	0.02

6 A climber's rope needs to be strong, but also light. The ratio UTS/ρ, where ρ is the density of the material, is a useful measure of strength per unit weight. Similarly, the ratio E/ρ gives a measure of a material's stiffness per unit weight. Use these criteria, and data in Tables 1 and 2, to find the most suitable material for a climber's rope.

For a metal, the Young modulus does not remain constant at higher values of stress. Beyond a point known as the limit of proportionality, stress is no longer proportional to strain. At a slightly higher stress, a material

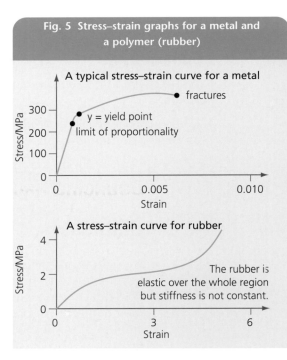

Fig. 5 Stress–strain graphs for a metal and a polymer (rubber)

A typical stress–strain curve for a metal

A stress–strain curve for rubber

The rubber is elastic over the whole region but stiffness is not constant.

begins to be permanently deformed; this point is the elastic limit or yield point (Fig. 5).

Metals obey Hooke's law over most of the elastic region, so the limit of proportionality and the elastic limit almost coincide. Some polymers, like rubber or silk, may be elastic right up until they break, but they often don't obey Hooke's law at all.

7 The graphs in Fig. 6 show the stress–strain curves for three different materials. Which material:

a is the stiffest?

b is the strongest?

c is the most ductile?

d has the lowest yield stress?

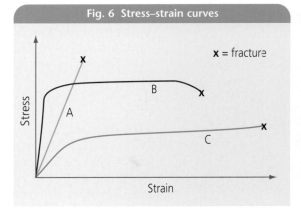

Fig. 6 Stress–strain curves

x = fracture

■ For materials which obey Hooke's law, force is proportional to extension (up to the limit of proportionality).

■ The Young modulus, E, is a measure of the stiffness of a material. E = stress / strain.

13.3 Bouncing back

'*The first half of the jump, when the cable is slack, is horrifying. You free-fall for up to 30 m with the ground rushing up at you at an alarming rate. Then the cable begins to stretch and slow your descent. The cords get tighter, until you slow to a stop and begin to accelerate back up. You get quite close to your original height, before you start falling again.*'

Elastic strain energy

As bungee cords stretch, the kinetic energy of the jumper is transferred to elastic strain energy in the cords. Work is done against the tension in the rubber cord and this is stored as elastic strain energy in the stretched cord. The work done by a constant force is given by:

work (J) = force (N) × distance moved (m)

But the force exerted by a bungee cord changes as the cord is stretched. The force varies from zero, for the unstretched cord, to a maximum force, F, when the cord reaches its full extension, e. If the cord obeys Hooke's law, the average force exerted is:

$$\frac{(0 + F)}{2} = \tfrac{1}{2}F$$

Therefore, the work done against the average force is:

$$W = \tfrac{1}{2}Fe$$
$$= \tfrac{1}{2}(ke)e = \tfrac{1}{2}ke^2$$

The strain energy stored in a stretched cord is equal to $^1/_2\,Fe$. If the cord was originally l metres long and has a cross-sectional area of A m^2, then its volume, V, equals $A \times l$. The strain energy stored per unit volume of the cord is given by:

$$\frac{W}{V} = \frac{\tfrac{1}{2}Fe}{Al}$$
$$= \tfrac{1}{2}\frac{F}{A}\frac{e}{l}$$
$$= \tfrac{1}{2}\,\text{stress} \times \text{strain}$$

Modern bungee jumping began on April Fool's Day, 1979, when some members of the Oxford Dangerous Sports Club jumped from the 75 m high Clifton Suspension Bridge in Bristol.

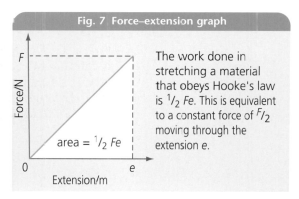

Fig. 7 Force–extension graph

The work done in stretching a material that obeys Hooke's law is $^1/_2\,Fe$. This is equivalent to a constant force of $^F/_2$ moving through the extension e.

187

For some materials, such as metal wire, it is possible to recover all of this stored energy (provided that the material has not been extended beyond its elastic limit). This is not the case for a rubber cord. More work is done in stretching a rubber cord than is released when the cord is unloaded. This type of behaviour is known as hysteresis (Fig. 8). Each time the rubber is stretched and released, some energy is transferred as internal energy in the rubber.

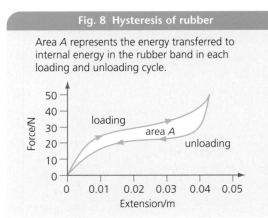

Fig. 8 Hysteresis of rubber

Area A represents the energy transferred to internal energy in the rubber band in each loading and unloading cycle.

Bungee cords can be made from a variety of natural or synthetic rubbers. Most types only obey Hooke's law over a limited range of extensions. Rubber tends to stretch easily at first and become much stiffer at high extensions; the expression for strain energy may only be approximately correct over part of the cord's extension.

If the rubber does not obey Hooke's law at all, then the expression $W = \frac{1}{2}Fe$ cannot be used to calculate the elastic strain energy. The work done in stretching the cord can be found by using a force versus extension graph (Fig. 8). The elastic strain energy recovered is the area below the curve as the rubber is unloaded. The area between the two curves is the energy transferred to the rubber as internal energy. The larger the area of the 'hysteresis loop', the greater the rise in internal energy of the rubber, and the hotter the rubber will get. A rubber is called **resilient** if it has a hysteresis loop with a small area.

The number of bungee cords attached to a jumper depends on the person's mass. At least three cords are used for a jumper of mass 80 kg. The cords will stretch until the jumper's potential energy, E_P, has been transferred as elastic strain energy in the bungee. For the type of bungee described in Fig. 9, this happens when the cords have stretched by about 12.75 m. The jumper will then have fallen a total distance of 27.75 m.

$$\Delta E_P = mg\Delta h$$
$$= 80\,\text{kg} \times 10\,\text{m s}^{-2} \times 27.75\,\text{m}$$
$$= 22\,200\,\text{J}$$

The elastic strain energy stored in each cord is therefore 22 200 J / 3 = 7400 J.

Since $\frac{1}{2}Fe = 7400\,\text{J}$, the tensile force exerted by each cord must be:

$$\frac{2 \times 7400\,\text{J}}{12.75\,\text{m}} = 1160\,\text{N}$$

The stress in each cord will then be:

$$\frac{1160\,\text{N}}{2.0 \times 10^{-4}\,\text{m}^2} = 5.8 \times 10^6\,\text{Pa},$$

well below the ultimate tensile stress of the rubber. The rebound height of the jumper depends on the type of rubber used for the bungee cord. Jumpers typically rebound to about 75% of their original height.

8 Spider's silk is stiffer than rubber and has a much lower resilience. What would a bungee jump be like if silk was used instead of the usual rubber cords?

9 What difference would it make to a bungee jumper if more cords were used?

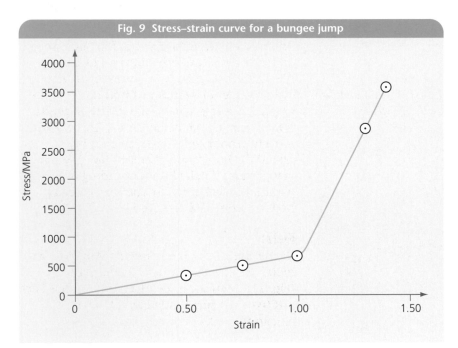

Fig. 9 Stress–strain curve for a bungee jump

10 'Sandbagging' is a variant on the bungee jump. A jumper holds onto a heavy sandbag, then drops it at the bottom of the jump. This has been banned in some countries as it puts spectators and the jumper in danger. Why is it dangerous to the jumper?

13.4 The secret's in the structure

As we have seen, there are huge differences in the mechanical properties of materials. These differences are due to the ways in which the atoms of each material are joined together.

Inter-atomic forces

Solid materials are held together by the forces between their atoms. These inter-atomic forces are due to the electrical forces between charged particles, i.e. electrons and positive ions. The force between two adjacent atoms depends on their separation (Fig. 10). Although the exact form of the interatomic force versus distance curve depends on the type of material, some features are common to all solids.

● There is an equilibrium separation between two atoms, x_0, where the resultant force on the atoms is zero.

● If two atoms are pushed closer than the equilibrium separation, a net repulsive force acts on the atoms, pushing them back to the equilibrium position. This force increases rapidly as the atoms are pushed closer together.

● If atoms are pulled apart by a tensile force, a force of attraction between positive nuclei and negative electrons acts to restore them to their equilibrium position. For small separations, this attractive force increases as the atoms are pulled further apart. However, as the distance between the atoms becomes larger, the force becomes weaker. The force approaches zero when the atoms are a long way apart.

● Atoms in a solid are not stationary; they vibrate around their average equilibrium separation, x_0, alternately repelling and attracting their neighbour atoms.

This simplified picture of the forces between atoms helps to explain some features of the behaviour of a solid. For example, on either side of the equilibrium position (Fig. 10) the graph is approximately linear. This suggests that, for small extensions and compressions, force is proportional to extension, i.e. materials should obey Hooke's law. We can gain a more detailed understanding of a material's mechanical properties by seeing how its atoms are arranged.

Metals

Metals are crystalline materials. Atoms in a metal are arranged in an ordered way (Fig. 11). Metals can be pictured as a matrix of positive ions surrounded by a 'sea' of electrons.

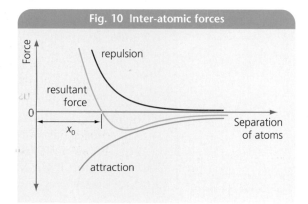

Fig. 10 Inter-atomic forces

189

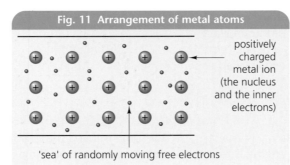

Fig. 11 Arrangement of metal atoms

positively charged metal ion (the nucleus and the inner electrons)

'sea' of randomly moving free electrons

The forces that act on each ion are largely isotropic; the force is the same in all directions. Each positive ion pulls on the surrounding electrons in the same way. This tends to create a close-packed structure.

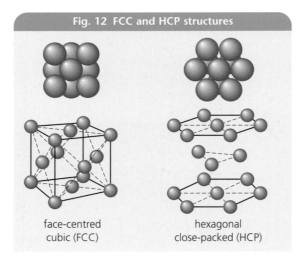

Fig. 12 FCC and HCP structures

face-centred cubic (FCC)

hexagonal close-packed (HCP)

Some metals can deform plastically under tensile stress. For example, copper is highly ductile. When the tensile stress is high enough, entire planes of copper atoms slide over each other. To accomplish this 'yielding' many atoms have to be pulled further apart. Plastic deformation is helped by the presence

Bubble rafts can be used to illustrate the types of defect that arise in crystal structures.

Metals can be etched to reveal their polycrystalline nature. This photograph shows the grain structure in a sample of copper.

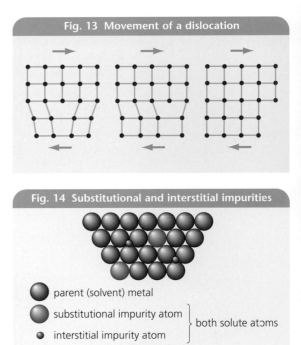

Fig. 13 Movement of a dislocation

Fig. 14 Substitutional and interstitial impurities

parent (solvent) metal

substitutional impurity atom

interstitial impurity atom

both solute atoms

of imperfections in the crystal called dislocations (Fig. 13). Because of these imperfections, metals yield at stresses that are thousands of times smaller than we would expect from the inter-atomic force curve.

Other imperfections in the crystal structure can affect a metal's mechanical properties (Fig. 14).

A real sample of metal is not a single crystal, it is actually a **polycrystalline** material. A metal is composed of millions of crystals, or grains, all at different angles to each other. However, it is possible, under carefully controlled conditions, to grow individual metal crystals that have an almost flawless structure. These are known as whiskers.

Glasses

Glass is an amorphous material. The atoms in an amorphous material may be arranged in an organised fashion over a very short range, but there is no long-range order as there is in a crystal. The arrangement of these atoms is similar to that of a liquid, though they are not as mobile as atoms in a liquid.

As a liquid cools to form a solid, the arrangement of the atoms is affected by the cooling rate. The longer the cooling period, the more crystalline the solid will be. If you melt some sugar and then cool it quickly, it forms an amorphous solid – a sort of clear, brittle toffee. If the liquid sugar is cooled more slowly, a crystalline, cloudy, fudge-like material is produced. It is possible to make amorphous samples of metal by cooling the molten metal quickly.

Amorphous materials tend to be brittle. Glass fractures with very little, if any, plastic deformation. The presence of a small crack will weaken a piece of glass, so that it breaks very easily. Because the area at the tip of a sharp crack or notch is very small, the stress at that point is very high. In a ductile material, some plastic deformation can take place, increasing the area at the tip of the crack and reducing the stress. A brittle material cannot undergo plastic deformation so the crack tends to propagate through the material, causing fracture.

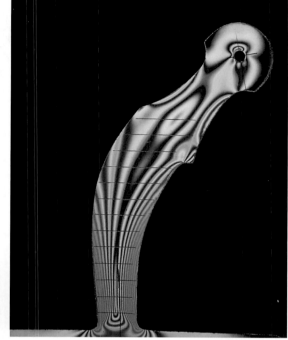

Coloured interference patterns are visible when a component, such as this model of an artificial hip joint, are photographed using polarised light. They can be used to locate regions of high stress, helping manufacturers to choose suitable materials and designs.

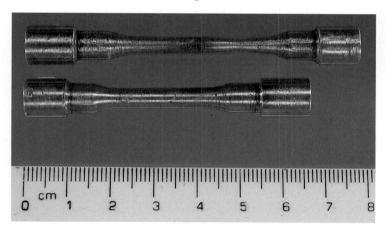

A ductile material fractures slowly under tension. A copper wire becomes narrow, forming a 'waist' before it breaks. A brittle material such as cast iron fractures suddenly when a crack travels through it at high speed.

EXTENSION

Polymers

Spider's silk is a polymer material made from giant chain-like molecules. Each molecule can contain thousands or millions of atoms. Rubber and silk are natural polymers. Perspex, polythene and Kevlar are all artificial polymers. Some polymers show plastic behaviour, while others are brittle.

Amorphous polymers

Some polymers have no long-range order – their molecules are arranged irregularly. The mechanical behaviour of these amorphous polymers depends on temperature. Each polymer has a glass transition temperature, T_C. Below this temperature, parts of the polymer chain cannot move because their thermal energy is too small to

Perspex has a glass transition temperature of 120°C, well above room temperature. Perspex safety glasses are brittle.

let them separate from neighbouring chains. The material is therefore stiff and brittle.

Above the glass transition temperature, the energy of the molecules is high enough to allow movement between adjacent molecular chains. The polymer in this phase behaves more like rubber than glass.

The rubber molecules in a bungee cord are initially tangled up and coiled in a random way. When the cord is put under tension the coiled molecules begin to unwind (Fig. 15). The long chains are prevented from slipping past each other by cross-links between the chains. When the stress is removed, these cross-links pull the molecules back into their original coiled shape and the bungee goes back to its original length. If more cross-links are added, the rubber becomes more difficult to stretch. A process known as vulcanisation adds cross-links, usually using sulphur atoms, to make the rubber stiffer, stronger and to improve its resistance to wear.

Semicrystalline polymers

Some polymers have well-ordered, crystalline regions. Long-chain molecules can fold to form parallel rows of atoms, known as lamella. At the ends of the folds are less ordered, amorphous regions (Fig. 16).

When a stress is applied to a semicrystalline polymer the lamella begin to unfold. The molecules become realigned to form fibrils. At very high values of stress, the fibrils break down and the polymer chains become highly ordered. The material is now extremely strong. You can demonstrate this process, known as 'cold-drawing', by stretching the polythene rings used to hold cans of drink together. The material has a small elastic region, but when you exert a higher stress the extension becomes permanent; the polythene flows into a neck that gradually increases in length. The polythene becomes very strong along its length, but weaker if you exert a force across its width. This is because the forces between atoms in the polymer chain are stronger than the forces between adjacent chains.

Fig. 15 Stretching polymer chains

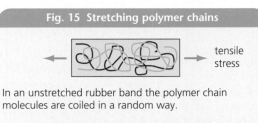

In an unstretched rubber band the polymer chain molecules are coiled in a random way.

Under stress the molecules untangle and become aligned.

Fig. 16 Polymer stretching

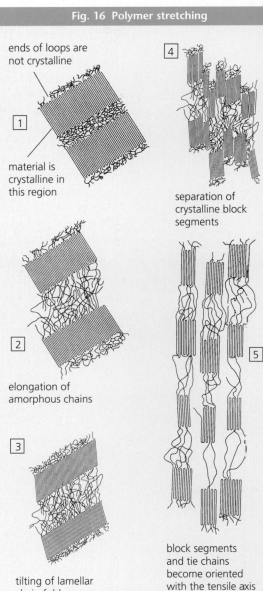

ends of loops are not crystalline

material is crystalline in this region

separation of crystalline block segments

elongation of amorphous chains

tilting of lamellar chain folds

block segments and tie chains become oriented with the tensile axis

11 Fibre-glass is used in the construction of boats and aircraft parts. It is made from glass fibres set in plastic resin. What are the benefits of using this combination of materials?

The spider's web

The silk produced by a spider is still puzzling the scientists who are trying to analyse and reproduce it. It is a semicrystalline polymer, with lines of up to ten amino acid molecules forming the lamella. The strength of such a polymer depends on its crystalline regions, and its elasticity is due to its amorphous regions. Spider silk seems to have less well-ordered crystalline regions than most polymers, but the amorphous regions are more orderly than normal. It takes about 20 different amino acids to build the chain, whereas most artificial polymers have only one or two basic building blocks. It may be that the secret of the spider's silk lies in the sheer complexity of its polymer chains.

KEY FACTS

- Polymers consist of long, chain-like molecules.

- Amorphous polymers are glassy below their glass transition temperature, T_G, and rubbery above it.

- Semicrystalline polymers have crystalline and amorphous regions.

- Some polymers, like rubber, are capable of very large elongation.

Stress and strain

When we use materials for any job, we want to be sure that the material will perform well and not let us down. Many modern materials show surprising responses to stress and can tell us in advance of any failures that may occur. Sometimes they can even repair themselves and return to their original shape after being stressed by a force.

We now have materials that respond to stress in these ways:

Shape-memory alloys – always go back to their original shape when subjected to temperature changes or stress, e.g. some makes of spectacle frames are made from shape-memory alloys so that if they are dropped they spring back into shape. Dentists have experimented with dental braces made from shape-memory alloys to avoid having to keep returning to the surgery to have the brace adjusted.

Fibre optic cable can provide feedback because when it is bent or stretched the frequency of the light travelling in it changes. There are plans to use this idea in aircraft so that the control system in the aircraft 'knows' when something is happening in its structure, e.g. a bird strike, or fatigue in structural members.

Liquid crystals familiar in lap top computers or TV monitors because they can change their colour (and other properties) when electrical energy is applied. They will also change colour when the load on them changes and have been put into climbers' ropes and carrier bags to alert the user when the load is too great for the material.

Piezoelectric materials will either give out an electric current when they are compressed or change shape when they have an electric current passed through them. Gas lighters use these materials which need no batteries to light the gas with a spark. Artificial muscle could be made with these materials in combination with plastics. Rotor blades in helicopters have been fitted with piezoelectric crystals to provide feedback in an effort to reduce noise and vibration in the cockpit.

1 Prepare a presentation to suggest some possible 'atomic models' which could explain one of the following smart materials and their effects:
Shape-memory alloys
Piezoelectric crystals
Fibre optic cables
Liquid crystal displays

You will need to look for ideas within this chapter and other chapters in this book and possibly on the Internet, in magazines and text books in your library or Resources Centre.

Your presentation should be no longer than 10 minutes and should use overhead projection transparencies or Powerpoint presentation software if possible. You could also prepare posters or large diagrams on a white / black board to help your audience understand what you are proposing. Also, be prepared for a question and answer session at the end of your presentation.

2 a Manipulate the formula for stress so that the equation is expressed in terms of *area*.

b Manipulate the formula for Young modulus so that the equation is expressed in terms of change in length.

c In a structure, the following data was recorded:

Force = -1.52×10^4 newtons;
Area = 3.23×10^2 millimetres

Calculate the stress in the structure (MN m^{-2}). Use scientific notation and write the answer correct to two decimal places.

What conclusion can you come to from the result?

1 A steel specimen is made for a certain tensile testing machine. The specimen has a circular cross-section in the shape shown in the diagram.

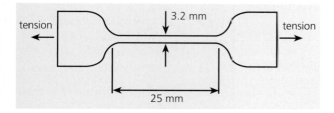

a The large diameter ends of the specimen are clamped in the jaws of the tensile machine. The specimen is designed so that when under test the narrow section, of effective length 25 mm, stretches while the large diameter end sections are considered not to stretch.

Explain why the large diameter end sections may be considered not to stretch when the specimen is under test. (2)

b Under test the specimen obeys Hooke's law up to the point where the stress is 2.0×10^8 Pa and the extension is 0.024 mm.

Calculate

(i) the extension of the specimen when the stress is 1.0×10^8 Pa,

(ii) a value for the Young modulus of the steel,

(iii) the cross-sectional area of the narrow section of the specimen,

(iv) the tension when the stress is 2.0×10^8 Pa. (5)

(AQA PH01 Jun 98 Q4)

2 a An alloy is made by mixing together two different metals. One metal has a density of 2500 kg m^{-3} and the other has a density of 8000 kg m^{-3}. The alloy is made by mixing together the two metals in the ratio of 2:1 by **volume**, with the higher proportion being the lower density metal.

Calculate

(i) the mass of a sample of the alloy having a volume of 0.30 m^3,

(ii) the density of the alloy,

(iii) the volume of a girder of mass 300 kg made from the alloy. (5)

b A new alloy is made by mixing the metals together in the ratio of 2:1 by **mass**, again with the higher proportion being the lower density metal. Calculate the density of this alloy. (3)

(AQA PH01 Jun 97 Q2)

3 a The Young modulus is defined as the ratio of *tensile stress* to *tensile strain*.

Explain what is meant by the two terms

tensile stress

tensile strain (3)

b A long wire is suspended vertically and a load of 10 N is attached to its lower end. The extension of the wire is measured accurately. In order to obtain a value for the Young modulus of the wire's material **two** more quantities must be measured.

State what these are and in each case indicate how an accurate measurement might be made. (4)

c Sketch a graph which shows how stress and strain are related for a ductile substance. (2)

(AQA PH01 Feb 97 Q1)

4 As part of a quality check, a manufacturer of fishing line subjects a sample to a tensile test. The sample of line is 2.0 m long and is of constant circular cross-section of diameter 0.50 mm. Hooke's law is obeyed up to the point when the line has been extended by 52 mm at a tensile stress of 1.8×10^8 Pa.

The maximum load the line can support before breaking is 45 N at an extension of 88 mm.

a Calculate

(i) the value of the Young modulus,

(ii) the breaking stress (assuming the cross-sectional area remains constant),

(iii) the breaking strain. (5)

b Sketch a graph to show how you expect the tensile stress to vary with strain. Mark the value of stress and corresponding strain at

(i) the limit of Hooke's law,

(ii) the breaking point. (4)

(AQA PH01 Mar 99 Q3)

5 Materials are often described as being *crystalline, polymeric* or *amorphous*.

Explain the meaning of each of the terms in italics and name **one** example of each type of material. (5)

(AQA PH01 Mar 98 Q7)

Glossary

Absolute zero   The lowest possible temperature; all molecular motion stops at absolute zero.

Absorption spectrum   A series of dark lines or bands that are characteristic of an absorbing material. Radiation emitted by a source can be selectively absorbed by a material between the source and the observer, e.g. absorption of a star's light by clouds of interstellar gas.

Acceleration, *a*   The rate of change of velocity (measured in $m\,s^{-2}$).

Activity   The number of decays (or emissions) per second in a radioactive source (measured in becquerel, Bq).

Air resistance (drag)   A force that acts to oppose motion relative to the air. The drag on a moving object increases if its speed relative to the air increases.

Alpha particle   Strongly ionising, short-range radiation emitted by some radioisotopes. An alpha particle is two neutrons and two protons tightly bound together.

Ammeter   An instrument of low resistance connected in series with a component to measure the current.

Amorphous   Materials that have no long-range order.

Analogue   A smoothly changing quantity used to represent information, e.g. the angle of hands on a clock represents time.

Annihilation   When particles of matter and antimatter meet, such as an electron and a positron, the particles disappear and their mass is transferred to energy. This is annihilation.

Anode   Positive electrode or positive terminal.

Antinode   The point on a standing wave where a quantity reaches a maximum. Usually refers to maximum displacement.

Antiparticles   A particle identical in mass to another more common particle, but different in other properties, e.g. charge, baryon number and strangeness. A bar over the particle letter, e.g. $\bar{p}$, indicates that it is an antiparticle.

Atom   The smallest particle of an element that shows the chemical properties of that element.

Atomic mass unit (u)   A small unit of mass used in nuclear physics. 1 u is defined as one-twelfth of the mass of a carbon-12 atom ($1\ u = 1.66043 \times 10^{-27}\ kg$).

Atomic number   The number of protons in the nucleus of an atom is known as its atomic number. The atomic number is also the number of electrons in the neutral (i.e. not ionised) atom.

Avogadro constant   The number of particles in a mole of anything: $N_A = 6.023 \times 10^{23}$ particles per mole.

Background radiation   The average level of radiation in the environment. It arises from both natural sources, such as radioactive rocks, and artificial sources, such as X-rays used in medicine.

Bandwidth   The width of the band of frequencies which can be passed by a circuit.

Baryon   A particle (a kind of hadron) with baryon number of +1. A baryon is made of three quarks. Protons and neutrons are baryons.

Baryon number   A number assigned to an observable particle which is the result of a combination of particular quarks. Baryons all have baryon number of +1, and their antiparticles have baryon number of –1.

Beta particle   A high-speed electron emitted from the nucleus of some radioisotopes.

Binding energy   In an atomic nucleus, this is the energy needed to pull it apart, i.e. to separate the individual neutrons and protons.

Black body   A perfect absorber of (heat) radiation. Black bodies are also the best possible emitters. A black body absorbs all of the radiation that falls upon it and reflects none. The temperature of a black body determines the amount of radiation that it emits at each wavelength.

Black hole   An astronomical body that is so dense that its gravitational field is strong enough to prevent even light escaping from it.

Boltzmann constant, *k*   The gas constant for a single ideal gas molecule ($k = R / N_A = 1.381 \times 10^{-23}\ J\,K^{-1}$).

Bosons   Particles which transmit force between other particles, e.g. the W boson which transmits the weak interaction. Bosons are particles with integral spin.

Bottom quark   A relatively heavy quark, discovered experimentally in 1977. Carries the conserved quantity, 'bottomness'.

Bound state   An atomic electron is held in orbit around the atom; energy is required to remove the electron from the atom. The electron's energy is defined as negative, and the electron is said to be in a bound state.

Brittle   A material which does not deform plastically before it fractures is said to be brittle, e.g. glass.

Capacitor   A device which stores electrical charge (and so electrical energy).

Capacity (of battery)   The total charge that a battery can supply to the circuit (measured in ampere-hours, A h).

Carrier wave   A wave which is encoded with information for transmission, e.g. light waves are the carrier wave in fibre optics.

Cathode   Negative electrode or negative terminal.

Cathode rays   The rays emitted from the heated cathode in a low-pressure gas tube. Later shown to be electrons by J.J. Thomson.

Centre of gravity   The point at which the weight of a body acts.

Centre of mass   For some applications, an object can be treated as if all its mass is concentrated at one point. This point is called the centre of mass. If the resultant force acting on a body passes through the centre of mass then the body will accelerate in a straight line. If the resultant force does not pass through the centre of mass the body will also spin.

Centripetal   Towards the centre.

Characteristic lines   X-rays emitted at specific frequencies which are dependent on the target material.

Charge   A fundamental property of matter; charged objects experience electrostatic forces. Charge may be positive, zero or negative.

Charge conservation   The total charge before and after a reaction between particles is always the same.

Charm   A quantity, similar to charge, which is conserved during particle interactions (carried by a charm quark).

Chromatic dispersion   The splitting of waves into different wavelengths during refraction, e.g. the coloured spectrum produced by a prism.

Cloud chamber   A device which gives a tiny cloud trail along the track of a charged particle.

Coherent   Describes waves which are of the same frequency, polarisation and amplitude and in a constant phase relationship.

Component   A vector may be replaced by several (usually two) different vectors known as components. Components are usually at right angles to each other, e.g. horizontal and vertical, and together have exactly the same effect as the original vector.

Compression   Region of a longitudinal wave where density is increased as particles move closer together.

Conductivity   A measure of how well a material conducts electricity (1/resistivity).

Conservation rules   Constraints on the type of particle interactions that are possible. Only some types of decays and interactions between particles are observed. Many possible interactions are never seen. One constraint is that charge remains the same before and after any interaction. There are other conservation rules, e.g. of baryon number and strangeness.

Constructive interference   Interference which results in an increased amplitude.

Conventional current   Consists of positive charge flow. It flows from the positive supply terminal, around the circuit, to the negative supply terminal.

Couple   The turning effect of two equal but opposite forces, F, separated by a distance d. Couple = $F \times d$.

Critical angle   The minimum angle at which total internal reflection occurs; the angle at which the refracted ray travels along the boundary between the media.

Current, I   The rate of flow of charge in a circuit (measured in amperes, A).

De Broglie relationship   Particles, e.g. electrons, can display wave behaviour. Their wavelength, λ, a wave property, depends on their momentum, p, a particle property, as described by de Broglie's relationship: $p = h / \lambda$

Decay constant, λ   The probability that a radioactive nucleus will decay in a given time period.

Degrees of freedom   Ways of moving which have energy linked with them, e.g. translation, rotation, vibration.

Destructive interference   Interference leading to decreased wave amplitude, and ultimately to complete cancellation.

Diffraction   The spreading out of the edges of waves to occupy areas which would otherwise be in shadow.

Diffraction grating   A grating of many narrow slits, each causing diffraction. These diffracted waves then interfere.

Diffusion   The spreading of the molecules of one substance between the molecules of another due to the random motion of molecules.

Digital   Digital quantities vary in big steps or jumps. Most systems use on/off switching, i.e. binary.

Displacement, s   The distance travelled in a certain direction from a given point. It is a vector quantity measured in metres, m.

Down quark   A fundamental particle, constituent of protons and neutrons.

Ductile   Describes a material which can withstand large plastic deformation. Copper is easily drawn into wires and is a ductile material.

Dynamic friction   The frictional force between two surfaces in relative motion; it acts so as to oppose the sliding.

Dynamo   A device which transfers kinetic energy to electrical energy.

E.m.f.   Abbreviation for electromotive force.

Efficiency   The ratio of useful energy output to total energy input, or power output to power input.

Elastic   A material that stretches under a load and then returns to its original dimensions when the load is removed.

Elastic collision   If the total kinetic energy before and after a collision is the same, the collision is said to be elastic, i.e. kinetic energy is conserved in an elastic collision.

Elastic limit   When an object is subjected to a force which is just large enough to cause permanent deformation, it is said to have reached its elastic limit.

Electric field   A region of space where charged objects experience a force.

Electromagnetic waves   Waves which propagate by swapping energy between electric and magnetic fields; includes radio waves, microwaves, infrared radiation, visible light, ultraviolet, X-rays and gamma rays.

Electromotive force   The energy per coulomb produced by a source of electricity; also the p.d. across a source when no current flows.

Electron   Charged particle of charge 1.6×10^{-19} C and mass 9×10^{-31} kg. The main charge carrier in metals.

Electron diffraction   High-energy electrons passed through very small gaps, such as the inter-atomic spaces in graphite, produce a diffraction pattern.

Electronvolt (eV)   A unit of energy used in atomic and nuclear physics. It is the energy gained by an electron when it is accelerated through a potential difference of 1 volt ($1 \text{ eV} = 1.6 \times 10^{-19}$ J).

Emission spectrum   The range of wavelengths emitted by a luminous source is known as its emission spectrum. It may be a line, band or continuous spectrum.

Energy   Energy is the stored ability to do work.

Energy level   Electrons in an atom can only have specific energy values. These are known as the atom's energy levels.

Equation of state   An equation which relates the state of a system (e.g. pressure and volume of a gas) to temperature.

Equilibrium position   The usual resting place of a system.

Excitation   When an electron absorbs energy and moves to a higher atomic energy level, the atom is said to be in an excited state.

Exponential decay   The name given to a mathematical relationship which has a constant reduction period, such as radioactive decay or the discharge of a capacitor.

Feynman diagrams   A representation of the exchange of particles in an interaction.

First law of thermodynamics   Heat supplied equals rise of internal energy of the system plus work done by the system: $\Delta Q = \Delta U + \Delta W$

Fission   The splitting of a large atomic nucleus, usually plutonium or uranium, into two smaller nuclei. The process releases a few free neutrons and a large amount of energy.

Fixed points   Measurements made at standard temperatures which are used to calibrate thermometers.

Flux (magnetic)   Imaginary lines through space, used to explain magnetic effects. Iron filings give a picture of flux patterns.

Frequency, f   The number of oscillations, or waves, in one second.

Fundamental   The fundamental frequency is the lowest natural frequency of oscillation in a system.

Fundamental particle   Constituents of all matter. These include quarks (which make up protons, neutrons, etc.), leptons (these include electrons and neutrinos) and bosons.

Fusion   The joining together of two light nuclei, e.g. isotopes of hydrogen, to form a heavier nucleus, such as helium. Energy is released in this process.

Gamma ray   Penetrating short-wavelength ionising radiation emitted by some radioisotopes.

Gauge bosons   See bosons.

Geostationary   Describes an orbit that keeps a satellite over exactly the same point on the Earth.

Gravitational field   The region around a mass where another mass would experience a gravitational attraction.

Gravitational field strength, g   The force exerted on a unit mass by a gravitational field (in N kg^{-1}). On Earth, g is roughly equal to 10 N kg^{-1}.

Gravitational potential energy   The energy due to the position of a mass, m, in a gravitational field. In a uniform field, such as that close to the surface of the Earth, the change in potential energy due to an increase in height, Δh, is $\Delta E_p = mg\Delta h$, where g is the gravitational field strength.

Graviton   The exchange particle that is supposed to carry the gravitational force. No experimental evidence has confirmed the existence of gravitons.

Ground state   An atom is said to be in its ground state when its electrons all occupy the lowest possible allowed energy levels.

Hadron   Particle composed of quarks. Hadrons include the baryons (e.g. neutrons and protons) and mesons (e.g. pions and kaons).

Half-life, $T_{1/2}$ The time taken for the number of radioactive nuclei in a source to drop to half its original value.

Half-wave dipole   A type of aerial designed to transmit, or receive, radio waves.

Heat   Energy transferred from one place to another because the places are at different temperatures.

Inelastic collision   In an inelastic collision, the total kinetic energy of the system decreases, i.e. kinetic energy is transferred as other forms of energy. Momentum is conserved in inelastic collisions.

Instantaneous   Values measured over an infinitesimally short period of time, Δt. The instantaneous speed of an object can be calculated from the distance travelled in a very small time interval, Δt.

Insulator   A material with a very high electrical resistance. A material where the atomic electrons are not free to move through the substance.

Intensity   The power through a given area (measured in W m^{-2}).

Interference   The addition of waves which leads to changes in amplitude.

Internal energy   The sum of all kinetic and potential energies of the component parts of a system. In ideal gases, the internal energy is equal to total kinetic energy.

Internal resistance   The resistance of the materials inside a source of electricity.

Inverse square law   The intensity of gamma radiation from a point gamma source is inversely proportional to the square of the distance from the source. If you double the distance between yourself and the source, you will receive one quarter of the radiation dose. This relationship is known as an inverse square law. It is important in other areas of physics, e.g. the strength of the gravitational field due to a spherical mass or the strength of an electric field due to a point charge.

Ion   An atom which has gained or lost one or more electrons.

Ionisation   The removal of electrons from an atom, or the addition of electrons to an atom.

Ionisation chamber   A device relying on charged particles ionising air. The ionisation current is proportional to the number of particles.

Isotope   Atoms of an element can exist in different forms. These forms, called isotopes, have the same number of protons and electrons but different numbers of neutrons.

Isotropic   The same in all directions.

Kinetic energy   The energy stored in a moving mass ($E_k = {}^1/_2 mv^2$).

Kirchhoff's laws   1st law: the sum of currents at a junction is zero (charge is conserved).

2nd law: the sum of e.m.f.s is equal to the sum of p.d.s around a closed circuit loop (energy is conserved).

Laser   A device which produces intense light by stimulated emission from excited molecules (light amplification by stimulated emission of radiation).

Latent heat   The heat which you need to supply to a material to change its phase, e.g. heat is needed to convert water into steam.

Lepton   The lepton family of particles include the electron, the muon and the neutrinos. They are fundamental particles, with no internal structure. They take part in weak interactions but do not feel the strong force.

Limiting friction   The maximum frictional force between two surfaces. An applied force greater than this will produce motion.

Longitudinal   Describes a wave where oscillations are in the direction of wave travel.

Magnetic flux density, B   The strength of a magnetic field, measured by the force on a current-carrying wire or moving charge (S.I. unit is the tesla, T).

Mass defect   The difference between the mass of a nucleus and the total mass of the nucleons which make up that nucleus.

Mean free path   The average distance travelled by a molecule before it collides with another molecule. Also used for neutrons travelling through a moderator.

Mesons   Particles (hadrons) made up of a quark and an antiquark.

mmHg   The pressure exerted by a column of mercury 1 mm high.

Molar heat capacity   The heat needed to warm up one mole of a substance by 1 °C (or 1 K).

Mole   The amount of material containing the same number of particles as 12 g of the isotope carbon-12.

Molecule   The smallest particle of a substance (element or compound), that shows the chemical properties of that substance. Often composed of a number of different atoms.

Moment   The turning effect of a force around a point. Moment = force × perpendicular distance to the point.

Momentum   The linear momentum of a body = mass × velocity. It is a vector quantity, measured in $kg\,m\,s^{-1}$.

Multimode dispersion   A sharp pulse of signal is dispersed after going through an optical fibre because rays take different paths.

Multiplier resistor   A high resistance which limits current through a moving coil meter, allowing it to function as a voltmeter.

Muon   A particle in the lepton family carrying the same charge as the electron but much more massive than the electron. Found in cosmic rays.

Natural frequency   For a vibrating system, this is the frequency at which the system oscillates when disturbed.

Neutron   A particle of zero charge found in the nucleus of almost all atoms. A free neutron is unstable and decays to a proton and an electron with a half-life of 11 minutes.

Neutron star   The very dense remnant left after the supernova of a star.

Newton   The S.I. unit of force. 1 newton is the force that will accelerate a mass of 1 kg at $1\,m\,s^{-2}$.

Node (waves)   The point on a standing wave where a quantity is zero. Usually refers to zero displacement.

Noise   An unwanted signal introduced, for example, by electrical discharges, other signals of similar frequency, etc.

Normal   At right angles to a surface.

Nucleons   Particles which form the atomic nucleus, i.e. neutrons and protons.

Ohm's law   The current through a conductor is proportional to the p.d., if temperature and other physical conditions stay constant.

Optical fibre   Thin fibre of very pure glass, normally coated with another layer of glass of lower refractive index. Light passes through the fibre by total internal reflection.

Optically dense   A material where light travels at a significantly lower speed than in a vacuum.

P.d.   Abbreviation for potential difference.

Pair production   In a pair production event a photon's energy is manifested as the masses of an electron and a positron.

Parallax   The apparent relative motion of two objects due to the motion of the observer, e.g. a nearby star appears to move against the background of stars due to the annual motion of the Earth.

Period   Time taken to complete one cycle of oscillation, one complete cycle of vibration, one complete wave or one complete rotation in circular motion.

Phase   A measurement of the relative timing of two oscillations of the same frequency.

Photoelectric effect   The emission of electrons from a metal surface caused by light of sufficiently high frequency.

Photon   A quantum of electromagnetic radiation. It carries an amount of energy, E, that depends upon the frequency, f, of the radiation. $E = hf$, where h is Planck's constant.

Pions   Type of meson that can act as an exchange particle between neutrons and protons at very short range (a few fm).

Plastic   A material which does not return to its original dimensions when a deforming force is removed is said to be plastic.

Plum pudding   Early model of the atom as a uniformly dense positive cloud, with electrons stuck into it, like plums in a pudding.

Point source of waves   A source which produces circular wavefronts as though they came from a single point in space.

Polarised   A transverse wave is polarised when the vibration of the wave is confined to one direction.

Polycrystalline   Materials, such as metals, that consist of a large number of small crystals, called grains, at various angles to each other.

Positron   A particle with the same mass as an electron, and equal but opposite charge (also called an antielectron).

Potential difference   The energy transferred per coulomb when charge moves through a circuit (measured in $J\,C^{-1}$ or V).

Potential divider   A pair of resistors which divide input p.d. in the ratio of the resistances.

Potential energy   The stored ability to do work. A body may have potential energy due to its position in a field, e.g. a mass raised above the surface of the Earth has gravitational potential energy due to its position in the Earth's gravitational field. Elastic potential energy is due to work done in changing the shape of an object, e.g. a stretched rubber band has elastic potential energy.

Power, P   The rate at which work is done. It can also be thought of as the rate at which energy is transferred (measured in watts, W).

Pressure, P   The normal force per unit area; pressure = force/area (measured in pascals, Pa; $1\,Pa = 1\,N\,m^{-2}$). Also measured in bars, atmospheres, mmHg.

Progressive wave   A wave which transfers energy from one place to another.

Propagation   The process by which a wave spreads itself through space.

Proton   A positively charged particle found in the nucleus of all atoms. Thought to be stable, until recently. Has a very long lifetime.

Quantum theory   This theory states that some physical quantities, like the energy of an electron in an atom, can only have certain discrete values. For example, charge is quantised in units of the charge of an electron; it is not possible to have a charge equivalent to 1.5 electrons.

Quarks   Fundamental particles which, in combination, make up all particles called hadrons. Three types of quark are of interest in considering the structure of protons, neutrons and pions. These are called the up, **u**, down, **d**, and the strange, **s**, quarks. (The three other quarks are: charm, top and bottom.)

Radioisotope   A form of a nucleus which is radioactive.

Rarefaction   A region of a longitudinal wave where the density is lower due to particles moving further apart.

Real image   An image that can be projected onto a screen.

Refraction   The change of direction of waves which results from a change of speed.

Refractive index   Light slows down in more dense media. The absolute refractive index of a material is the speed of light in a vacuum divided by the speed in the material.

Resilient   Materials that can undergo repeated deformations without transferring a significant amount of energy as internal energy.

Resistance, R   A measure of a component's tendency to oppose electrical current; ratio of p.d. to current ($R = V / I$).

Resistivity, ρ   A measure of the resistance of materials; resistance of a specimen of unit length and unit cross-sectional area.

Resonance   This occurs when a system accepts energy from a driving source at its natural frequency – the amplitude increases greatly.

Resultant   It is possible to combine a number of vectors into a single vector which has the same effect. This single vector is called the resultant.

Root mean square, r.m.s.   The square root of the average of the squares of the values; a useful average if quantities can be both positive and negative, e.g. the arithmetic mean of ($+3$, -4, $+6$, -5, 0) is 0, but the r.m.s. value is 4.14.

S.I.   Stands for Systeme Internationale and refers to the system of units based on the kilogram, metre and second. S.I. units are nearly universally used by scientists.

Scalar   A physical quantity which has magnitude but no direction. Mass, speed, temperature and potential difference are examples of scalar quantities.

Secondary wavelet   Every point on a wavefront is a disturbance of the medium, and so acts as a tiny point source of waves called secondary wavelets.

Shunt resistor   A low value resistor which increases the ammeter range by allowing most of the current to bypass the meter.

Snell's law   The refractive index of a material = sin (angle of incidence) / sin (angle of refraction). The angles are measured from the normal. Snell's law relates angles to refractive indices.

Special relativity   Einstein's theory of mechanics, published in 1905. The theory gives results which are identical to Newton's laws except when relative velocities approach the speed of light.

Specific   This term means 'per unit mass' (in S.I. units, the value per kg).

Specific heat capacity   The heat which you need to supply to 1 kg of material to warm it up by 1 °C (or 1 K).

Specific latent heat   The latent heat required per kg of material.

Spontaneous   A spontaneous event is one that occurs without an external cause. Radioactive decay is a spontaneous event.

Standing wave   A state of oscillation of a system which can be regarded as resembling a wave standing still.

Stationary wave   Alternative term for standing wave.

Steady-state (thermal)   If all temperatures have stabilised throughout the specimen/apparatus, it is said to be in steady-state.

Stiffness   This is a measure of how difficult it is to stretch a material. Tensile stiffness is measured by the ratio: stress/strain (known as the Young modulus).

Strange quark   A fundamental particle carrying the conserved property of 'strangeness'.

Strangeness   Property of some quarks and hence of some hadrons. The need to conserve strangeness is a rule that particle interactions follow. This explains why many interactions – which would otherwise be seen – do not happen.

Stress   The force per unit cross-sectional area (measured in Pa).

Strong nuclear force   One of the fundamental forces. The strong nuclear force acts between nucleons over a very short range and holds the nuclei of atoms together.

Superconduction   At low temperatures, some materials lose all electrical resistance, i.e. they become perfect conductors.

Tensile strain   Extension per unit length (has no units).

Tensile stress   The force per unit cross-sectional area which is tending to elongate an object.

Tension   A force which acts so as to elongate an object, e.g. a tow rope would be in tension.

Terminal p.d.   The p.d. across the terminals of a source when current is drawn; energy per coulomb delivered to a circuit.

Terminal velocity   An object falling through the atmosphere reaches a top speed, known as its terminal velocity. This happens when the opposing forces of weight and air resistance are equal.

Tesla (T)   Unit of magnetic flux density.

Thermal equilibrium   If objects are in thermal equilibrium, there is no net flow of heat between them; they are at the same temperature.

Thermal radiation   Electromagnetic radiation emitted by objects as a result of the random thermal motion of their particles. The spectrum of emitted radiation depends on the surface temperature of the object (see black body).

Thermionic emission   The emission of electrons from a heated cathode.

Thermocouple   A thermometer formed by joining two dissimilar metals. A small e.m.f. is produced that depends on the temperature.

Thermodynamics   The study of the movement of heat through systems.

Thermometric property   Any material property which varies reliably with temperature, and so can be used to make a thermometer.

Threshold frequency   The minimum frequency of light which can cause photoelectric emission.

Top quark   A fundamental particle. The heaviest of the quarks, 35 000 times more massive than the up and down quarks, experimentally verified at Fermilab in 1995.

Torque   The rotational equivalent of a force. An unbalanced torque causes an object to spin, i.e. gives it angular acceleration.

Total internal reflection   At high angles of incidence to a less dense medium, all incident radiation is reflected inside the more dense medium.

Transverse   Describes a wave where vibrations are at right angles to the direction of wave travel.

Ultimate tensile stress, UTS   The breaking stress of a material.

Ultraviolet catastrophe   The conflict of wave theory with the observations of black-body radiation. The theory predicted that small wavelengths should be accompanied by a large intensity. Only low intensities are observed. The cause of this low intensity was impossible to explain using a wave model of light.

Universal molar gas constant, R $R = PV / T$ for one mole of gas. It is universal, i.e. the same for all gases when their behaviour is close to ideal ($R = 8.31\,\mathrm{J\,K^{-1}\,mol^{-1}}$).

Up quark   A fundamental particle, one of the constituents of protons and neutrons.

Upthrust   The buoyancy force on an object in a fluid. Upthrust is due to the difference in fluid pressure on the top and bottom surfaces of the object.

Vector   A physical quantity which has a direction as well as a magnitude. Force, velocity and electric field strength are examples of vector quantities.

Velocity, v   Velocity is the rate of change of displacement measured in $m\,s^{-1}$.

Virtual image   An image which can be seen through an optical instrument but cannot be formed on a screen.

Virtual particle   Particle exchanged between other particles during interactions. A particle which transmits force between other particles.

Voltage   An alternative term for potential difference.

Voltmeter   An instrument of very high resistance connected in parallel with a component to measure the potential difference.

Wave–particle duality   The term used to describe the fact that light behaves as a wave and a particle. Subatomic particles, such as electrons, show wave and particle properties.

Wavelength, λ   The distance travelled by a wave in one period of oscillation; the length in space of one cycle.

Weak interaction   Many particles change into other particles by processes that cannot be explained by the strong force, gravity or electromagnetism. The short range influence responsible for such changes (or decays) is the weak interaction. Beta decay is an example of a particle change governed by the weak interaction.

Weight, W   Force on a mass, m, due to a gravitational field, measured in newtons, N ($W = mg$).

Work   Work, W, is done by a force, F, when it moves its point of application in the direction of the force. If there is an angle θ between the direction of the force and the displacement, s, then $W = Fs \cos \theta$. Work is a scalar quantity (measured in joules, J).

Work function   The energy needed to remove an electron from a material in thermionic or photoelectric emission processes.

X-rays   Very penetrating, ionising radiation from the short wavelength (high frequency) end of the electromagnetic spectrum. An X-ray is produced by rapid deceleration of a charged particle or by a high-energy electron transition in an atom.

Young modulus, E   A measure of the stiffness of a material, equal to tensile stress divided by tensile strain (measured in Pa).

Answers to Questions

Chapter 1

1 Smaller soot particles have a lower mass so collisions with water molecules would have a greater effect on their velocity.

Water molecules will move faster if the liquid is heated, they will collide faster (and more often) with the soot particles, increasing the Brownian motion.

Diffusion rate is less with more massive particles. At any given temperature, any molecule has the same average kinetic energy, so more massive molecules move slower, reducing the rate of diffusion.

2 Diffusion increases with temperature, because the molecules are moving faster.

3 **a** 1.45 GW
   b 142×10^{-12} m or 1.42×10^{-10} m

4 An atom cannot be bigger than the thickness of the film, but the film could be many atoms thick.

5 To improve the accuracy of measuring the volume; otherwise, measuring the volume of 1 drop can be achieved using the apparatus shown in Fig. 3(a), p. 9.

6 Measure the thickness of the book, divide by the number of pages. This gives the thickness of 1 sheet of paper as about 0.1 mm. If atomic size $\approx 1 \times 10^{-10}$ m, the paper is about 1×10^6 (i.e. a million) atoms thick.

7 The mass of the electron is very small compared with molecules of air. An electron beam passing through the air would very quickly be scattered and would not reach the fluorescent screen.

8 Nuclear radius of $^{12}_{6}$C is 3.04×10^{-15} m
Atomic mass = 19.932×10^{-27} kg

$$\text{Density} = \frac{\text{mass}}{\text{volume}} = \frac{19.932 \times 10^{-27}}{{}^4/_3\pi(3.04 \times 10^{-15})^3}$$

$$= 1.7 \times 10^{17} \text{ kg m}^{-3}$$

(subtracting the mass of the electrons would make only a small difference).

9 92 protons, 92 electrons, 235 − 92 = 143 neutrons.

10 U-238 has 3 more neutrons than U-235. It is otherwise identical.

11 Heavier elements have larger nuclei, so more neutrons are needed to overcome the longer-range electrostatic repulsion between the protons.

12 Short-range (max 5 fm), attractive between 1–5 fm, strongly repulsive at less than 1 fm.

Chapter 2

1 $100 \times 10^3 \times 1.6 \times 10^{-19} = 1.6 \times 10^{-14}$ J

2 $100 \times 10^9 \times 1.6 \times 10^{-19} = 1.6 \times 10^{-8}$ J

3 $0.106 / 0.934 = 0.1135$ u $= 1.88 \times 10^{-28}$ kg

4 The magnetic field will curve an upwards electron, or a downwards positron, in the same direction (Fleming's left-hand law). The lead slows the particle down so the track will curve more. This shows that it is a positron moving down.

5 $E = 2mc^2 = 2 \times 1.672 \times 10^{-27} \times (3 \times 10^8)^2 = 3.01 \times 10^{-10}$ J
   $= 1.88 \times 10^9$ eV
   $= 1.9$ GeV

6 A neutrino *is* emitted in beta decay, its mass may be zero (though the latest measurements suggest not). They *are* electrically neutral.

7 **a** High hydrogen content means lots of protons for the reaction with antineutrinos.
   b A nuclear reactor releases lots of beta particles and (hence) antineutrinos from fission reactions and from the decay of radioisotopes created by fission.

Chapter 3

1 **a** $1 \neq 0 + (-1)$ Not allowed, charge is not conserved

    b $(-1) + 1 = (-1) + (1)$ Allowed. Charge is conserved

    c $(-1) + (1) \neq (-1) + 1 + (-1)$ Not allowed, charge is not conserved

    (a) and (c) are forbidden.

2 **a** $1 = 1 + 0$ Baryon number is conserved

    b $1 + 1 \neq 1 + 1 + 1$ Baryon number is not conserved

    c $1 + 1 = 1 + 1 + 0 + 0$ Baryon number is conserved

    b is forbidden

3 **a** $0 + 0 \neq -1 + (-1)$ Strangeness is not conserved
    b $0 + 0 = -1 + (-1)$ Strangeness is conserved
    c $1 + 0 \neq 0 + (-1)$ Strangeness is not conserved

4 **a** $Q\checkmark$ $B\checkmark$ $S\times$ forbidden, strangeness not conserved

    b $Q\checkmark$ $B\times$ $S\checkmark$ forbidden, baryon number not conserved

    c $Q\checkmark$ $B\checkmark$ $S\checkmark$ allowed

    d $Q\checkmark$ $B\checkmark$ $S\checkmark$ allowed

    e $Q\checkmark$ $B\times$ $S\checkmark$ forbidden, baryon number not conserved

    f $Q\checkmark$ $B\times$ $S\times$ forbidden, baryon number and strangeness not conserved

5 X must carry no charge, and have a baryon number of 0, and a strangeness of 0. X must have a L_μ value of 1 and must carry opposite spin. A muon-neutrino satisfies these criteria.
$\pi^+ \rightarrow \mu^+ + \nu_\mu$

6

	u	d	d	neutron
Q	$2/3$	$-1/3$	$-1/3$	0
B	$1/3$	$1/3$	$1/3$	1
S	0	0	0	0

	$\overline{u}$	$\overline{d}$	$\overline{d}$	antineutron
Q	$-2/3$	$1/3$	$1/3$	0
B	$-1/3$	$-1/3$	$-1/3$	-1
S	0	0	0	0

7 Mesons are 2 quarks, always a quark and an antiquark. Mesons can contain 1 strange quark, s , or antistrange quark, $\overline{s}$, but *not* 2 strange quarks.

    Baryons can contain up to 3 strange quarks.

8 In some ways a neutron has 'hidden charge' – it carries three charged quarks whose total charge is zero. A meson made of a strange and an antistrange quark, $s\overline{s}$, would have no obvious strangeness.

9

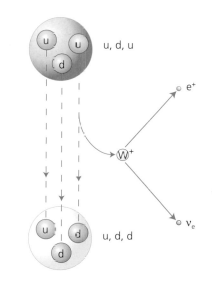

10 Gravity and electromagnetic forces are both infinite. Their bosons are massless. Gravity is only attractive, whereas electromagnetism is attractive and repulsive because two different charges, plus and minus, exist.

11 They only interact with matter via the weak interaction (very short range) and gravity (a weak force).

12 a electromagnetism
    b strong interaction
    c weak interaction

Chapter 4

1 A wave on a string does not carry energy along the string, but the sound wave *does* carry energy through the air.

   The wave on the string has nodes which do not vibrate; the sound wave does not.

   The wave on the string is a transverse wave; the sound wave is longitudinal.

2 Half a wavelength is now less than it was. If the wavelength gets less, the frequency must increase (while speed stays constant).

3 Using $c = f\lambda$, wavelengths are between 17 m and 17 mm.

4 a $f = c/\lambda = 3 \times 10^8\,\text{m s}^{-1} / 1500\,\text{m} = 200\,\text{kHz}$
   b $f = c/\lambda = 3 \times 10^8\,\text{m s}^{-1} / 700 \times 10^{-9}\,\text{m} = 4.29 \times 10^{14}\,\text{Hz}$

5 a

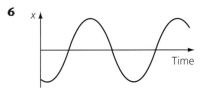

10 cm

Wavelengths are 1, 1/3, 1/5, 1/7, etc of fundamental

   b Wavelength could be 20.0 cm, 6.7 cm, 4.0 cm, etc. Using $c = f\lambda$ gives frequencies of 1.50 GHz, 4.50 GHz, 7.50 GHz, etc.

6

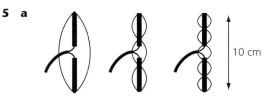

7 Difficult! With lateral inversion, no true inversion has taken place, because each point on the image is actually opposite the corresponding point on the object.

8

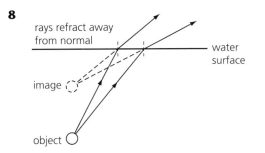

rays refract away from normal

water surface

image

object

9 Using $n = c/v$ and time = distance / speed, the times for the two colours are 164.04 and 164.00 µs. The difference of arrival times is therefore 0.04 µs, or 40 ns.

10 The relative refractive index is $1.60/1.40 = 1.143$
   A ray incident at 30° would refract at 25.9°, so strike the wall at $(90 - 25.9) = 64.1°$

11 The speed of light in the fibre is $c/n = 1.875 \times 10^8\,\text{m s}^{-1}$, and you can show that for every unit along the fibre, the critical angle path is 1.0667 units; so times are:
   straight path → $1\,\text{km}/v = 5.333 \times 10^{-6}\,\text{s}$
   longest path → $1.0667\,\text{km}/v = 5.689 \times 10^{-6}\,\text{s}$
   The time delay per kilometre is therefore 0.356 ms.

12 Over a 10 km cable, there would be a time delay of 3.56 ms. You could not transmit waves with a period longer than this. The maximum frequency is therefore $f = 1/T = 284\,\text{kHz}$. (This would be unacceptably low – real fibre optic cables have very close refractive indices for core and cladding to minimise the time delays.)

13 In a coherent bundle, each fibre carries information about one image point. The more image points, or pixels, there are, the more detailed the image will be. Fine fibres closely packed together will give a high resolution image. Incoherent bundles just carry light, not image information, and so the fibres can be much thicker.

Chapter 5

1 Kinetic energy of the incoming electron can excite an atomic electron to a higher energy level. As the electron returns to the ground state the atom will emit a photon of light.

2 a Three (From 3 to 2, 3 to 1 and 2 to 1)

   b 3 to 1: $\Delta E = -1.5 - (-13.6) = 12.1\,\text{eV} = 1.94 \times 10^{-18}\,\text{J}$

   $f = \Delta E/h$

   $= 1.94 \times 10^{-18} / 6.6 \times 10^{-34} = 2.94 \times 10^{15}\,\text{Hz}$

   Similar calculations give frequencies of $5.47 \times 10^{14}\,\text{Hz}$ and $2.47 \times 10^{15}\,\text{Hz}$

3 The largest possible energy change is $13.6\,\text{eV}$.
   This gives $\lambda = 91\,\text{nm}$.

4 The cooler atmosphere has many more atoms in their ground state so that absorption can take place. If the gases were as hot as the Sun there would be just as much emission as absorption.

5 The heat of the flame will excite some of the electrons in the sodium atoms to a higher energy level. These emit yellow light as they return to the lower energy level.

   With strong sunlight shining through the flame, there is more absorption in the sodium vapour; this makes the lines look darker.

6 Increasing the voltage means that the electrons have more energy. If they lose all that energy in one collision they will emit X-rays with a shorter wavelength. The electrons may now have enough energy to knock out an atomic electron from a lower energy level, leading to more characteristic lines.

7 The minimum wavelength only depends on the energy gained by the electrons as they are accelerated across the tube. This is fixed by the tube voltage. Atoms with higher atomic number have more tightly bound electrons. It takes more energy to knock them out of the lower energy levels and so the X-rays which are emitted have shorter wavelengths.

8 a No electrons are emitted, no matter how bright the red light is.

   b The number of electrons would increase as the blue light got brighter.

   c The maximum kinetic energy of the electrons is not affected by the brightness of the light. The kinetic energy would increase if higher frequency light, UV for example, was used.

9 Energy of ingoing photon $= hf$
   $= 6.6 \times 10^{-34} \times 3.4 \times 10^{19} = 2.24 \times 10^{-14}\,\text{J}$
   energy of outgoing photon $= hf$
   $= (6.6 \times 10^{-34} \times 3 \times 10^{8}) / (415 \times 10^{-9}) = 4.77 \times 10^{-19}\,\text{J}$
   energy absorbed $= \dfrac{(2.24 \times 10^{-14}\,\text{J} - 4.77 \times 10^{-19}\,\text{J})}{(2.24 \times 10^{-14}\,\text{J})} = 99.8\%$

10 $\phi = hf_T = hc/\lambda$
   $= (6.6 \times 10^{-34} \times 3 \times 10^{8}) / (415 \times 10^{-5})$
   $= 4.77 \times 10^{-19}\,\text{J} = 3\,\text{eV}$

11 Walking speed $\sim 2\,\text{m s}^{-1}$
   mass $\sim 60\,\text{kg}$
   momentum, $p = 120\,\text{kg m s}^{-1}$
   $\lambda = h/p = 6.61 \times 10^{-34} / 120 = 5.51 \times 10^{-36}\,\text{m}$
   Diffraction is noticeable if $d \sim \lambda$, that would need a *very* small doorway!

Chapter 6

1 Velocity is a vector quantity. Every time that the athletes change direction they are also changing their velocity. Speed is a scalar quantity. If the athletes are running equal distances in successive equal time intervals their speed stays the same.

2 **a** average speed = total distance / time = 10 000 / 1813.74
= 5.513 m s^{-1}

b average velocity = displacement / time = 0 m s^{-1}

3 The runner with the highest average speed wins. They will cover the distance in the shortest time.

4 It is the instantaneous speed at the moment of take-off which determines the length of the jump; the average speed of the run up is not important.

5 No. An object is only stationary relative to an observer. Another observer using a different frame of reference might see the object as moving. For example, you may be stationary relative to this book, but relative to the Sun you are hurtling through space at almost 30 km per second.

6 Horizontally, the Earth is stationary relative to the high jumper. Relative to an observer in space (who is not rotating with the Earth) the high jumper and the Earth are both moving with a horizontal velocity of up to 465 m s^{-1}.

7

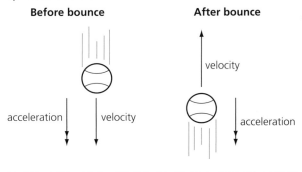

shot velocity
= 12.5 m s^{-1}

41°

horizontal component
= 12.5 cos 41° = 9.43 m s^{-1}

8 Just after the ball is dropped, its velocity and acceleration are downwards. After the ball has bounced, the velocity is upwards but the acceleration is still down.

Before bounce　　　　　　**After bounce**

velocity

acceleration　velocity　　　acceleration

9 **a** Acceleration is the slope of the graph
$a = 8/2 = 4$ m s^{-2}

b distance covered is the area under the graph. Do this in 2 stages, from 0–2 s and from 2–8 s.
distance = $\frac{1}{2}(2 \times 8) + (8 \times 6) = 56$ m

10

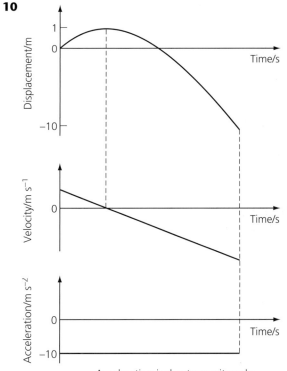

Acceleration is due to gravity only.

11 Use $a = (v - u) / t = (75 - 0) / 0.0005 = 150\,000\ \mathrm{m\ s^{-2}}$. This is 15 000 times the acceleration due to gravity!

12 At the top of the jump $v = 0\ \mathrm{m\ s^{-1}}$; $u = 4.8\ \mathrm{m\ s^{-1}}$; acceleration is due to gravity and acts down, $a = -9.8\ \mathrm{m\ s^{-2}}$. Rearrange $v^2 = u^2 + 2as$ to give:

$$s = \frac{v^2 - u^2}{2a} = \frac{0 - 23.0\ \mathrm{m^2\ s^{-2}}}{2 \times (-9.8\ \mathrm{m\ s^{-2}})} = 1.18\ \mathrm{m}$$

This is the height gained by the centre of mass, so add 0.95 m to give a height of 2.13 m for the centre of mass. (A top class athlete will jump with her centre of mass as close to the bar as possible.)

13 a Consider vertical motion first, use $s = ut + \frac{1}{2}at^2$ to find the time of flight. Since the jumpers move horizontally at first, $u = 0\ \mathrm{m\ s^{-1}}$ so:

$$t = \sqrt{\frac{2s}{a}} = \sqrt{\frac{2 \times 26.7\ \mathrm{m}}{9.8\ \mathrm{m\ s^{-2}}}} = 2.33\ \mathrm{s}$$

Horizontal distance must be at least 8.22 m so horizontal velocity must be at least $8.22\ \mathrm{m} / 2.33\ \mathrm{s} = 3.52\ \mathrm{m\ s^{-1}}$

b Horizontal velocity is approximately constant $= 3.52\ \mathrm{m\ s^{-1}}$

Vertical velocity is: $v = u + at = 0 + 9.8 \times 2.33$
$$= 22.8\ \mathrm{m\ s^{-1}}$$

Use scale drawing (or Pythagoras' theorem) to combine these. Final velocity $= 23.1\ \mathrm{m\ s^{-1}}$ at 81.3° to the horizontal.

14 Long jumpers can't manage the 'optimum take-off angle' without dropping their horizontal velocity to match their maximum vertical speed. This would be counter-productive. Some gymnastic events use a springboard which allows the gymnasts to get much closer to 45°.

Chapter 7

1 a $80 \times 9.8 = 784\ \mathrm{N}$
b $128 / 80 = 1.6\ \mathrm{N\ kg^{-1}}$

2
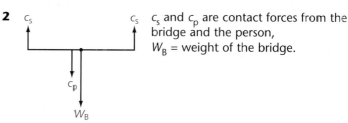
c_s and c_p are contact forces from the bridge and the person, W_B = weight of the bridge.

3 No. A larger weight means a larger contact force which means more friction, so the car is less likely to skid.

4 Actual contact area could be 0.01% of 4 cm², say $4 \times 10^{-8}\ \mathrm{m^2}$. Pressure = weight / area
weight $= \rho g V = 8000 \times 10 \times 8 \times 10^{-6} = 0.64\ \mathrm{N}$
so pressure at points of contact $= 0.64 / 4 \times 10^{-8}$
$= 16 \times 10^5\ \mathrm{Pa} = 16\ \mathrm{MPa}$

5 a $F = \mu N = 0.02 \times 500 = 10\ \mathrm{N}$
b Because the normal contact force is now less than the weight. Surfaces are not pressed together as hard.

6 Forces are weight, tension from cables and contact force from ground. Cables are in tension, the mast is in compression.

7
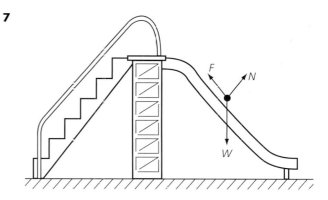
W = child's weight
N = normal contact force
F = friction acting on child

8

W_B → W_L → W_C →

← R_2 ← R_1

9

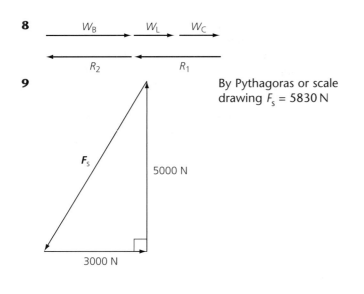

By Pythagoras or scale drawing $F_s = 5830$ N

10

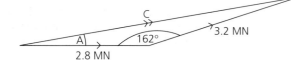

Resolve the weight.
Perpendicular to the slope,
$10\,000 \times \cos 15° =$
$N = 9660$ N

Parallel to slope,
$10\,000 \times \sin 15° = F =$
2600 N

11 Using the cosine rule:

$c^2 = (2.8)^2 + (3.20)^2 - 2 \times 2.8 \times 3.2 \times \cos 162°$
$c = 5.92$ MN
Using the sine rule:
$\sin A / 3.20 = \sin 162° / 5.92$
$\sin A = 0.167, A = 9.6°$
The resultant force is 9.6° above the force from tug B, which is 1.6° North of East.

12

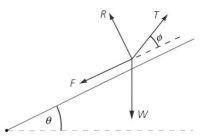

where T = tension in tow rope
F = friction
R = normal contact force
W = skier's weight

For equilibrium along the slope:

$F + W \sin \theta = T \cos \phi$

For equilibrium at right angles to the slope:
$R + T \sin \phi = W \cos \theta$

13 The increased flow over the roof surface leads to a drop in pressure above the roof. The higher pressure below can lift the roof off.

14 As the mast is lifted, the angle increases from 25°. The component of T perpendicular to the mast also increases. The moment of the weight decreases, because the perpendicular distance to X gets smaller.

15

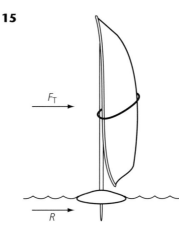

The transverse force caused by the wind would tip the sailboard over. The resistive force of the water on the daggerboard helps to balance this.

Chapter 8

1 In a head-on collision the front of the car is rapidly brought to a halt. Any rear seat passengers will continue at their original velocity until acted upon by a force, in accordance with Newton's first law. It may take a force equal to the weight of an elephant, say 35 000 N, to stop them. Without rear safety belts this force could be provided by the front seat passengers.

2 When a car is hit from behind, it is accelerated forwards. The car seats will accelerate with it, pushing a passenger's body forward. Without an external force to accelerate it, a passenger's head will retain its original velocity, lagging behind the rest of the body until the muscles of the neck pull it forwards. This results in 'whiplash' injuries. A head restraint provides an external force and accelerates the head at the same rate as the body.

3 Using $F = ma$, $F = 10\,kg \times 200\,m\,s^{-2} = 2000\,N$. This is close to the force required to beat the world weightlifting record. It would be impossible for an adult to provide this force to restrain a baby in a crash.

4 $s = 23 - 9 = 14\,m$, $v = 0\,m\,s^{-1}$,
$u = 48.3 \times 1000 / 3600 = 13.4\,m\,s^{-1}$.
Using $v^2 = u^2 + 2as$, $a = (v^2 - u^2) / 2s = -6.4\,m\,s^{-2}$.
Since $F = ma$, $F = 1500 \times 6.4 = 9600\,N$.

5 The crash barrier takes time to deform. This extends the duration of the collision. Force = rate of change of momentum (Newton's second law), so if the momentum change takes place over a longer time, the force is reduced.

6 a

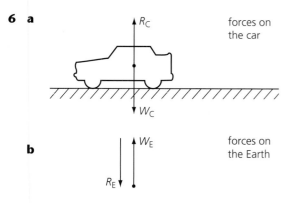

forces on the car

b

forces on the Earth

W_C = gravitational pull of the Earth on the car (the car's weight)
W_E = gravitational pull of the car on the Earth
R_C = contact force of the Earth's surface on the car
R_E = contact force of the car on the Earth's surface

c Because the car and the Earth are in equilibrium, Newton's first law says that there must be no net force, so $R_C = W_C$ and $R_E = W_E$.

d Newton's third law says $R_C = R_E$ and $W_E = W_C$.

7 A car's wheels are turned by the force provided by the engine. The wheels push the road backwards via the friction between the tyres and the road surface. The road exerts an equal but opposite force on the car (Newton's third law). It is this force which pushes the car forward.

8 Kinetic energy is proportional to speed *squared*. A car travelling at 20 mph has only a quarter of the kinetic energy that it would have at 40 mph. Cutting your speed by half will drastically reduce the effect of a collision.

9 a $E_k = \frac{1}{2}mv^2 = 500\,kJ$
b All the kinetic energy needs to be transferred, so work = 500 kJ
c work = force × distance
force = work / distance
$= 500\,kJ / 38 = 13\,kN$

10 a power = force × velocity,
so $F = P / v = 112\,000 / 8.9 = 12.6\,kN$ at 20 mph
and $112\,000 / 17.8 = 6.3\,kN$ at 40 mph.
b To find acceleration use $a = F / m$, but F is the resultant force. We need to know the resistive force acting to find the resultant force.

11 Treat the horizontal and vertical components of momentum separately.
Horizontally: as the Volvo accelerates forwards from rest at the top of the building it pushes the Earth backwards (Newton's third law). The gain in the forward momentum of the car is exactly matched by the gain in the Earth's 'backwards' momentum. When the Volvo skids to a halt on the ground below, friction will act equally on the car and the Earth, changing the momentum of the Earth and the car by the same amount.
Vertically: as the car accelerates under gravity it gains momentum in a downwards direction. The car exerts an equal but opposite gravitational pull on the Earth (Newton's third law), so the Earth gains an equal, but opposite, momentum in an upwards direction. During the collision the contact forces act equally, and for the same time, on the Volvo and the Earth. Both bodies lose their vertical momentum. At all times, the total vertical momentum is zero.

Chapter 9

1 $E = mc^2 = 1 \times (3 \times 10^8)^2 = 9 \times 10^{16}$ J

2 mass = density × volume

$= 2000 \times \frac{4}{3}\pi (500)^2 = 2.1 \times 10^9$ kg

$E_k = \frac{1}{2}mv^2 = \frac{1}{2} \times 2.1 \times 10^9 \times (10 \times 10^3)^2 = 1 \times 10^{17}$ J

3 $E_p = mg\Delta h = 400 \times 1000 \times 10 \times 500 = 2 \times 10^9$ J per second

4 $E_p = 7 \times 10^6 \times 1000 \times 10 \times 500 = 3.5 \times 10^{13}$ J

5 Initial $E_k = \frac{1}{2}mv^2$

Final $E_p = mg\Delta h$

so $\Delta h = \frac{1}{2}v^2/g = \frac{1}{2} \times 400/10$

$\Delta h = 20$ m

6 Typical room volume, 3 m × 3 m × 6 m = 54 m³
Energy = $mc\Delta\theta = 1.3 \times 54 \times 993 \times 20 = 1.4 \times 10^6$ J

7 Energy required to bring water to the boil is:
$Q = mc\Delta\theta = 2 \times 4200 \times 90 = 75\,600$ J

kettle transfers 2200 J s⁻¹
time taken = 75 600 / 2200 = 344 s or 5.7 minutes

8 **a** $\frac{1}{2}mv^2 = \frac{1}{2} \times 800 - (30)^2 = 360\,000$ J
b 25% of 360 000 = 90 000 J
$\Delta\theta = Q/mc = 90\,000 / 2 \times 500 = 90\,°$C rise
Fortunately the brakes are air-cooled, rapidly.

9 The latent heat of vaporisation will be transferred to the skin as the steam condenses.

10 Energy required to turn 2 kg of water to steam, is $Q = ml$
$= 2 \times 2260 \times 10^3$
$= 4.52 \times 10^6$ J
Energy required to raise 2 kg of water from 20 °C to 100 °C is
$= mc\Delta\theta$
$= 2 \times 4200 \times 80 = 672\,000$ J
Total energy = 5.19×10^6 J
Kettle delivers 2000 J per second; in 5 minutes this is:
$5 \times 60 \times 2000 = 600\,000$ J or 0.6×10^6 J
This is not enough energy to boil the kettle dry.

11 a Work done = $100 \times 10^3 \times (73.75 \times 10^{-3}) = 7\,375$ J

b $Q = 0.2 \times 3.94 \times 10^5 = 18\,800$ J
c The difference, 11 425 J, is used in overcoming inter-molecular forces, i.e. increasing the potential energy of the benzene molecules.

Chapter 10

1 At constant volume, no external work is done, so all the heat transfers to internal energy. At constant pressure, the substance expands, so you need to supply extra heat to do the work associated with expansion.

2 Using $Q = mc\Delta T$ gives $Q = 70$ J at constant volume.
80 J was supplied, so 10 J of external work has been done.

3 Celsius = Kelvin − 273.15 = 273.16 − 273.15 = 0.01 °C

4 a Boyle's Law gives that pressure is doubled.
b Same mass, half the volume, so the density is doubled.
c Same temperature, so the molecules are travelling at the same speed. (If the gas is ideal, there are no forces between the molecules, so squashing them together doesn't affect speed.)

5

Assumption	In section
molecules small	2, 4
perfectly elastic	1, 2, (4)
collisions are quick	2, (4)
no inter-molecular force	4
large numbers	4, (5)
random directions	5
Newton's laws hold	1, 2

6 $V = RT / P = 0.0224$ m³ = 22.4 litres

7 Using density = mass / volume, the volume of one mole of air would also be 22.4 litres. It obeys accurately the equation of state of an ideal gas at s.t.p.

Chapter 11

1 1 kWh is 1000 J/s for 3600 seconds,
$1000 \times 10^3 \times 60 \times 60 = 3.6 \times 10^9$ J

2 $100 \times 24 \times 60 \times 60 = 8.64 \times 10^6$ J
or $0.1 \times 24 = 2.4$ kWh

3 $26.4 \times 10^3 \times 60 \times 60 = 9.5 \times 10^6$ J
or 9.5 MJ

4 $E_k = 247$ kJ. This takes 25.5 s.

5 a it accelerates faster

  b no change of E_k
  c higher top speed

6 a Gain in kinetic energy = $^1/_2 \times 1000 \times (25)^2 = 312\,500$ J
This is achieved in 10 s, average power = 31 250 W
= 31 kW

  b at 30% efficiency we need a power input of 31 250 / 0.3
= 104 kW
total capacity of tank = $50 \times 50 = 2500$ MJ
$2\,500 \times 10^6 / 1040 \times 10^3 = 2\,400$ times

7 6.25×10^{18} electrons.

8 Overall, 10 C of charge passes in 2 s, giving $I = 5$ A
(conventional current to the right).

9 $I = Q/t = 32\,C / 0.2\,s = 160$ A

10 $I = P/V = 1400/240 = 5.8$ A   13 A fuse

11 $I = P/V = 7000/240 = 29$ A. Standard plug is only designed to carry 13 A, so showers need to be directly wired.

12 $W = QV = 2\,C \times 160\,V = 320$ J

13 a $Q = It = 15$ C
  b $W = QV = 180$ J
  c $P = E/t = 36$ W

14 a Energy = $IVt = 77 \times 60 \times 60 \times 343 = 95.1 \times 10^6$ J
  b Power of charger = $220 \times 30 = 6600$ W
$95.1 \times 10^6 / 6600 = 14\,410$ s (240 minutes or 4 hours)

15 Resistance should be low to avoid wasting power heating the wire.
$0.002\,\Omega \rightarrow 0.2$ V $0.1\,\Omega \rightarrow 10$ V
Note that headlamps use far less than 100 A.

16 6 V, assuming the heating element obeys Ohm's law.

17 Battery p.d. is 42 V, giving a current of 143 A.
Power loss in the wires is 102 W. Efficiency is 98%.
This p.d. is safer and loss of efficiency is small.

18 P.d. across internal resistance is 6 V
terminal p.d. is 12 V – 6 V = 6 V
efficiency is 6 V / 12 V = 0.5 = 50%

19 $E = V + Ir = 168 + (120 \times 0.1) = 180$ V

20 Using $P = I^2R \rightarrow I = 4.0$ A
Using $E = I(R+r) \rightarrow r = 0.5\,\Omega$

21 a $R_{lamp} = 3\,\Omega$, $R_{total} = 1.5\,\Omega$, current = 8.0 A
  b (12 Ω in parallel with 6 Ω) = 4 Ω $\rightarrow I = 3.0$ A
  c (30 Ω in parallel with 15 Ω) = 10 Ω $\rightarrow I = 1.2$ A

22 a 12 V   **b** 11 V   **c** 8 V

23 P.d. across 10 Ω resistor $\leq (14 - 9) = 5$ V

so power $\leq V^2/R = 2.5$ W

24 a 0.3 A   **b** 0.1 A

25 a 6 V   **b** 50 V   **c** 4 V   **d** 6 V

26 A moving coil meter could be connected in parallel with a supply lead. The lead becomes the shunt resistor. The p.d. across the lead will be up to 300 A × 0.003 Ω = 0.9 V. You could use any meter where the p.d. across its terminals is around 1 V at full scale deflection, e.g. 100 mA, 10 Ω.

27 For resistance of 0.001 Ω you need $A = 6.75 \times 10^{-4}$ m^2. With steel plate 1 mm thick, a width of 0.675 m is needed.

28 Initially the bulb filament is cool and its resistance is low. The filament quickly heats up (to around 1000 °C) and its resistance is much higher, allowing less current to flow.

Chapter 12

1 A higher work function means that more energy is needed to free electrons from the surface. You need a higher thermal energy, so higher temperature.

2 The high heater current is for resistive (I^2R) heating. A high anode–cathode p.d. is needed to accelerate the electrons away from the cathode.

3 Using $1 / C = 1 / C_1 + 1 / C_2$
gives $C = 24\,\mu F$
The charge on each plate is $Q = CV = 0.024\,C$
Using $V = Q / C$, p.d.s are $400\,V$ and $600\,V$ for the $60\,\mu F$ and $40\,\mu F$ capacitors respectively.

Chapter 13

1 1 kg is equal to 1000 g
$1\,m^3$ is equal to $1 \times 10^6\,cm^3$
so $1000\,kg\,m^{-3} = 1000 \times 1000 / 1 \times 10^6 = 1\,g\,cm^{-3}$

2 Volume = mass / density = $1 / 21\,450 = 47 \times 10^{-6}\,m^3$

3 Cylinder volume = $\pi r^2 h = \pi\,(0.25)^2 \times 1 = 0.196\,m^3$.
Since mass = volume $\times$ density,
mass = $0.196 \times 1000 = 196\,kg$

4 **a** $F = A\sigma = \pi \times (1 \times 10^{-3})^2 \times 85 \times 10^6 = 267\,N$, approximately 27 kg
   b $F = 267 \times 5 = 1335\,N$
   $A = F / \sigma = 1335 / (85 \times 10^6) = 15.7 \times 10^{-6}\,m^2$, so the diameter = 4.48 mm

5 strain = extension / length = $7.5 \times 10^{-2} / 50 = 1.5 \times 10^{-3}$

6 specific strength of Kevlar = $2.15\,MPa\,kg^{-1}$

   specific stiffness of Kevlar = $86.1\,MPa\,kg^{-1}$
   Although carbon fibre is stiffer, it is not as strong.

7 **a** B **b** A **c** C **d** C **e** A

8 Because the silk is stiffer, it requires a greater force to stretch it, so the bungee jumper wouldn't fall as far.
   The silk's lower resilience means that more energy is lost through hysteresis, so the jumper wouldn't rebound as high.

9 More cords would result in a greater force on the jumper for the same extension. The cords wouldn't stretch as far.

10 Increasing the mass of the jumper means that the cords stretch further and more energy is stored as elastic strain energy. When the bag drops, the mass is decreased and so the jumper rebounds much higher, possibly crashing into the platform they left only a brief moment earlier.

11 The glass fibres are very stiff and prevent the fibre glass from deforming very much under stress. The plastic resin prevents cracks propagating through the material and stops brittle fracture.

Data Section

Fundamental constants

Quantity	Symbol	Value	Units
speed of light in vacuo	c	3.00×10^8	$m\,s^{-1}$
charge of electron	e	1.60×10^{-19}	C
the Planck constant	h	6.63×10^{-34}	$J\,s$
the Avogadro constant	N_A	6.02×10^{23}	mol^{-1}
molar gas constant	R	8.31	$J\,K^{-1}\,mol^{-1}$
the Boltzmann constant	k	1.38×10^{-23}	$J\,K^{-1}$
the Stefan constant	σ	5.67×10^{-8}	$W\,m^{-2}\,K^{-4}$
the Wien constant	α	2.90×10^{-3}	$m\,K$
electron rest mass	m_e	9.11×10^{-31}	kg
electron charge/mass ratio	e/m_e	1.76×10^{11}	$C\,kg^{-1}$
proton rest mass	m_p	1.67×10^{-27}	kg
proton charge/mass ratio	e/m_p	9.58×10^7	$C\,kg^{-1}$
neutron rest mass	m_n	1.67×10^{-27}	kg
gravitational field strength	g	9.81	$N\,kg^{-1}$
acceleration due to gravity	g	9.81	$m\,s^{-2}$

Mathematical constants and equations

$e = 2.72$ $\pi = 3.14$ 1 radian $= 57.3°$

circumference of circle $= 2\pi r$

area of circle $= \pi r^2$

area of cylinder $= 2\pi rh$

volume of cylinder $= \pi r^2 h$

area of sphere $= 4\pi r^2$

volume of sphere $= \frac{4}{3}\pi r^3$

arc $= r\theta$

$\sin^2 \theta + \cos^2 \theta = 1$

For small angles, $\sin \theta \approx \tan \theta \approx \theta$

$y = mx + c$ – equation of a straight line

Properties of solids

At 293 K

Substance	Density	Electrical resistivity	Yield strength	Young modulus	Melting point	Specific latent heat of fusion	Specific heat capacity
	$kg\,m^{-3}$	$\Omega\,m \times 10^{-8}$	$Pa \times 10^{6}$	$Pa \times 10^{9}$	K	$J\,kg^{-1} \times 10^{4}$	$J\,kg^{-1}\,K^{-1}$
alumina, ceramic	3800	–	–	245	2300	–	800
aluminium	2710	2.65	50	71	932	38	913
brass	8500	8.0	450	100	1300	–	370
brick, building	2300	–	–	–	–	–	–
carbon, graphite	2300	–	–	1200	–	–	710
carbon, diamond	3300	–	–	207	3800	–	525
concrete	2400	–	–	14	–	–	3350
constantan	8880	47	–	170	1360	–	420
copper	8930	1.7	75	117	1356	21	385
epoxy resin	1120	–	–	4.5	–	–	1400
gold	19 300	2.4	–	71	1340	7	132
iron	7870	10	165	206	1810	27	440
lead	11 340	21	12	18	600	2.6	126
marble	2600	–	–	–	–	–	880
perspex	1190	–	–	3.0	350	–	1500
phosphor bronze	8900	7	420	120	–	–	–
platinum	21 450	11	–	150	2042	11	136
polystyrene	1050	–	–	3.1	510	–	1300
quartz fibre	2660	–	–	73	2020	–	788
rubber	910	–	–	0.02	300	–	1600
silver	10 500	1.6	180	70	1230	10	235
stainless steel	7930	96	230	200	1800	–	510
steel, piano wire	7800	–	–	210	1700	–	–
titanium carbide	4500	–	–	345	–	–	–
zinc	7140	5.9	–	110	693	10	385

Useful equations

Statics

$F = \mu R$

Dynamics

$v = u + at$

$s = \left(\dfrac{u+v}{2}\right)t$

$s = ut + \dfrac{at^2}{2}$

$v^2 = u^2 + 2as$

$p = mv$

$F = \dfrac{\Delta(mv)}{\Delta t}$

$P = Fv$

$\text{efficiency} = \dfrac{\text{power output}}{\text{power input}}$

Refraction

$_1 n_2 = \dfrac{\sin\theta_1}{\sin\theta_2} = \dfrac{c_1}{c_2} = \dfrac{n_2}{n_1}$

$\sin\theta_c = \dfrac{1}{n}$

Electricity

$\in = \dfrac{E}{Q}$

$\in = I(R + r)$

$R_{series} = R_1 + R_2 + R_3 + \ldots$

$\dfrac{1}{R_{parallel}} = \dfrac{1}{R_1} + \dfrac{1}{R_2} + \dfrac{1}{R_3} + \ldots$

$P = I^2 R$

$\rho = \dfrac{RA}{l}$

Alternating current

$I_{r.m.s.} - \dfrac{I_0}{\sqrt{2}}$

$V_{r.m.s.} = \dfrac{V_0}{\sqrt{2}}$

Solids

$\text{Young modulus} = \dfrac{F/A}{e/L}$

$\text{elastic strain energy} = \tfrac{1}{2}Fe = \text{energy stored}$

Thermal properties

$$c = \frac{\Delta Q}{m \Delta T}$$

$$l = \frac{\Delta Q}{m}$$

$$pV = \tfrac{1}{3} N m \overline{c^2}$$

$$\tfrac{1}{2} m \overline{c^2} = \tfrac{3}{2} kT = \frac{3RT}{2N_A}$$

Nuclear physics

$$E = mc^2$$

Photoelectric effect

$$E = hf$$

$$hf = \phi + E_k$$

$$hf = E_1 - E_2$$

Wave–particle duality

$$\lambda = \frac{h}{p}$$

$$\lambda = \frac{h}{\sqrt{2meV}}$$

Index

α particles *see* alpha particles
absolute zero 138, 141
absorption spectra 77
a.c. 176–9
acceleration 89, 91, 92–3, 124
   due to gravity 90, 92
addition, vector 88–9, 104–5
aerials 57, 59–60
aerodynamic forces 107
air bags 113, 123
air resistance 90, 94, 106–7, 116, 121
alpha particles 13–14, 30
alternating current 176–9
aluminium 166, 167
ammeters 165
amorphous materials 190–2, 193
analogue meters 165
Anderson, Carl 25
annihilation 25, 26, 27
antibaryons 40, 44
antileptons 33
antimatter 25, 27
   see also antiparticles
antineutrinos 30, 45, 50
antineutrons 40, 44
antinodes 56
antiparticles 23, 25–8
   hadron family 40
   lepton family 30, 33
   quarks in 44–5
   in weak interaction 50
antiprotons 26, 40, 44
antiquarks 44–5
astronomy 72, 84
   telescopes 36, 60, 84
atomic mass number 17
atomic number 16
atomic radii 9
atoms 6–10, 12–13
   equilibrium separation 101, 189
   nucleus 13–18, 19, 44
   orbital model 57, 74–5, 76–7
   spectra 42
average velocity 87

β+ *see* positrons
β– *see* beta particles
background radiation 138
Balmer series 76

baryon number 39–40, 44
baryons 40, 42, 50
   structure 43, 44
batteries 153, 154, 158–60
   energy and power 155, 156
Bernoulli effect 107
beta particles (beta minus) 31, 45, 50
   energies of 29–30
beta plus (positrons) 25, 27, 50
binding energy 24
black body radiation 76
blocking capacitors 177
Bohr, Niels 42, 74
Boltzmann, Ludwig 7
Boltzmann constant 146
bosons 42
   see also gauge bosons; Higgs boson
bottom quark 47
bound state 74
Boyle, Robert 142
Boyle's law 142, 144
braking, vehicle 118–24
breaking stress 183
Bremsstrahlung radiation 78
bridges 98, 101
brittle materials 184, 191
Brown, Robert 7
Brownian motion 7–8
bungee jumping 187–9
buoyancy 106

capacitors 177
capacity, battery 154
carbon 18, 22, 27
cars 113, 150
   circuits in 160, 161, 162, 164
   collisions 113–14, 115–24
   electric *see* electric cars
   petrol cars 151, 152, 153
cathode rays 10–12, 171–2
cathode-ray tubes (CRTs) 171, 172–4
   in oscilloscopes 175–7
CCDs (charge coupled devices) 84
Celsius scale 139, 141
centre of gravity 99
centre of mass 94, 99
CERN 6, 34, 36, 49, 51
Chadwick, Sir James 17
characteristic lines 78

charge 153
   on antiparticles 23
   conservation 26, 39
     in Kirchhoff's laws 154–5
   and the electromagnetic force 19
   on particles 12, 17, 33, 44
charge carriers
   in metals 156–7, 167
   in semiconductors 168
charge coupled devices (CCDs) 84
charge-to-mass ratio 12
charging insulators 153
Charles, Jacques 145
Charles' law 145
charm quark 46
chromatic dispersion 65
circuits 160, 161–2, 163
   parallel and series 154, 155, 161–2
cloud chambers 25
coefficient of friction 100
coherent bundles 69
cold-drawing 192
collisions 75, 122–3
colour, quark 51
communications *see*
   telecommunications
components 88–9, 94–5, 103–4
compression 101, 102, 189
compressions (waves) 55
conductivity 166–7
conductors 153, 157
conservation of baryon number 39–40
conservation of charge 26, 39, 154–5
conservation of energy 24, 119, 127–8
   in first law 140
conservation of leptons 42, 46
conservation of momentum 122, 123
conservation of strangeness 40–1, 49
constant-volume ideal gas thermometer
   141
contact forces 99–100
Cooper pairs 84
copper 166, 167, 190
   wires 62, 70
cosmic rays 32
couples 109
crack propagation 191
critical angle 68
cross-links 192

CRTs *see* cathode ray tubes
crumple zones 116–17, 123
cryogenics 138, 148
crystalline materials 189–90
    liquid crystals 171, 180, 194
    semi crystalline polymers 192–3
current 154, 163, 165
    a.c. 176–9
    and batteries 158–9
    in Fleming's left-hand rule 174

Dalton, John 7
dark matter 28–9
Davisson, C.J. 83
de Broglie, Prince Louis 83
de Broglie wavelength 83
deceleration 89, 124
deflection system, CRT 173–4
degrees of freedom 147
Democritus 6
density 183
detectors, light 84
deuterium 18, 20
diffraction 15, 61, 73, 83
diffraction gratings 73
diffusion 8
digital meters 165
diodes, semiconductor 157
Dirac, Paul 25, 37, 51
direct current 177, 178–9
dislocations 190
dispersion 65, 69
displacement 86–7, 92–3
displacement–time graphs 91, 92
display screens, CRT 173
distance 87
    see also displacement
down quark 43
drag forces 90, 94, 106–7, 116, 121
ductile materials 184, 190, 191
dynamic friction 100

efficiency 152, 160
Einstein, Albert 23, 24, 80, 128
elastic collisions 123
elastic limit 184
elastic materials 184
elastic scattering 75
elastic strain energy 187–9
electrical potential energy 128

electric cars 150–2, 154, 156
    batteries 156, 158–9
electric fields 55, 156
electricity
    hydroelectric generation 130
    mains 155, 179
electric motors 109
electromagnetic force 19, 20, 21, 50
    photons as exchange particles for 48
electromagnetic radiation 72–3
    in electron transitions 74–5, 76–7,
    78–9
    photons *see* photons
    see also gamma rays; infrared; light;
    radio waves; ultraviolet; X-rays
electromagnetic waves 55, 56, 59, 72–3
electromotive force 159–60, 163
electron guns 173
electron microscopes 83
electrons
    in atoms 12–13, 14, 15, 16, 18
        orbits 57, 74–5, 76–7
    as cathode rays 12, 171–2
    Cooper pairs 84
    diffraction 15, 83
    discovery 9, 10–12
    in electronvolt definition 24
    energy levels 74–5, 76–7, 78–9
    in fields 12, 173–4
    forces acting on 50
    free 156–7, 167, 190
    in lepton family 33, 38, 42
    particle collisions 50
    in photoelectric effect 79–80, 82
    spin 43
electronvolts 24, 25, 76–7
electrostatic fields 12, 173–4
electrostatic forces 16, 17, 48
electroweak theory 21
elements 17, 18, 77
e.m.f. 159–60, 163
emission spectra 73–4
endoscopes 69, 70
energy 119
    of alpha particles 30
    of beta particles 29–30
    binding energy 24
    in collisions 75, 123
    conservation of 24, 119, 127–8, 140

elastic strain energy 187–9
    internal energy 131–5, 140, 188
    kinetic *see* kinetic energy
    mass equivalence 24, 25, 26, 128
    measuring in electronvolts 25
    of molecules 139, 141, 142, 146–7
    in photoelectric effect 79–80, 82
    potential energy 119, 128–9, 131
    and power 151
    quantisation of 74–5, 76, 80
    transfer 126–37
        by waves 55, 56
    in virtual particle creation 28
    see also power; work
energy levels 74–5, 76–7, 78–9
equations of linear motion 92–4
equation of state 145
equilibrium
    and forces 102–4, 108, 109
    inter-molecular separation 101, 189
    thermal 139
exchange particles (gauge bosons) 38,
    47–50
excitation 74–5
expansion 135, 140
extension 184
    force–extension graphs 187, 188

falling objects 90, 131
    bungee jumping 187–9
    projectile motion 94–5
Faraday, Michael 6, 7, 21
FCC structures 190
Fermi, Enrico 30
fermions 42
ferrite 59
Feynman diagrams 47–8, 49, 50
fibre optics *see* optical fibres
fields *see* electric fields; electrostatic
    fields; magnetic fields
fixed points 139, 141
Fleming's left-hand rule 174
fluids 106, 107
fluorescence 173
forces 98–107
    addition 104–5
    aerodynamic forces 107
    contact forces 99–100
    drag 90, 94, 106–7, 116, 121
    electrostatic 16, 17, 48

force–extension graphs 187, 188
friction 100–1, 109, 116, 121, 153
fundamental forces 19–21, 47–50
   gravity *see* gravity
   inter-atomic forces 189
   inter-molecular forces 101, 135
   in laws of motion 114–17
   moments of 108, 109–10
   polygon of forces 101
   resolving 103–4
   resultant 99, 102–3, 104
   in roof design 111
   and stress 183
   tension 101–2, 189
   weight 98–9
   in windsurfing 106–7
   and work done 118–19
free-body force diagrams 102
free electrons 156–7, 167, 190
free fall 90
frequency 58, 61, 176
   in photoelectric effect 79–80
   television broadcasting 59
friction 100–1, 109, 153
   rolling resistance 116, 121
   see also air resistance
fuel cells 169
fundamental (waves) 57
fundamental forces 19–21, 47–50
   gravity *see* gravity
fundamental particles 33, 46, 47, 51
   atoms as 10
fuses 155
fusion
   nuclear 20
   specific latent heat of 134

γ rays *see* gamma rays
gamma camera 81
gamma rays 27, 81
gas constant, universal molar 145
gases 7–8, 139–47
   ideal 141–4, 146–7
gas laws 139, 142, 144–6
gauge bosons (exchange particles) 38, 47–50
Geiger, Hans 13
Gell-Mann, Murray 40, 43
Germer, L. 83
Glashow, Sheldon 21, 29
glasses 184, 190–1
glass transition temperature 191–2

gluons 48, 50
grand unification theories (GUTs) 21
gravitational field strength 98, 128–9
gravitational potential energy 128–9
gravitons 50
gravity 19, 20, 128–30
   acceleration due to 90, 92
   particles affected by 50
   in the Universe 28, 31
   and weight 98–9
ground state 74
GUTs (grand unification theories) 21

hadrons 38, 44, 47, 50
   conservation laws 39–41
half-life 22
half wave dipole 59
harmonics 57
HCP structures 190
heat 131–2
   and work 140
   see also internal energy
heat capacity 132–3
heating, resistive 157
Heisenberg's uncertainty principle 28
helium 17, 20, 24, 77
Hertz, Heinrich 10
hidden bottom 47
hidden charm 46
Higgs boson 6, 21, 51
Hooke's law 185, 186, 188, 189
horizontal deflection, oscilloscope 175
horizontal motion 94–5
Huygens' construction 61
hydroelectric power 130
hydrogen 17, 18, 20, 133
   spectra 74–5, 76–7
hysteresis 188

ideal gas equation 145–6
ideal gases 141–4, 146–7
images, real and virtual 63
incoherent bundles 69
inelastic collisions 123
inelastic scattering 75
information transfer 62
   see also optical fibres
infra-red 65, 73, 76
instantaneous acceleration 89
instantaneous velocity 87
insulators 153, 168

inter-atomic forces 189
   see also intermolecular forces
intermediate vector bosons 49, 50
inter-molecular forces 101, 135
   see also inter-atomic forces
internal energy 131–5, 140, 188
internal resistance 159–60
interstitial impurities 190
ionisation 75, 153
isotopes 18, 22, 27

Joule, James Prescott 127, 140

kaons 40, 45
Kelvin temperature scale 139, 141
kinetic energy 119, 120, 129–31
   in collisions 75, 123
   of gas molecules 139, 141, 142, 146–7
   of photoelectrons 80, 82
kinetic theory 141–4, 146
Kirchhoff, Gustav 77
Kirchhoff's laws 163

Lamb shift 28
lasers 65
latent heat 133–5
lateral inversion 63
LCDs 171, 180, 194
LEDs (light emitting diodes) 65
left-hand rule 174
LEPs (light emitting plastics) 180
leptons 31–3, 38, 42, 46
   forces acting on 50
   as fundamental particles 33, 46, 51
Libby, Willard 22
lift 107
light 72, 73
   detectors 84
   from electron transitions 76
   particle behaviour of 82
   in the photoelectric effect 79–80
   reflection of 62–3, 68–9
   refraction 64–7
   speed of 24, 128
   transmitting signals with 62
   see also optical fibres; photons
light emitting diodes (LEDs) 65
light emitting plastics (LEPs) 180
light leakage 68
limiting friction 100
line spectra 73–4, 75, 76, 78

liquefaction of gases 140, 144
liquid crystals 171, 180, 194
longitudinal waves 55–6
Lyman series 76

Mach, Ernst 7
magnetic fields 12, 55, 174
magnets, superconducting 148
Marconi, Guglielmo 10
Mariotte, E. 142
Marsden, Ernest 13
mass
    of dark matter 28–9
    energy equivalence 24, 25, 26, 128
    measuring in electronvolts 25
    of particles 51
        electrons 12, 17
        leptons 33
        neutrinos 29, 31
        nucleons 17
    relative atomic mass 17
    unified atomic mass constant 17
    and weight compared 98
materials
    resistance 155–8
    strength 182–94
    structure 189–93
matter 6
    dark matter 28–9
    particles in 23, 51
    wave properties of 83
Maxwell, James Clerk 6, 7
Maxwell distribution 141, 142
mean free path 8
medical applications
    computer controlled robotics 54
    of CRTs 172, 175
    gamma camera 81
    of optical fibres 69, 70
    PET scanning 27
mesons 40, 42, 50
    quark structure 44, 45
metals 186, 189–90
    resistance 156–7, 167, 168
meters 165, 179
Millikan, Robert 82
mirrors 63
mobile phones 54, 61
molar heat capacity 146
    see also specific heat capacity

molecules 7–8
    energy of 139, 141, 142, 146–7
    kinetic theory 141–4, 146
moments 108, 109–10
momentum 114, 115, 122, 123
monomode fibre 69
motion 86–97
    equations of 92–5
    Newton's laws of 114–17
    vehicle braking 118–24
motion graphs 89, 90, 91–2
motors, electric 109
moving coil meters 165
multimode dispersion 69
multiplier resistors 165
muons 32–3, 37, 42, 50
musical instruments 57

naked bottoms 47
near Earth objects (NEOs) 126
negative charges 19
neutral atoms 16
neutrinos 29–32, 50
neutrons 16–18
    decay of 38, 45, 46, 50
    quark structure 44
Newton's laws of motion 114–17
NMR scanners 148
nodes 56
non-ohmic conductors 157
nuclear fusion 20
nuclear magnetic resonance (NMR)
    scanners 148
nucleon number 17
nucleons 15, 17
    see also neutrons; protons
nucleus 13–18, 19, 44

Ohm, Georg Simon 157
ohmic conductors 157
Ohm's law 157
optical fibres 64, 65–9
    applications 54, 62, 70, 194
orbits, electron 57, 74–5, 76–7
order of magnitude 8
oscillations, waves as 55
oscilloscopes 175–7
overtones 57

pair production 26, 28
parabolic motion 94
parallax 63

parallel circuits 154, 155, 161–2
particle accelerators 24, 36
    see also CERN
particles 23–8, 36–8
    alpha particles 13–14, 30
    beta particles 29–30, 31, 45, 50
    de Broglie wavelength 83
    exchange particles 8, 47–50
    in fields 12, 156, 173–4
    fundamental 33, 46, 47, 51
    hadron family 39–41
    lepton family 29–33, 42
    quarks 43–7, 51
    virtual particles 28, 47
    wave–particle duality 15, 57, 83–4
    see also atoms; electrons; molecules;
    photons
Paschen series 76
Pauli, Wolfgang 29, 30–1
Pauli exclusion principle 42
p.d. see potential difference
peak power 178
period 58, 175–6
petrol cars 151, 152, 153
PET scanning 27
phase 60, 176
phase changes 133–4
    see also liquefaction
phosphorescence 173
photocathode detectors 84
photoelectric effect 12, 79–80, 81
    in photocathode detectors 84
    stopping voltage 82
photomultiplier tubes 82
photons 76–9, 80
    and antimatter 25, 26
    as exchange particles 48, 50
    as fermions 42
    see also electromagnetic radiation
piezoelectric materials 193
pi-mesons (pions) 44, 45, 48, 49
pixels 84
Planck, Max 74, 76
Planck's constant 28, 76
plane mirrors 63
plane surfaces, refraction at 64–7
plasma screen television 171
plastic deformation 184, 190, 191
plugs, electrical 155
plum pudding model 12–13
pollution from cars 150
polycrystalline materials 190

polygon of forces 101
polymers 184, 186, 191–3
positive charges 19
positron emission tomography 27
positrons 25, 27, 50
potential difference 154–5, 158–60
   in Kirchhoff's laws 163
   measuring 165, 179
   on oscilloscopes 176–7
   r.m.s. 178–9
   stopping voltage 82
potential dividers 164–6
potential energy 119, 128–9, 131
power 119–20, 151
   electrical 155, 158–9, 178–9
prefixes 8
pressure 106
   and lift 107
   and temperature 139, 141, 145
   and volume 142, 144
prisms 65
progressive waves 56–7
projectile motion 94–5
propagation, wave 55
proton number see atomic number
protons 16–18, 20
   collisions 50
   decay of 21, 41
   quark structure of 44
pulse spread 65

QCD (quantum chromodynamics) 46
quantisation of energy 74–5, 76, 80
quantum theory 74, 76
quarks 43–7, 49, 51

Rabi, I. 37
radians 60
radiation
   background radiation 138
   black body radiation 76
   electromagnetic see electromagnetic radiation
   see also alpha particles; beta particles
radioactive isotopes 22, 27
radiocarbon dating 22
radio waves 54, 57, 59–61
ramp waveform 175
rarefactions 55
ray diagrams 62
Rayleigh–Jeans curve 76
reaction (force) 99–100

real gases 144, 146–7
real images 63
reflection 62–3, 68–9
refraction 64–7
refractive index 64, 66–7
   chromatic dispersion 65
   in total internal reflection 68
Reines, F. 31
relative atomic mass 17
relative motion 88
relativity, special theory of 24
resilience in rubber 188
resistance 155–9
   in potential dividers 164–5
   superconductivity 148
   and temperature 167–8
resistive forces 116, 121
resistivity 166–7
resistors 161–2, 165
resolving vectors 88–9, 103–4
resultant force 99, 102–3, 104
resultant vector 88–9
r.m.s. (root mean square)
   speed 142, 144
   voltage 178–9
rolling resistance 116, 121
Röntgen, Wilhelm 10
roofs, forces on 111
root mean square see r.m.s.
ropes 182–3
rubber 186, 188, 192
Rubbia, Carlo 21
Rutherford, Ernest 13, 74

Salaam, Abdus 21
satellites 54
scalars 86–7
   pressure as 106
   work as 118
scale drawing 88, 89, 102, 103
scales
   on meters 165
   and order of magnitude 8
   of temperature 139, 141
scientific notation 8
Searle's apparatus 185
seat belts 117
semiconductor diodes 157
semiconductors 168
semi crystalline polymers 192–3
sensors 160, 164
series circuits 154, 155, 161, 162

shape-memory alloys 194
shells, electron 75
shunt resistors 165
signal transmission 62
   see also optical fibres
silk, spider's 182, 184, 191, 193
size
   atomic radii 9
   nuclear radii 14, 15
   and order of magnitude 8
Snell's law 66–7
sound waves 55
specific heat capacity 132–3
   see also molar heat capacity
specific latent heat 133–5
spectra 42, 72–9
speed 86, 87
   of light 24, 128
   of molecules 141–4, 146
   r.m.s. speed 142
   of waves 58, 64, 66
   see also velocity
spider's silk 182, 184, 191, 193
spin, particle 30, 42, 43
sports 86, 88, 90, 94–5
   see also windsurfing
standard model 6, 46–7, 51
standing waves 56–7
stationary waves 56–7
stiffness 185–6
STJs (superconducting tunnel junctions) 84
stopping voltage 82
strain 184, 185–6, 194
strangeness 40–1, 44, 49
strange quark 43
strength of materials 182–94
stress 183–4, 185–6, 194
stretching 101, 184–9, 192
strings, standing waves on 57
strong nuclear force (interaction) 16–17, 19, 48–9, 50
structure 189–93
substitutional impurities 190
Sun 20, 73, 77
   neutrinos from 29, 32
superconducting tunnel junctions (STJs) 84
superconductivity 148
SUSY (supersymmetry) 29
sweep waveform 175
systems 119, 122, 127

tau particle 33, 42, 46
telecommunications 54, 61, 62, 65
    see also optical fibres
telescopes 36, 60, 84
television 60, 61, 62
    broadcast frequencies 59
    electron guns in 173
    screen technology 171
temperature 139–41
    absolute zero 138, 141
    glass transition temperature 191–2
    in heating 131–2
    low temperatures 138, 148
    and kinetic energy of gas 141
    and pressure 139, 141, 145
    and resistance 167–8
    and specific heat capacity 132–3
    and thermistors 164
    and volume 145
    and wavelength emitted 73
tensile strain 184
tensile stress 183
tension 101–2, 189
terminal p.d. 159–60
terminal velocity 90
thermal energy 131
    see also internal energy
thermal equilibrium 139
thermal radiation 73
thermionic emission 172, 173
thermionic valves 172
thermistors 164
thermodynamics, first law of 140–1
thermometers 139, 141
thermometric properties 139, 141
Thomson, Sir J.J. 9, 10–12

threshold frequency 79–80
time
    in equations of motion 92–3
    on motion graphs 89, 90, 91–2
time base, oscilloscope 175
top quark 47
torque 109
total internal reflection 68–9
transverse waves 55–6
trigonometry for vector addition 88, 89
triple point of water 141
tritium 18
turning effect 108, 109–10

ultimate tensile stress (UTS) 183
ultraviolet 76
unified atomic mass constant 17
uniform velocity 87
universal molar gas constant 145
Universe 23, 28–9, 31, 36
up quark 43
upthrust 106
UTS (ultimate tensile stress) 183

vaporisation, specific latent heat of 134
vectors 86–7, 89, 102
    resolving 88–9, 103–4
velocity 87, 88–9
    in equations of motion 92–3
    terminal velocity 90
    see also speed
velocity–time graphs 89, 90, 91, 92
vertical deflection, oscilloscope 176–7
vertical motion 94–5
virtual images 63
virtual particles 28, 47
voltage *see* potential difference

voltmeters 165, 179
volume, gas 142, 144, 145

water 133, 134, 141
wavelength 58, 61, 65
    X-rays 78–9
wavelets 61
wave–particle duality 15, 57, 83–4
waves 58
    diffraction 15, 61, 73, 83
    electromagnetic 55, 56, 59, 72–3
    motion of 55–60
    particle duality 15, 57, 83–4
    reflection 62–3, 68–9
    refraction 64–7
weak interaction 19–20, 21, 49–50
weakly interacting massive particles
    (WIMPs) 29
weight 98–9
Weinberg, Steven 21
WIMPs (weakly interacting massive
    particles) 29
windsurfing, forces in 106–7, 109–10
work 118–19, 127, 140
    and e.m.f. 159
    in expansion 135
    and potential difference 154–5
    in stretching 187–8
work function 79, 80, 172

X-rays 78–9

yield stress 184
Young modulus 185–6
Yukawa, H. 47, 48

Zweig, George 43